COVID19 - SHORT PATH TO 'YOU'LL OWN NOTHING. AND YOU'LL BE HAPPY.'

Welcome to the new Age of Tyranny

"It is for your protection and safety!"

By Jeffrey Hann

Journalistic Revolution

Paperback: 979-8-9874490-0-4
Hardcover: 979-8-9874490-1-1
Ebook: 979-8-9874490-2-8

Library of Congress Control Number: 2022923264

First edition February 2023.

Published by:
Journalistic Revolution, LLC
PO Box 130
Eatonville, WA 98328

https://www.journalisticrevolution.com

Table of Contents

Preface

"Persons attempting to find a motive in this narrative will be prosecuted; persons attempting to find a moral in it will be banished; persons attempting to find a plot in it will be shot. BY ORDER OF THE AUTHOR per G.G., CHIEF OF ORDNANCE" – Mark Twain, *The Adventures of Huckleberry Finn*, 1885

My path to this book has been decades in the making. My background consists of many avenues of knowledge and experiences. I am part of the Oregon Trail generation -1985 Apple II computer game- or a Xennial, which allowed me to live through the start of computers and video games, moving from an analog childhood to electronic adulthood. I have enjoyed freedom of movement -the root definition and context of the word free- during my youth, being out in the world at a young age with significantly fewer restrictions than what exists today. The number of federal and local laws and regulations have significantly increased across the board from when I was a child.

I experienced the freedom the Internet initially offered, being able to explore and experience it without the worry of laws and restrictions or fear of something or someone constantly monitoring my every move for any misstep. I experienced the electronic music scene, raves -pre and post-9/11- and the freedom of listening to music when no one was being victimized. I witnessed the scene become vilified and condemned for enjoying the freedom it offered from those who had no understanding beyond what the government and mainstream media explained. I experienced the freedom that cryptocurrency, e.g.,

Bitcoin and Ethereum, brought until government laws and regulations were enacted against them.

As a Network and Systems Administrator, I have worked on routers, switches, and servers. I have designed and developed websites and graphics. I have been a United States (U.S.) Army soldier experiencing military life as an Infantryman and Signals Intelligence (SIGINT) and Cyber Intelligence Analyst. I have held a top-secret clearance and have been entrusted with what some consider the nation's greatest secrets. I have worked for years in the public sector as a Business and Solutions Analyst, trying to see how it would be possible to make positive changes regarding the freedom and rights of citizens -you can't unless you amass power and resources and are elected to high levels of public office. I have worked on analyzing laws and regulations while learning and understanding how industries of practice initially become regulated.

Many of the ideas and principles I have learned, gathered, and developed during these experiences have helped guide me down my path as I have evolved into what I am today. With sadness, I recognize that my children will not be able to experience these things the way I did -to enjoy and experience the freedom that should come with life while navigating the pitfalls and dangers that freedom can come with. That is what it should mean to be an adult; we should be free to experience life as long as we do not victimize and violate the natural rights of others. I have witnessed freedom and the idea and understanding of freedom erode over the decades. Government restrictions and regulations in many aspects of our lives and trade industries continue to grow with no end.

I went through the Orlando, Florida, public education system from 1st through 12th grade. I hold several degrees; an Associate of Science in Digital Media and Computer Engineering, an Associate in Applied Science in Intelligence Operations Studies, a Bachelor of Science in Liberal Arts, and a Master of Business Administration in IT Management. Throughout these educational experiences and extensive self-growth educational research, I have realized that public education encouraged me to be a literacy slave, competent enough to work but not competent enough to think for myself, with blind obedience towards authority mixed in.

In 2015, I was taught the Trivium Method of Critical Thinking -a proper way to think critically as a skill set. This was one of those life-changing moments for me. In the following years, I published works and articles that corrected the rhetoric I had held as the truth -rhetoric that the government and the public education system had heavily influenced. Far from any semblance of fact in many bodies of knowledge, I discovered -with horror- how confused and systematically manipulated we all have been. When first seen, the truth can be painful, but it is within all of us to think critically as a skill set and to know and accept the truth without fear and pain.

"In a highly developed society, the Establishment cannot survive without the obedience and loyalty of millions of people who are given small rewards to keep the system going: the soldiers and police, teachers and ministers, administrators and social workers, technicians and production workers, doctors, lawyers, nurses, transport and communications workers, garbage men and firemen. These people-the employed, the somewhat privileged-are drawn into alliance with the elite. They become the guards of the system, buffers between the upper and lower classes. If they stop obeying, the system falls." – Howard Zinn, *A People's History of the United States*, August 2nd, 2005

What is obedience? Obedience is to submit to being ruled by authority or compliant with tyrannical laws and policies. Slaves are obedient, which is achieved through violence and intimidation. Free and innocent people should not be ruled, nor should they be forced to be obedient to anyone over them through violence and intimidation. The idea of government, and the legitimacy of government, is around the "consent of the governed," not being "forced to be governed." However, the "consent of the governed" is still a fallacious idea and thought, and I will show you why in this book.

Being ruled or controlled through non-voluntary means is akin to being a slave; varying degrees of slavery require different levels of control and force. Tyranny is force, and at a government level, it is forced through a monopoly on violence. The idea that we must be obedient to authority through a monopoly on violence is slavery. Documentaries on the idea of the monopoly on violence are *The Monopoly on Violence* and *Overpoliced*, directed by Chris Cofer, and are documentaries that I helped produce.

The U.S. was officially established with the Declaration of Independence on July 4th, 1776. A declaration to be independent of British tyrannical rule -which Thomas Jefferson drafted using many ideas and teachings from philosopher and physician John Locke. The founders of the U.S. and most of those in the original colonies no longer wanted to be obedient to a tyrant. To gain independence and freedom, resistance against tyranny was an absolute requirement, which led to the U.S. Revolutionary War. Resistance in this context is defined as organized opposition to rulers and tyranny. This resistance to government tyranny provided the pathway for the U.S. to maintain its independence and to usher in a couple hundred years of advancement that supposedly boasted freedom for all, even though slavery continued to be standard practice after the signing of the Declaration of Independence and the U.S. Constitution.

"Reading is for the improvement of the understanding. The improvement of understanding is for two ends: first, our own increase of knowledge; secondly, to enable us to deliver that knowledge to others." – John Locke, *Some Thoughts Concerning Reading and Study for A Gentleman*, 1703

Why is it now that blind obedience to governmental authority is viewed as being a "good citizen," and resistance to what some see as government tyranny is viewed as "terroristic behavior"? Has all understanding of how this country was formed vanished? Why does the government-run public education system not teach the essential ideologies many of the founders used as justification for the Revolutionary War?

Many do not understand these ideas about freedom from tyranny. Each of us should be able to judge our current political climate and issues without only repeating the rhetoric of others. We should be able to form and create our rhetoric by using critical thinking to process all information available to determine our rhetoric and truth. Why do you think the government-run education system teaches individuals what to think and not how to think?

The U.S. Education System comprises the Classical Trivium - Classical Education- and the Prussian Education System. The Classical Trivium -designed by the Catholic Church- was used to create a circle body of knowledge and to keep people within that body of knowledge. Stepping outside that body of knowledge is viewed negatively and quickly "corrected." This system is used to create literacy slaves, those competent enough to work but not competent enough to think for themselves. The Prussian Education System was designed after the Prussian army -and its mercenaries- lost against Napoleon's army from 1806 to 1807. The Prussian Parliament determined that its soldiers and mercenaries lost due to independent thought -thinking for themselves- so it changed the educational system to create blind obedience to authority with a focus on creating mercenaries and nation-building. The Prussians later evolved into Nazi Germany. The U.S. Education System comprises these two systems and aims to generate literacy slaves who have blind obedience towards authority. What we see today is a direct result of this system teaching and indoctrinating multiple generations.

Our Natural Rights -Life, Freedom, and Property- are inalienable rights that everyone in the world has and shares, and they are being attacked at every step. Most people accept it without question or any protest or resistance. We are on the precipice of human evolution or devolution; which way do you want to go?

In his *Five Types of Regimes*, Plato -arguably the most influential person in Western philosophy- said thousands of years ago that government has a lifecycle. Government is not a static thing. Plato explained that Revolution comes after Tyranny, which, if a Revolution is successful, citizens are revolved into a previous, less restrictive version of government. This less stringent government version is still statism and eventually leads to Tyranny. We are at a point in this global government lifecycle where no revolution against government tyranny would be televised or otherwise published by any tyrannical government trying to maintain control and power over the innocent. Unless, of course, it is politically advantageous to do so. It is up to all of us to stand up against tyranny and voice the ideas that made the U.S. an arguably once great nation; defiance in the face of tyranny.

In 2016, I wrote an article asking myself, "what made America great?" From this article, I came up with the saying "Make America Defiant Again" (MADA), a response to President Donald Trump's campaign slogan "Make America Great Again" being pushed at the time. President Trump's campaign slogan was a blatant ripoff of the year President Reagan used "Make America Great Again" as his campaign slogan. Since then, I have used this MADA statement as a motto for where we need to go and how we must be as a society collectively. With this article, I defined patriotism and learned what it was to be a patriot.

Patriotism comes from the words patriot + -ism; patriot from the Late Latin word patriota, "fellow-countryman" + -ism as a system or practice (Online Etymology Dictionary), so a system or practice of being a fellow-countryman -a government supporter. Using context and theme, a country is defined as a landmass controlled by a government. This is the root definition of a patriot; however, in the 18th century, patriot was also used as "a factious disturber of the government" (Online Etymology Dictionary). When viewed with context and theme, should patriot -how Thomas Jefferson and the other founders used it in the 18th century- be considered a fellow redcoat or a factious disturber of the redcoats and the tyrannical British government? Would the likes of Thomas Jefferson and others view where we are today as American flag-waving patriots -the U.S. flag being the U.S. government's coat of arms- or would they be factious disturbers of a tyrannical government in search of a Revolution and new coat of arms to distinguish themselves from said tyrannical symbol?

"If patriotism were defined, not as blind obedience to government, nor as submissive worship to flags and anthems, but rather as love of one's country, one's fellow citizens (all over the world), as loyalty to the principles of justice and democracy, then patriotism would require us to disobey our government, when it violated those principles. We have thrown away the most valuable asset we had — the individual's right to oppose both flag and country when he believed them to be in the wrong. We have thrown it away; and with it, all that was really respectable about that grotesque and laughable word, Patriotism. We grow up in a controlled society, where we are told that when one person kills another person, that is murder, but when the government kills a hundred thousand, that is patriotism." – Howard Zinn, *Declarations of Independence: Cross-Examining American Ideology*, January 1st, 1991

Individually, a single person cannot stop government tyranny, but an individual can be the start of a movement of defiance and disobedience, which progresses Tyranny through Revolution. We can evolve past the need for government, the need to be controlled, and an endless cycle of tyranny that has lasted thousands of years. But to get to this point, defiance in the face of tyranny is a must which would be the catalyst to end Tyranny and progress us to the beginning of Revolution.

The etymology of the word defiance is a "challenge, declaration of war" (Online Etymology Dictionary). We must be defiant in the face of oppression from a government that does not represent the wishes or wills of those it supposedly represents. Defiant against those who wish to violate the rights of the innocent when seeking more power and resources. If this stance and defiance against government tyranny do not happen, then we, and our children, will be in this phase of tyranny for many years to come; we are only at the beginning stages of this new Age of Tyranny.

It is not the goal of this book to teach you how to think critically but to provide you with the tools and knowledge to start understanding the path we are heading down and the bleak outlook the future might hold for us. We can get through it and survive what is coming over the next few decades, but it will get very rough. This book will focus on everything I could find on COVID19 while showing how COVID19 is the new 9/11 helping to usher in the Great Reset and a short path to "You will own nothing. And you'll be happy." (World Economic Forum). I hope this book helps open others' eyes to the truth as I see it and the potentially dangerous direction we are heading. We can enact real change in this new Age of Tyranny if we meet the issues we face with a sense of purpose focused on helping expose the horrors committed against innocent people worldwide. It is up to us to speak up, or the servile insanity will continue for generations.

Jeffrey Hann

Critical Thinking

"He is the best of all who thinks for himself in all things. He, too, is good who takes advice from a wiser (person). But he who neither thinks for himself, nor lays to heart another's wisdom, this is a useless man." – Aristotle, *The Ethics Of Aristotle (Vol. I)*, translated by Arthur Humphreys, 1902

Critical thinking using root definitions is a skill set that allows an individual, by themselves, to judge and settle disputes as well as set limits on what is considered to be morally ethical and correct manners of someone who has one's behavior in society. However, critical thinking is much more than its root definition. Critical thinking is skillfully defining, intellectualizing, analyzing, and evaluating data and information gathered from all sources and producing belief and action in rhetoric that provides clarity and consistency through evidence and reason. The steps to critical thinking as a skill set, using the Trivium Method of Critical Thinking: Grammar (Input), Logic (Processing), and Rhetoric (Output) in that order. It is a never-ending process for determining the truth in any subject and situation. Critical thinking is a necessary skill for all to have if we are to enjoy a peaceful life and true freedom while respecting the natural rights of everyone around us.

Critical thinking has roots in western philosophy, from the influential philosophers Socrates, Plato, Aristotle, and Isocrates. Socrates, who lived from ~ 470 BC to 399 BC in Athens, was one of the founders of Western philosophy and is considered the first moral philosopher, a lover of truth and wisdom. The word philosopher comes from the word sophist but was used to differentiate between the negative aspect of sophist and a modest wise teacher, a philosopher.

Socrates created the Socratic method, a logical process with dialogue between individuals who ask and answer questions geared towards encouraging critical thinking between those discussing a topic at hand. He came up with this method when many in Athens started to view him as the wisest man in Greece. As he viewed it, this paradox was discussed by a series of questions that came to be known as the Socratic Method. The Socratic Method is used in which a defending point of view is questioned and refuted, giving the defending individual an opportunity to respond in kind. This process allows each debater to make an inquiry and instruction on the point of view while trying to elicit a clear and consistent expression that is agreed upon by rational thinkers. The back-and-forth of questions and answers is typical in debates, whereby a hypothesis can be eliminated when contradictions and logical fallacies are found.

This process took on a new form called the Scientific Method - determining truth from falsehoods by using laboratory-controlled experiments to test hypotheses. Science is not true or false but a process to determine if something is true or false. There can be many reasons why the results of research we are told could be incorrect. Many today see science as a belief structure -always true- but only if it confirms their biases (Science!^{TM}), which makes it difficult to convince and persuade, not manipulate, others into thinking differently, even if laboratory studies show their point of view is potentially incorrect.

"If you are trying to get at me as a public health official and scientist, you're really attacking not only Dr. Anthony Fauci, you are attacking science." – Dr. Anthony Fauci, *MSNBC Interview*, June 9th, 2021

Grammar, the art of letters, is a structured set of rules about words and phrases and the meaning behind those in an understandable format -words have objective meanings. In the sense of the Trivium, Grammar is the place we methodically and coherently gather factual data in its raw and root forms. It is the place where we gather root and modern definitions, themes, and context around the data. It is the place where objective reality is separated from subjective reality. It is a place to order the evidence into a systematic knowledge base. This body of knowledge is the foundation for Rhetoric. As new information is presented, it must be checked against the body of knowledge that has been previously collected to determine if it changes anything. Debating cannot start and end in the world of Rhetoric unless the goal is to control and manipulate others.

Root definitions are the earliest we can go back to a word's meaning. Root definitions provide a foundation from which objective and subjective language can be separated and objective reality can be agreed upon. A major problem with communication in today's society is that it is common to be sloppy or purposefully sophist when defining terms -making words extremely subjective. From a root definition, a theme presents itself with how the word was used and evolved.

"A definition is the start of an argument, not the end of one." – Neil Postman, *Crazy Talk, Stupid Talk : How We Defeat Ourselves by the Way We Talk and What to do About It*, 1976

Many words have themes and topics attached to them that have relationships to other identified characteristics, creating the subject and focus of what is being discussed. These connections and relationships play into context, a communicative tool that provides the framework of the event and resources for the interpretation of that event. Context can provide evidence of when and why the meaning of a word changes during an event. Context comes with its own common vernacular -its colloquialism- which includes everyday speech, language, and slang, which can alter and change the meaning of a word. Now, this doesn't mean the use of the word is correct, only that the usage of the word changed during that period. It is still a subjective word usage and doesn't reflect the truth of the definition and theme. Words can be broken down into greater detail if required, but the purpose of a word shouldn't change unless you want to be a sophist.

Objectivity is the condition or quality of being a tangible thing, something presented to our senses. Objectivity requires the ability to think critically about an object or subject, reducing the subjective opinions of oneself and external influences. Objectivity is required to seek out, determine, and understand the truth of our reality. This truth is only as strong and correct as the information and data used at the start of the process. Grammar requires objectivity, or the truth will constantly shift and move, never being really understood. Trusting in a body of knowledge must be based on factual and observable objective evidence, not made up of subjectivity that convinces us of something that isn't true. Reality is based on facts, rules, laws, and principles, while our interpretation of this reality is subjective and tends to be wrong.

Logic provides the ability for self-growth by processing the knowledge base collected during Grammar, then removing paradoxes, fallacies, and biases that we all have within ourselves and removing these from the rhetoric of others. Logic came from the Greek root word Logos, meaning word, reason, speech, and idea. Words convey meanings and ideas, and they must be rooted in objective reality to be effective, or confusion will remain. Logic, when used properly, should reflect the rules on how to process reality. Some people's perception of logic might be less logical than that of others. We need to be careful because the semantics of a single word can change the truth conditions within logic. This is another reason why the first step of the Trivium -Grammar- is so important, especially regarding root definitions. Logic and the concept of truth are found and discussed in all fields of study in everyday life we find ourselves. We use Logic to process information to determine whether it is subjective -relative- or objective -absolute. The why of a subject is answered during the Logic process of the Trivium, bringing us toward a systematic understanding of the subject being discussed. Even during the Logic process, if new information is presented, we must move back up to Grammar and start the process over.

A paradox occurs when one's statement contradicts one's stated opinion; it is an analysis examining contradictory information in which conclusions are used to justify or reconcile the conflicting information. One of the oldest known paradoxes is the Epimenides paradox (~600 BC), when Epimenides, a Cretan, claimed that "all Cretans are liars," creating a paradox and a fallacious generalized statement. This statement can be true or false depending on the meanings behind the statement as well as the subjective opinion being used to view the statement. Is he lying or telling the truth? Many paradoxes are only subjective twists in language using words within a statement that could have multiple meanings, creating confusion and paradoxes. Many different paradoxes arise from sophistry and the use of only rhetoric.

Western logic started and flourished under Aristotle creating Syllogism and Term logic, but Stoic logic and Propositional logic also held sway during that time. Syllogism is a logical argument using deductive reasoning based on two or more propositions viewed as either true or false. The difference between inductive and deductive reasoning is that the conclusion of inductive reasoning may be probably true, while conclusions of deductive reasoning are certainly true. The conclusion can be false using inductive reasoning, so premises are viewed as either strong or weak versus valid or invalid, as with deductive reasoning.

Logical fallacies are broken into two categories: formal and informal fallacies. Fallacies are reasoned thoughts and statements with defects in the logical structure that misleads and deceives those receiving them. The difference between the formal and informal variants is that informal fallacies are valid in form but have one or more false premises, making the conclusion false. A few of the significant logical fallacies I see being used en masse are:

- **Appeal to Authority** "I am a doctor, so you should trust me without question" or "Government said x to be true, so it must be true"
- **Appeal to Emotion** "Think of the children!" or "Think of the hospital workers!"
- **Ad hominem** "You are selfish if you do not do this!"
- Idiom **Moving the Goalposts** "two weeks," "get one or two injections, and you can stop wearing masks," or "only one booster is needed"

Additionally apt is the Broken Window fallacy -coined by French economist Frédéric Bastiat in 1850- is an illusionary concept used by governments, where someone breaks a window, someone else fixes it, then people cite the exchange of money, resources, and labor as proof that the economy is growing and is healthy. Bastiat used this parable to show that the money spent to fix the broken window is not a net benefit to the economy and society.

We need to look at facts and the process of science to avoid the pitfalls of fallacies, but be wary of using it as a crutch. The Argument from Fallacy -or Fallacy Fallacy- is the fallacy that uses the assumption that if the statement has a fallacy, therefore, the conclusion is false. We know that a conclusion can be true even with logical fallacies found within. There are countless logical fallacies in existence, and we will continue to discover more as we evolve and grow in the field of Logic.

Cognitive bias is an expedient means of processing information and data. I want to mention here that not all cognitive biases are useless or irrational, e.g., heuristics: "rule of thumb," but it must be remembered that it is a practical method, so it is not perfect. The human brain uses heuristics to practically solve problems and learn by speeding up the process to solution and resolution. From this process, biases are formed to help process the information quickly. Most of the time, cognitive biases have paradoxes and fallacies found within them, creating a bad mental habit that further degrades an individual's critical thinking skill set. As long as we are aware of these mental shortcuts and that they need to be challenged with the truth and evidence, we will continue to grow our skill set in critical thinking.

Once we start removing our paradoxes, logical fallacies, and cognitive biases, we will begin to gain a systematic understanding of the presented information. This systematic understanding of information grows as we increase our knowledge base, setting us up for the final step of the Trivium, Rhetoric. Even with objectively factual evidence, we will most likely have flawed rhetoric if we have poor and inefficient logic. Proper Grammar and Logic are fundamental to understanding reality and consciousness.

Rhetoric is where we ask and answer the how questions. This is where we turn the knowledge base of the objective reality of a subject, and the evidence that supports it, absent paradoxes, logical fallacies, and cognitive biases that we find, into systematically usable knowledge and understanding of the conclusions from Grammar and Logic. At any point when new information is provided, the process repeats in a never-ending cycle of determining truthful Rhetoric. Sophists have mainly used rhetoric to manipulate others without the use, or incorrect use, of Grammar and Logic.

Rhetoric started in Mesopotamia, ~2000 BC, with Akkadian literature containing enormous amounts of text regarding mythology, science, letters, legality, and rights. Still, the structure for Rhetoric we know today started with Aristotle's stand against sophistry. Aristotle's work on Rhetoric came in the form of three books which looks more like student notes potentially not meant to be published. Aristotle viewed rhetoric as having three means of persuasion: Ethos, Pathos, and Logos. Ethos is our habitual character, beliefs, morals, and ideals at an individual and community level. Pathos is the potential pain and suffering of the experience of going through something and the appeals made to the emotion and ideals of that experience. Logos is our speech, discourse, and accounts of a given situation tempered with reason and understanding.

Isocrates was one of the ten Attic orators that pushed rhetoric -the art of discourse- as a primary art form emphasizing eloquent public speaking above all, not necessarily the truth. Dialectics and rhetoric are different in that dialectics are used for truth-based discovery where the purpose of the discourse is to come to a reasoned truth; rhetoric without a subjective logic like emotional appeals. Isocrates started the first academy in Rhetoric as he felt that rhetoric was the best tool to inform, persuade, manipulate, and motivate others in political life using heuristics. Isocrates' main work on rhetoric was written in *Against the Sophists*, in which he responded to some of the negative criticisms of sophistry at the time. Isocrates was the main reason the word sophist took a negative connotation still seen today. Socrates, Plato, and Aristotle's negative view of sophistry came from orators having a weak knowledge base, faulty logic, and providing rhetoric that was used to control and govern the minds of society.

Rhetoric concerns itself with the effects on the audience more so than if the statements being made were true and correct or if the statements purposely omitted facts. This is different from the Rhetoric of the Trivium, which focuses on the systematic understanding of objective reality's truth; facts should not be omitted nor overlooked. Therefore, Rhetoric must be accompanied by Grammar and Logic. This is good to remember when rhetoric is being spoken to us since most politicians are skilled rhetoricians. If it doesn't have proper Grammar and Logic, chances are it is being used to manipulate and control, I mean to govern, you.

If new information changes our rhetoric, then so be it. We want the truth, correct? We must accept that we could be wrong and be willing to move from deeply held beliefs and biases to seek our reality's truth. Trust in your ability to learn critical thinking as a skill set, but it starts with the understanding that we must address our logical fallacies and hard-held beliefs. Everyone has fallacies and errors in their thought processes, believing in things that are not factually true, so it is up to us to correct our thought processes.

"I part with the book with deep seriousness, in the sure hope that sooner or later it will reach those to whom alone it can be addressed; and for the rest, patiently resigned that the same fate should, in full measure, befall it, that in all ages has, to some extent, befallen all knowledge, and especially the weightiest knowledge of the truth, to which only a brief triumph is allotted between the two long periods in which it is condemned as paradoxical or disparaged as trivial. The former fate is also wont to befall its author." – Arthur Schopenhauer, *The World as Will and Representation*, 1819

Trusting Government

"We are fast approaching the stage of the ultimate inversion: the stage where the government is free to do anything it pleases, while the citizens may act only by permission; which is the stage of the darkest periods of human history, the stage of rule by brute force." – Ayn Rand, *The Virtue of Selfishness*, 1964

First, we need to define government. What is government to you? How do you define it? When you think about any government, do you feel a sense of pride and admiration toward it? Do you think the government, people in power over you who can dictate your life at any level, really are there to protect and serve you? Do governments and its agents have your back in dangerous situations? What if the government causes these dangerous situations? Think about these questions and reflect on them throughout this chapter and book because your health and safety depend on the answers to these questions.

Government, govern (control) + -ment (tool or action), using root definitions, means a tool or action of control. How different is this definition from the one you thought of? Innocent people can't be free if they are being controlled. Who should be controlled? Criminals - those who create victims. No victim, no crime. What do you do when criminals, unethical individuals, and secretive groups run the government and have power and influence over those stopping criminals? In this situation, do you think the justice system would act with ethical morality, or would it be a corrupt institution?

To answer this, let's first start with the family unit. In a broader sense, children should be controlled by their parents, but this isn't a government regarding the theme and context of the word government used throughout this book and society. Of course, this doesn't mean parents are allowed to beat and abuse their children. Parents are still capable of victimizing their children and should face justice when it happens. Anyone is capable of victimizing someone else. Capability doesn't imply guilt. We are all born with the same inalienable rights: Life, Freedom, and Property. This idea isn't only bound to U.S. citizens, but it is an idea that spans all of humanity and can be found written within the fabric of nature and our reality. Think of rights like bubbles around each of us. When an issue happens, and a bubble is popped, it must be determined if a right was violated by accident or with intent and if fault can be assigned and restitutions determined. If no bubbles are popped, everyone can go about their lives without needing to be controlled or restrained.

"Of liberty I would say that, in the whole plenitude of its extent, it is unobstructed action according to our will. But rightful liberty is unobstructed action according to our will within limits drawn around us by the equal rights of others. I do not add "within the limits of the law" because law is often but the tyrant's will, and always so when it violates the rights of the individual." – Thomas Jefferson, *Letter to Isaac H.*, April 4th, 1819

When you say the word government, it elicits a response from others. For most, I would bet, a very adverse reaction, even though most cannot accept a reality where the government doesn't exist. When you are dealing with words, you need to understand the root definition, theme, and context of how the word is being used, as well as when it is being used, or translation can be lost. Sophistry is a real thing, and it is used to control and manipulate the masses. Plato said the government has a lifecycle, which still holds today, even though most don't realize this truth. We are witnessing the progression of government on a global scale heading toward full-blown tyranny. After Democracy comes Tyranny, and I believe that we have entered this late-stage government, Tyranny. This should be concerning for everyone because it will only worsen exponentially.

In 2016, I published an article covering the definition of terrorism and how it has changed with how the government defines terrorism. Many don't understand that the root definition of terrorism is "government intimidation […] great fear, alarm, panic" (Online Etymology Dictionary). The idea of terrorism was coined when the French government committed atrocities against its civilians during the Reign of Terror (1793 – 1794). As we move through this chapter, I will make the case that the U.S. government is the world's largest terrorist organization based on the root definition of terrorism.

In 2021, the U.S. had 750 military bases in 80 countries, with a military budget larger than the following ten largest countries combined. For the fiscal year 2022, the U.S. military budget was $1.5 trillion. This is our tax dollars hard at work. Over the last 70 years, the U.S. government has operated militarily and with special operation units in over 80 counties, dropping over 300 thousand bombs over the past 20 years. Yet, in early 2022, the masses in the U.S. were very upset that Russia invaded a country run by a government with heavy ties to Nazis? Where was the outrage about what our government has been doing for decades worldwide? Being upset with one and not the other is fallacious thinking. If we include all governments throughout history, there are thousands of years of evidence showing governments consistently committing atrocities and tyrannical acts, with many against its citizens. This chapter will focus on the U.S. government.

Why does the U.S. government define terrorism as not including government actions against its citizens? Maybe it is because if it defined terrorism as government intimidation, many would associate the U.S. government and governments worldwide with terrorist organizations. This change in definition is sophistry in action used to manipulate and control. The belief that government is anything but tyrannical is a fallacy. Government always leads to tyranny; therefore, it is tyrannical in nature.

A conspiracy theory is a point of view that a group is plotting something sinister -often in secret- using direct movements and actions to control what is being seen, like in the sense of theater. A good conspiracy can be hard to prove. Conspiracy theories are absolutely real, but not every conspiracy theory is accurate or real. If they never existed, how did the phrase come into existence? It was in 1967 that the Central Intelligence Agency (CIA) focused on turning the term conspiracy theory into a negative connotation, making it easier to discredit the truth from being discovered around the John F. Kennedy (JFK) assassination. The official dispatch describing the focus and push was titled *Countering Criticism of the Warren Report* and was declassified in 1998.

In 2019, the Federal Bureau of Investigation (FBI) started identifying conspiracy theorists as domestic terrorists, which means if we don't believe in the approved government rhetoric being pushed, we are considered domestic terrorists. Do you think that questioning the government is indicative of terroristic behavior? When you think of the phrase "conspiracy theory," what reaction does it elicit? Is it in a negative or positive light? If negative, could it be due to the constant push by the government to turn "conspiracy theory" into a negative connotation for the last 55 years?

With the proper symbols and words, one can elicit changes in consciousness in the viewers. This an important aspect to remember when researching conspiracy theories. Symbols are significant, highly important, and can be seen in things like money - all-seeing eye-, government logos, and have been used throughout history to signify something potentially important. These symbols also include numbers like 666 -the Mark of the Beast (*A Revelation to John* 13:1-18)- which has been associated with evil and Satanic rituals for two millennia. Secret societies and groups have used symbols and numerology as far back as written history can take us and should never be discounted or discredited as only a crackpot conspiracy when the theory involves a religious and spiritual aspect.

The government has perfected psychological operations (psyops) and uses them constantly in expertly planned propaganda campaigns that have stoked the fires of fear for years. During the Iraq war, the U.S. government spent over $500 million on creating fake Al-Qaeda propaganda videos that helped sway U.S. public opinion on the war and atrocities being committed in Iraq. This was reported in the media, but as with anything important, it was buried in other "news." Over the last few years, billions in taxpayer funds have been used to create COVID19 propaganda for citizens, primarily focusing on pushing vaccines created by corporations with liability protection provided by the government. These vaccines have generated billions in taxpayer funds for for-profit organizations and pharmaceutical corporations. Do you not see the conflict of interests and issues this has created or the large swaths of wealth being transferred to the few from the many?

The vast majority of the U.S. money supply is debited and credited digitally to commercial banks, which the commercial banks then order money to be created for use and distribution. Trillions in new currency have been made between the Federal Reserve, increasing their asset-liability to $9 trillion, and commercial banks putting in orders for new currency. 80% of all U.S. dollars in circulation were printed in 2020 and 2021, with the majority in the name of COVID19 relief and support. This flood of newly printed currency in circulation, and the creation of a greater supply of assets on paper, is both correlative to and causative of the extremely high inflation rates that the U.S. economy was seeing in 2022. Things will only worsen with the national debt reaching $31 trillion in 2022. Anyone who paid attention to basic economics would know that printing new money devalues currency, changing supply and demand. Yet, we are told that the "experts" didn't understand why inflation is so high even though plenty of people said this would happen. Even trying to question this immoral and unethical funding issue surrounding COVID19 government responses is considered anti-science and terroristic behavior by the masses. At least, that is what mainstream media pushes as the narrative.

What are police (law enforcement officer)? The etymology of the word police has the same meaning as policy, "way of management," and comes from the Latin word *politia*, "civil administrator," and the Greek word *polis*, "ancient Greek city-state." Enforcement means "constraint, compulsion" and comes from the Old French word *enforcier*, "strengthen, reinforce; use force (on), offer violence (to); oppress; violate, rape" (Online Etymology Dictionary). The word officer comes from Latin *officium*, "a service, a duty." A police enforcement officer is someone whose service and duty are to force us to comply, "management," with a city-state's regulations and policies, which has a theme and context around the idea of violence and rape. The duty of the police is that of a policy enforcer. Policy enforcers enforce policies set down without care for the nature of the policy nor the level of tyranny it executes. This is not the actions of peacekeepers.

What is a peacekeeper? Peace comes from the Latin word *pacem*, "compact, agreement, treaty of peace, tranquility, absence of war," and keeper, "one who has charge of some person or thing, warden," so a peace-keeper is someone who has taken charge and become a warden of peace and the absence of war (Online Etymology Dictionary). Police enforcement officers have become militarized over the years, which is the opposite of what a peacekeeper should be. Police are policy enforcers; they are not peacekeepers and should not be confused with peacekeepers. Modern-day policy enforcers are tantamount to the redcoats from the Revolutionary War. This is the current state of our police force within the United States. There will always be those willing to commit violence on someone's behalf, whether for a gang ruler or a government ruler. Why should we appeal to their authority and blindly be obedient to them? Thomas Jefferson said that the law was often nothing but a tyrant's will, and those who enforce that will enforce tyranny. There is no law too small that the government will not kill over.

Appellate court case *Warren v. District of Columbia*, 444 A.2d 1 (D.C. Ct. of App. 1981), found that the "fundamental principle of American law is that a government and its agents are under no general duty to provide public services, such as police protection, to any individual citizen." Later the Supreme Court case *DeShaney v. Winnebago County Department of Social Services*, 489 U.S. 189 (1989), determined that the government only had a duty to protect and serve those physically restrained by the government, those in prisons and jails, and who could not defend themselves. These two court cases show that "protect and serve" was always a myth and lie, regardless of how often it was said. Can we trust police enforcement if they have no duty to protect and serve?

For instance, at the time of writing this section, the Texas Uvalde shooting had recently occurred. As more information came out, it was clear that the police and government agents failed at every step to stop a mass shooting of children while waiting up to an hour to intervene as children were being killed. Worse, some policy enforcers went into the school to secure *their* children, not worrying about the rest, before attempting to stop the shooter. Government policy enforcers are only here to enforce laws and policies set before them, even if the orders are tyrannical. Nazi soldiers and Nazi policy enforcers were enforcing the policies set before them, correct? There will always be those willing to commit evil at the command of others.

Slavery has existed as far back as government, with some historians providing evidence of slavery existing roughly 11,000 years ago. Most would agree that slavery is inherently wrong and should be abolished throughout the world, yet U.S. law and the U.S. Constitution allow slavery; therefore, the idea of the law as a basis for what is acceptable as a standard for how we should coexist with each other is a poor litmus test. Many would disagree that slavery is legal in the U.S., but they have failed to realize what was legalized when the Thirteenth Amendment was written.

U.S. Constitution - Thirteenth Amendment

"Neither slavery nor involuntary servitude, except as a punishment for crime whereof the party shall have been duly convicted, shall exist within the United States, or any place subject to their jurisdiction."

Read it again. The Thirteenth Amendment legalized slavery using the exception of being "duly convicted" of a "crime." It did not abolish slavery; it only limited it in scope so a profitable industry - slave labor- could be easier to control.

Who defines the word crime, and who is targeted with enforcement of the crime? Being duly convicted of a crime is a generic and broad-reaching statement based on what the government views as a crime (e.g., jaywalking). Slavery is very much alive and well in the U.S. Look no further than in the U.S. prison system to see legalized slavery which disproportionately targets black people (e.g., jaywalking) or other specific minorities when it suits the government. Roughly 20% of the world's prison population is found within the U.S., and many jailed are minorities. It is a fact that U.S. law at all levels was built atop views of racism and bigotry. How many feel President Lincoln, who "freed the slaves," was a great president? Did you know that Lincoln's Emancipation Proclamation, which set slaves free, was only targeted at the rebellious Southern states and that in the Northern states, slavery continued without issue for years later? If Lincoln could have saved the Union without setting a single slave free, he would have done it without question. Lincoln was very open about his views on blacks and slavery.

"I am not, nor ever have been, in favor of bringing about in any way the social and political equality of the white and black races, that I am not, nor ever have been, in favor of making voters or jurors of negroes, nor of qualifying them to hold office, nor to intermarry with white people; and I will say in addition to this that there is a physical difference between the white and black races which I believe will forever forbid the two races living together on terms of social and political equity ... I will add to this that I have never seen, to my knowledge, a man, woman, or child who was in favor of producing a perfect equality, social and political, between negroes and white men." – Abraham Lincoln, *Campaign Speech*, September 18th, 1858

If someone is duly convicted of a crime, they can be a legal slave and have their life, liberty, or property forfeited. Due process is essential to protecting freedom and rights -innocent until proven guilty, as they allegedly say- but in the U.S., it has become guilty until proven innocent. Even if someone can prove innocence, they may continue to lose all their rights and freedoms and be sent to jail or prison. This can be seen in the explosion of civil asset forfeiture over the years and an ever-increasing jail and prison population. Policy enforcers have abused forfeiture laws so much that civil asset forfeiture outpaces criminal theft each year.

U.S. Constitution - Fourteenth Amendment

"All persons born or naturalized in the United States, and subject to the jurisdiction thereof, are citizens of the United States and of the state wherein they reside. No state shall make or enforce any law which shall abridge the privileges or immunities of citizens of the

United States; nor shall any state deprive any person of life, liberty,
or property, without due process of law; nor deny to any person
within its jurisdiction the equal protection of the laws."

The Fourteenth Amendment, which surrounds the idea of privacy
and bodily autonomy -e.g., *Roe v. Wade*, 410 U.S. 113 (1973)- has
been slowly eroding for decades. On June 24th, 2022, the Supreme
Court overturned Roe v. Wade; this is a slippery slope because of the
bodily autonomy aspect of the case -ignoring the debate around what
is considered a human life with guaranteed rights. If we do not have
bodily autonomy, "my body, my choice," then we do not have the
choice to say, "no, I do not want that medicine injected into my
body," nor can we say, "no, I do not want X taken from my body."
The path we are heading down could easily lead us to mandatory
injections or abortions due to some pandemic or climate emergency.

"The very word "secrecy" is repugnant in a free and open society;
and we are as a people inherently and historically opposed to secret
societies, to secret oaths and to secret proceedings...Our way of life
is under attack. Those who make themselves our enemy are
advancing around the globe...no war ever posed a greater threat to
our security. If you are awaiting a finding of "clear and present
danger," then I can only say that the danger has never been more
clear and its presence has never been more imminent...For we are
opposed around the world by a monolithic and ruthless conspiracy
that relies primarily on covert means for expanding its sphere of
influence—on infiltration instead of invasion, on subversion instead of
elections, on intimidation instead of free choice, on guerrillas by
night instead of armies by day. It is a system which has conscripted
vast human and material resources into the building of a tightly knit,
highly efficient machine that combines military, diplomatic,
intelligence, economic, scientific and political operations. Its
preparations are concealed, not published. Its mistakes are buried,

not headlined. Its dissenters are silenced, not praised. No expenditure is questioned, no rumor is printed, no secret is revealed." – John F. Kennedy, *President and the Press*, April 27th, 1961

JFK -35th president of the U.S.- was assassinated on November 22nd, 1963, in Dallas, Texas, during a presidential parade. During his time in office, JFK spoke out against secret societies and the invisible hand directing the U.S. from within high levels of the government while standing against government operations that targeted U.S. citizens, e.g., Operation Northwoods. The official narrative of the assassination of JFK was that it would blame Lee Harvey Oswald -a Marine veteran- who was gunned down by Jack Ruby two days after the JFK assassination on live TV. Before his death, Oswald claimed he wasn't responsible for JFK's assassination and was being used as a "patsy" for a government intelligence operation. A picture exists of what looks to be Oswald standing in front of the book depository as the motorcade drives by, which means -if true- Oswald could not have assassinated JFK, and we all have been lied to for decades.

Oswald was initially arrested for the murder of J. D. Tippit -former Army veteran and 11-year veteran with the Dallas Police Department- which occurred 45 minutes after the JFK assassination before being blamed for the death of JFK. A declassified document released in October 2017 showed that Tippit was identified as the real JFK assassin by an FBI informant. The FBI informant noted that a week before JFK's assassination, Tippit met with Oswald at Ruby's nightclub. The FBI informant provided this information to the FBI on March 26th, 1964. Dr. Lousi Jolyon West -an MKUltra psychiatrist who researched LSD and brainwashing- was appointed as Ruby's psychiatrist after his murder of Oswald, in which Dr. West deemed Ruby psychotic and delusional.

In 1957, during his time in the Marines, Oswald was stationed at Atsugi naval air base in Japan -the CIA researched psychedelic drugs to study mind control. James Wilcott Jr. -a finance clerk working for the CIA- claimed in a memorandum from 1978 that the CIA had hired Oswald during his time at Atsugi. In December 2022, the CIA released all but a few thousand documents related to the JFK assassination by order of President Joseph Biden. Through this release, additional information has come out potentially showing that Oswald was involved in a CIA intelligence operation in the summer of 1963 -months before JFK was assassinated- and had been in contact with a KGB agent in Mexico City on September 28th, 1963. Why is the CIA refusing to release all documents related to the JFK assassination? Would those documents confirm that the CIA had a pivotal role in the death of JFK? Why should we trust a government that potentially kills its president and lies to the public with impunity hiding the truth?

To add confusion to the conspiracy, Milton William Cooper - writer of the 1991 book *Behold a Pale Horse*- presented evidence that JFK was assassinated by his driver, Secret Service agent William Greer, who supposedly used a compressed air -gas-powered- handgun to fire the fatal shot that entered JFK's head killing him. One video captures the assassination on film in which Greer looks to be pulling something out into his left hand, turning to face JFK -breaking security procedures in the process- then seems to point something at JFK over his right shoulder turning quickly back to face forward after JFK's head explodes. This would explain the "back and to the left" movement of JFK's head that led many to think there was a second shooter on the Grassy Knoll. The video is somewhat unclear and shaky, so it is hard to confirm that Greer had a device in his hand; however, the technology existed and could have been used. For an operation like this, multiple shooters would have resulted in a higher chance of success. The lone gunman theory is unlikely. Could Trippit have been the initial shooter, with Greer completing the mission objective?

Cooper explained that the assassination was due to JFK's plan to release evidence that extraterrestrials were plotting to take over Earth.

This, of course, sounds crazy and unbelievable, but is it? On December 8th, 2020, former Israeli Defense Ministry's Space Security Chief Haim Eshed announced that extraterrestrials were real, that there was a galactic federation, and that these aliens had been in contact with the U.S. and other country government officials for decades, but were waiting until humanity reached a higher level of technological advancement before making themselves known publicly. If this is true, and JFK was going to release this information, he would have been viewed as a security risk needing to be taken out.

The U.S. government has conducted experiments on innocent non-consenting individuals, poisoned and massacred the innocent en masse, destabilized regions, toppled foreign governments, and ran guns and drugs to terrorist organizations, cartels, and inner-city communities. Groups of rulers and influencers that sway power to enact global changes often meet in secret -or what is discussed is kept secret- which has negatively affected many worldwide since ancient times. Here is a short list of U.S. government actions, experiments, and secret societies in the U.S. showing evidence of this truth:

Alcohol Prohibition – From 1920 to 1933, a push from protestant religious members helped enact a federal ban on the production, manufacture, transportation, and sale of alcohol which caused an increase in crime and violence by gangs and mafias entering the bootleg alcohol market. To combat the bootleg sale of alcohol, the federal government decided to increase the number of specific chemicals (e.g., benzene, mercury, and methanol) found in industrial alcohols used to create bootleg alcohol. Roughly 10,000 individuals died from a direct cause of the federal government adding poison to the supply chain.

Tuskegee Experiment – The United States Public Health Service, under the guise of free healthcare, experimented on untreated syphilis using 600 black men. Free injections were given as treatment for "bad blood," infecting 399 with syphilis and 201 as the control. Informed consent was not gathered. Roughly 30 died directly because of syphilis. Approximately 100 died of related complications. Dozens passed syphilis on to their partners, which also caused children to be born with congenital syphilis. The study was conducted from 1932 to 1972.

Operation Paperclip – The U.S. government brought more than 1,600 Nazi scientists, engineers, and technicians to the U.S. to work for the government instead of facing crimes for their atrocities between 1945 -1959. Many of the experiments were continued in secret in the U.S. and continue to this day, with projects and experiments being given new names once discovered. In June 1946, the U.S. established the Gehlen Organization intelligence agency in occupied Germany, headed by Reinhard Gehlen -Major General and head of military intelligence on the Eastern Front for the Nazis during WWII. The Gehlen Organization hired hundreds of former Nazi Party members. On April 1st, 1956, the Gehlen Organization was rebranded to the Federal Intelligence Service, which is still Germany's foreign intelligence agency.

Operation Sea-spray – The U.S. Army conducted bacterial warfare tests across the country in multiple cities from 1949 to 1969 by releasing live bacteria into the fog over non-consenting citizens. It was only discovered because of a spike of infections in local hospitals at the time of spraying, with one person dying. How many other operations like this have been conducted or are still ongoing without the knowledge of the public? Don't discredit those who talk about chemtrails because the government has openly admitted to spraying the skies with chemicals for experiments and other purposes. This spraying has not stopped nor slowed down.

On June 29th, 2016, CIA Director John Brennan gave a speech at the Council of Foreign Relations where he admitted that the CIA had been working on geoengineering, weather modification, and spraying the sky using stratospheric aerosol injection -chemtrails. I find it interesting that Brennan -who voted for the communist party in 1976- was the station chief of Jeddah, Saudi Arabia in the 1980s and station chief of Riyadh, Saudi Arabia, leading up to 9/11. 15 out of 19 hijackers from Saudi Arabia had their visas stamped from the U.S. Consulate in Jeddah and the U.S. Embassy in Riyadh. In March 2001, Brennan became the deputy executive director of the CIA.

MKUltra – With the help of dozens of scientists, the CIA conducted LSD mind control experimentation on many non-consenting and unsuspecting subjects. Sidney Gottlieb ran this operation. These tests included brainwashing and psychological torture. Experiments and studies took place from 1953 to 1973. Dr. Henry Murray, who trained CIA spies during World War II, conducted some psychological experiments and torture at Harvard University. One Harvard test subject was 16-year-old Ted Kaczynski, who later became the Unabomber.

Dr. Louis Jolyon West was another psychiatrist working under the MKUltra project researching LSD and brainwashing techniques from Cornell University. Dr. West admitted that he developed the ability to implant false memories in subjects. Freelance journalist Tom O'Neill wrote *CHAOS: Charles Manson, the CIA, and the Secret History of the Sixties*, in which he connects Charles Manson to MKUltra and CIA mind control experiments. CIA Director Richard Helms ordered the destruction of files and evidence around MKUltra, hampering investigation efforts into these atrocities. How many Manchurian candidates does the CIA have as resources to push political agendas? How much of these efforts have been perfected over the decades?

Operation Midnight Climax – A sub-operation of MKUltra, this project was set up in multiple safehouses in multiple cities where the CIA paid women to lure subjects to a bugged and monitored room, have the women slip LSD to the subjects, and prod the subjects with leading questions to see if they would reveal secrets or if they would be susceptible to commit crimes. This took place from 1953 to 1964. The CIA had several other projects and operations dealing with controlling and convincing others to do things.

Human Radiation Experiments – The U.S. Department of Energy and its predecessors conducted hundreds of studies on many non-consenting subjects, many from state-run mental wards, by injecting plutonium and radium into unsuspecting individuals. Informed consent was not gained. The studies took place from the 1940s to 1970s.

COINTELPRO – With the support of congressional leadership, the FBI established a counterintelligence program in 1956 to monitor, expose, disrupt, misdirect, and discredit the Black Panther Party, the Communist Party, the Socialist Workers' Party, White Hate Groups, and the New Left. The Black Panther Party took the most focus, with Martin Luther King (MLK) Jr. under surveillance for years until his assassination. MLK Jr. was targeted by the FBI to be discredited and removed as an obstacle. It is not a stretch to think that the FBI had a hand in MLK Jr.'s assassination. Do you think the FBI has become more or less corrupt since the 1950s?

Operation Mockingbird – A CIA project from the 1950s through the 1970s that targeted U.S. journalists and religious clergy to use in intelligence operations to gain significant influence over newspapers and wire agencies. This operation was highly successful and has only grown in control and power over the decades. Government rhetoric highly influences mainstream media. This was also the time and operation when the CIA started to affect Hollywood and the production of commercial films. The CIA has gained further influence and control over the film industry as the decades have passed.

Operation Northwoods – On March 13th, 1962, U.S. military leaders developed and formally proposed a plan to kill Americans in a terrorist attack, blaming it on Cuba to drum up support for intervention. Think 9/11. JFK rejected this proposal. JFK was assassinated in 1963, with evidence suggesting the CIA's involvement. How many presidents since then have been shown evidence of the assassination and made to bend to the will of those controlling them by threat and intimidation? This operation proves that the U.S. government will target U.S. civilians to push agendas.

Operation CHAOS – A CIA domestic espionage operation that targeted Americans from 1967 to 1974. President Lyndon Johnson and President Richard Nixon approved this operation. The operation consolidated all domestic surveillance activities to determine any foreign contacts established to provide intelligence to foreign governments. The CIA had documented files on thousands of Americans and had reported that it found no evidence of foreign espionage among those targeted. How much evidence found was used as blackmail instead of being reported through official channels?

Kent State Massacre – On May 4th, 1970, during a peace rally opposing the Vietnam War's expansion into Cambodia at Kent State University (Kent, Ohio), the Ohio National Guard murdered four and wounded nine unarmed students. The National Guard had been called in due to rumors of businesses being threatened, students with caches of weapons, and plots to spike water supplies with LSD. On this day, roughly 2,000 protesters gathered on campus peacefully. After refusing to disperse, with teargas being deployed ineffectively, some students started throwing rocks at the guardsmen, which caused the National Guard to order the advancement on the students. At some point, a sergeant started shooting into the crowd of students causing other guardsmen to begin shooting, who later cited "fearing for their lives" as to why they started shooting. After 13 seconds of shooting, roughly 67 rounds had been fired into an unarmed crowd of students.

CIA-Contra Controversy Allegations – Contras was a U.S.-backed right-wing rebel group active in the 1980s and 1990s that committed terrorist attacks and violated human rights. The Contras trafficked cocaine for the CIA, helping bring massive amounts into the U.S. to help fund other operations and coups worldwide. The CIA ran the cocaine into the U.S., processed it into crack cocaine, then flooded it specifically into black communities during the 1980s. Laws were passed to target crack cocaine users where the sentencing disparity between crack and powder cocaine had a 100:1 ratio. This ratio was later reduced to 18:1 through the Fair Sentencing Act. Does that still seem fair, primarily when it generally targeted black communities?

I bring these allegations and evidence up because of Afghanistan and the opium trade. Before the U.S. entered Afghanistan in 2002, the Taliban banned growing opium in 2000. After the U.S. entered Afghanistan, the CIA took over the production of opium, using U.S. soldiers to protect the fields, which increased Afghanistan's output from 10% to 90%+ of the world's opium trade. I find it suspicious that the opium epidemic in the U.S. took off after the CIA started cultivating and dealing with opium from Afghanistan. There are pictures and stories from soldiers who had to risk their lives protecting these fields while deployed.

Northfield Laboratories, Inc. Blood Substitute (PolyHeme) – In 1997, Northfield Laboratories started a government trial testing their blood substitute, PolyHeme, with surgery patients in serious need of blood. By August 2001, Northfield Laboratories shut down the surgery trial before the completion date due to multiple heart attacks in the test group. In December 2003, the Food and Drug Administration (FDA) approved Northfield Laboratories to test PolyHeme with unconscious and non-responsive emergency patients who could not give informed consent; the trial focused on getting 360 patients who would receive the blood substitute and 360 patients would receive a saline solution. Of the 712 patients enrolled in the government study, the group given PolyHeme saw a 13.2% mortality rate, while the control group given the saline solution saw a 9.6% mortality rate. Due to the excess deaths caused by the product, the FDA denied the regulatory approval of its use in the market.

Operation Fast and Furious – From 2009 to 2011, this operation, one of the operations under Project Gunrunner (a project to combat Mexican Drug Cartels), the U.S. government helped arm Mexican Drug Cartels, which led to a sharp increase in violent crimes. You read that correctly. The U.S. government deliberately gave drug cartels weapons and resources under an operation with the stated goal of combating the drug cartels.

Operation Timber Sycamore – In 2013, the U.S. government, through the CIA under the Obama administration, armed Syrian rebels in an attempt to overthrow the Syrian government, which stood in alliance with Russia. Saudi Arabia and Israel also joined in with the CIA in funding and supplying these rebels with many resources, making their way to major terrorist organizations through the black market and not the "moderate" rebels that were promised to receive the resources. Evidence suggests that the CIA, with Israel's Intelligence Agency (Mossad), created ISIS/ISIL in the Middle East to help destabilize the region.

Bilderberg Group – Every year, roughly 130 political leaders, religious leaders, "elites," and experts from multiple industries gather privately to discuss issues and foster dialogue between Europe and North America. Scant details about agendas, no resolutions are released to the public, no votes are cataloged, and no thorough policy statements are issued. This secretive group annually plots the movements and actions of what the masses see and hear. Is believing that such a group -or some involved with this group- are potentially meeting for nefarious purposes that hard of a concept to accept?

Bohemian Grove – Another secretive elite invitation-only social club with an annual meeting. Founded in 1872, this club has had all types of political leaders, royalty, celebrities, artists, actors, lawyers, and journalists as members. In 1942 members of the Manhattan Project -which led to the creation of the atomic bomb- attended and discussed plans at the annual meeting. These individuals and groups significantly sway how society has operated and changed over the years. The meetings have been reported as being known for sex, drugs, and a culmination event of ritually burning a small empty coffin in front of a giant owl.

Freemasonry – One of the oldest secretive fraternal organizations, boasting a recorded 6 million members, has its roots in 13th-century stonemasons. Members gradually gain knowledge and understanding of Masonic ritualism and symbolism as they progress in standing and status within the organization. The Freemasons are made up of several groups, which comprise a worldwide network of men who share the same or similar thoughts and ideas. Many prominent figures like royalty, politicians, and celebrities throughout history have been members, e.g., Ludwig van Beethoven, Benjamin Franklin, Frederick the Great, J. Edgar Hoover, and many U.S. presidents like George Washington, Thomas Jefferson, Andrew Jackson, William Taft, Franklin D. Roosevelt, and Harry Truman.

Order 322 – This is the Skull and Bones secret society based out of Yale University, founded in 1832. Three members of the Skull and Bones secret society became U.S. presidents; William Taft, George H.W. Bush, and George W. Bush. Secret societies are very real and have had a direct influence over our entire lives.

Bavarian Illuminati – I bring this up because of the connection to Freemasonry and the modern usage of Illuminati. A former Jesuit named Adam Weishaupt founded the Bavarian Illuminati, -a secret organization- on May 1st, 1776, in Bavaria -now part of Germany. This movement and organization initially focused on "republican free thought" -ending all governments- while replacing Christianity and other religions with a religion of reason. This organization partnered with Freemasonry members and lodges to achieve its goals. Some figures suggest that roughly 600 to 2000 members were part of the Bavarian Illuminati at its peak. By 1785 -after infighting among members- the organization ceased activity; however, it is assumed that some within the organization continued with its efforts. On January 31st, 1800, Thomas Jefferson wrote to Bishop James Madison about Adam Weishaupt and the Bavarian Illuminati. There have been multiple Illuminati "enlightened" secret organizations that even predate the Bavarian Illuminati. The Eye of Providence "all-seeing eye" was used by Freemasonry and added to U.S. currency but was never associated with the original Bavarian Illuminati organization.

Here are some tools that have been used or are still in use to violate privacy and our rights. There are more that have yet to be publicly disclosed:

US-98XN – Also known as Prism, US-98XN was a top-secret National Security Agency (NSA) program birthed after the attacks of September 11th, 2001, and in operation during the Bush and Obama administration, where the government was given the legal authority to secretly collect intelligence data on US citizens from major tech companies and Internet providers.

Pegasus – A hacking tool that breaks into mobile phones and extracts the data and contents within the device. Pegasus was developed by the Israeli spyware company NSO Group Technologies Ltd. Due to a Freedom of Information Act (FOIA) request, it was released that the FBI had purchased Pegasus for "research purposes" and that the FBI had pressed to deploy hacking tools from late 2020 to early 2021 -created by the NSO Group. These tools were to be and are being used against U.S. citizens.

XKeyscore – An NSA program and tool that allows the NSA to collect nearly everything millions of users do on the Internet; emails, social media, browsing history, etc. NSA analysts had full access to all data without needing prior authorization for searches, which is against U.S. law. In July 2013, evidence of this program was released to the public by Edward Snowden.

Here are some of the U.S. interventions since WWII: Bomb attacks, assignations, sabotage, coups, and attempted regime changes:
- China, 1945-1946, 1950-1953
- Syria, 1949, 2011-2022
- Korea, 1950-1953
- Iran, 1953, 1987-1988
- Guatemala, 1954, 1964, 1967-1969
- Tibet, 1955-1970s
- Indonesia, 1958, 1965
- Cuba, 1959
- Democratic Republic of Congo, 1961, 1964
- Vietnam, 1961-1973
- Brazil, 1964, 2016

- British Guiana, 1964
- Laos, 1964-1973
- Dominican Republic, 1965-1966
- Peru, 1965
- Greece, 1967
- Cambodia, 1969-1970, 1980-1995
- Chile, 1970-1973
- Argentina, 1979
- Angola, 1976-1992
- Turkey, 1980
- Poland, 1980-1981
- El Salvador, 1981-1992
- Nicaragua, 1981-1990
- Lebanon, 1982-1984
- Grenada, 1983-1984
- Libya, 1986, 1989, 2011
- Philippines, 1989
- Panama, 1989-1990
- Haiti, 1991, 2004
- Iraq, 1991, 1992-1996, 1998, 2002-2022
- Kuwait, 1991
- Somalia, 1992-1994, 2006-2007, 2020, 2022
- Bosnia, 1995
- Sudan, 1998
- Afghanistan, 1998, 2001-2022
- Yugoslavia, 1999
- Yemen, 2002-2022
- Honduras, 2009
- Ukraine, 2014
- Bolivia, 2019
- Venezuela, 2019
- Guyana, 2020

Convicted pedophile and billionaire Jeffrey Epstein -a financial consultant- had close ties to many of the world's rich and powerful, e.g., President Donald Trump, President Bill Clinton, Bill Gates, and Prince Andrew. Epstein traveled the world, creating robust networks of connections and resources over decades. Epstein donated heavily to politicians in the U.S. and worldwide. Epstein flew presidents, politicians, and celebrities worldwide on his private jet -Lolita Express. Lolita is a book about a middle-aged literature professor having an obsession and fixation on a 12-year-old girl whom the professor sexually molests. President Clinton flew on Epstein's plane dozens of times. No client of Epstein has been brought to justice for participating in child sex trafficking, nor even their names released to the public.

Through his consulting firm, Intercontinental Assets Group, Inc., and financial management firm, J. Epstein & Company, Epstein found himself helping governments and the highly wealthy recover their stolen money and manage their vast assets. Epstein had clients worldwide. At one point, Epstein claimed that he worked for the CIA as an intelligence agent but later recanted that claim. Epstein even invested in a startup, Reporty Homeland Security, which is heavily connected to Israel's defense industry and Israeli Defense Forces (IDF). Epstein had significant leverage and evidence on the clients he serviced by concealing cameras throughout his properties that recorded his clients and associates sexually exploiting underage children to be used as blackmail and insurance policies. Several of Epstein's victims have publicly spoken out that Epstein had videos of highly-public and connected men raping underage children. The FBI has these videos, yet Epstein's clients have not been arrested, nor have the public seen this treasure trove of evidence. Could the FBI be using this evidence to blackmail these clients?

In August 2019, Epstein had been on suicide watch -after being arrested a second time for sex with minors and trafficking children- but was taken off of suicide watch and placed in a regular cell within the Special Housing Unit at the Metropolitan Correctional Center (MCC) in New York City. Two cameras were monitoring Epstein's cell door -no cameras inside his cell- yet both "malfunctioned" on the night of Epstein's "suicide." At the same time, guards failed to perform their regularly scheduled checks due to taking long extended breaks leaving Epstein unguarded. Reports indicate that other prisoners heard a struggle coming from Epstein's cell at the time of his supposed suicide. The autopsy found multiple broken bones in Epstein's neck consistent with strangulation rather than a simple bedsheet being self-administered, restricting oxygen and blood flow to the brain. In December 2019, months after his death, Epstein's bank -Southern Country International- had $15.5 million transferred to it by Epstein's estate, under Judge Carolyn Hermon-Purcell's control. The money was emptied from the account by the end of December 2019, and there is still no explanation for who authorized the transfer or withdrew the funds.

Epstein committing suicide is unlikely. More likely scenarios are that he was murdered, or a body double was murdered in his stead and Epstein is free -possibly living in some remote region after plastic surgery. One thing is certain, Epstein didn't kill himself. His supposed suicide was a boon for his known and unknown associates -e.g., Gates as their relationships became increasingly public in 2019 before the COVID19 pandemic began.

After Epstein's death, information released indicated that Epstein was working with Mossad and the CIA, gathering intelligence on the world's influential players. On September 9th, 2019, the former senior executive for Israel's Directorate of Military Intelligence, Ari Ben-Menshe, said during an interview with investigative journalist Zev Shalev that Epstein and Ghislaine Maxwell -girlfriend and co-conspirator- were working with Israeli intelligence in the 1980s. Maxwell's father, Robert Maxwell, had ties to the British Royal family, British Secret Intelligence Service (MI6), the Soviet KGB, and Mossad, with six current and former heads of Mossad attending his funeral in Israel in 1991. What if Epstein was an agent for these intelligence agencies and gathered intelligence and leverage against some of the most influential and connected individuals in the "elite" and corporation circles?

Child sex trafficking is a billion-dollar business industry that can only be done to this scale with the help of those working in governments worldwide. Ben Swann -an independent investigative journalist- addressed the concerns and questions that mainstream media journalists and news outlets weren't being investigated about the leaked Podesta emails potentially tying the Podesta brothers and some of the political elite to child sex trafficking. After Swann's special on Pizzagate, he was promptly shut down and reduced to only conducting generic news stories while his website was taken down. Swann's investigation brought up serious, legitimate questions about what was found in the leaked emails. Pizzagate can't be discounted when countless politicians, government officials, and those who work with children, e.g., teachers and school officials, have been criminally charged with child molestation and trafficking and distributing child pornography.

Here is a very small sample of examples of those in the political landscape having charges of child exploitation:
- Republican Party Chairman of Thurston County, Washington, Paul Ingram, was convicted in 1988 of sexually abusing his daughters in satanic rituals.
- Puerto Rican Republican Representative, Edison Misla Aldarondo, was arrested and convicted in 2002 for molesting his step-daughter and one of her friends and was sentenced to nine years in prison.
- Defense attorney and chairman of the Sussex County Republican Committee, Jeffrey Patti, was convicted in 2006 for possessing and distributing child pornography of a five-year-old victim.

- Former top Senate GOP aide, Jesse Ryan Loskarn, committed suicide in 2014 after being charged with possessing child pornography.
- Democratic Illinois State Representative Keith Farnham pleaded guilty in 2014 to distributing child pornography and was sentenced to eight years in prison. He had once bragged about molesting a six-year-old girl. Farnham had co-sponsored two bills that increased penalties for those convicted of child pornography.
- Former Democratic mayor of Dawson, Georgia, Christopher Wright, pleaded no contest in 2016 to child molestation and rape of a 12-year-old girl and was sentenced to 20 years on probation.
- Former Democratic mayor of Hubbard, Ohio, Richard Keenan, pleaded guilty to raping a four-year-old over two years and received a life sentence in 2017.
- Democratic Representative Anthony Weiner -husband to Huma Abedin (vice chair of Hillary Clinton's 2016 presidential campaign)- pleaded guilty in 2017 to child pornography charges and sexting with a 15-year-old minor.
- Republican Pennsylvania State Senate politician, Michael Folmer, pleaded guilty in 2020 to possessing child pornography and was sentenced to up to two years in county jail plus eight years of probation.

With the potential that any politician in office could be a pedophile seeking greater power and resources to continue their immoral and abhorrent behavior, things like Pizzagate cannot be discounted outright as fake news because the government and mainstream media say so. Legitimate questions exist and should be investigated. This small list is mainly of those who have been voted and elected into their positions. Corrupt people seek power and control over the innocent to continue their immoral and unethical conduct.

Voting is not and has never been the cause of a successful revolution to greater freedom. Voting harder is not a solution; it is part of the problem. Voting for the lesser evil is still evil and has taken us down a slow, then-fast path toward tyranny. The speed at which we reach greater depths of tyranny depends on the votes or manufactured votes counted and how they can manipulate people into voting. Remember all this information the next time there is a shooting and the government starts to push for greater control and restriction against our ability to defend ourselves from a tyrannical government or low-level common criminals. How many mass casualty events were perpetrated and pushed by the government and blamed on something else to drive or cover up a classified agenda that we might never know the truth about? It is healthy and essential for our future to have a natural distrust of the government and government-forced authority. We all should be able to agree that the government should not be trusted at face value.

"From the standpoint of policy and program, the focal point of the World Population Conference (WPC) at Bucharest, Romania, in August 1974, was the World Population Plan of Action (WPPA). The U.S. had contributed many substantive points to the draft Plan. We had particularly emphasized the incorporation of population factors in national planning of developing countries' population programs for assuring the availability of means of family planning to persons of reproductive age, voluntary but specific goals for the reduction of population growth and time frames for action. As the WPPA reached the WPC it was organized as a demographic document. It also related population factors to family welfare, social and economic development, and fertility reduction. Population policies and programs were recognized as an essential element, but only one element of economic and social development programs." – Henry Kissinger, *National Security Study Memorandum 200: Implications*

of Worldwide Population Growth for U.S. Security and Overseas Interests (NSSM200), The Kissinger Report, December 10th, 1974

The classified report *National Security Study Memorandum 200: Implications of Worldwide Population Growth for U.S. Security and Overseas Interests (NSSM200)* -known as the *Kissinger Report*- was a directive published on December 10th, 1974, by Henry Kissinger and the U.S. National Security Council, in partnership with the CIA, U.S. Agency for International Development (USAID), and the U.S. Departments of State, Defense, and Agriculture. The report focused on reducing population growth in dozens of third-world countries as a way for the U.S. to maintain socio-political and economic control in various regions worldwide.

One of the premises of the report, which has been shared over the decades by many of the political elites, explained that rapid population growth could lead to worldwide food scarcity issues, reduction of shared resources, and supply chain disasters that would cause significant disruptions throughout all developed nations. The report cautioned that any population growth policies enacted against the identified third-world countries should also be passed within the U.S. to avoid the appearance of an industrialized country creating and enforcing population growth policies directly aimed at third-world countries.

These population growth controls and reduction strategies suggested using various types of political pressure, military force, forced sterilizations, socially accepted abortions, political blackmail, and other focused economic warfare to achieve the strategy and goals within the Kissinger Report. The report was released within two years of the famous *Roe v. Wade* decision that legalized the right to have abortions in the U.S. The adopted guidelines and policies for population growth reduction led to the support and funding of the U.N. Population Fund (UNFPA), which has been accused of supporting government programs that included forced abortions and coercive sterilizations.

There are plenty of other examples of American imperialism and expansion, with atrocities committed worldwide. This should at least set the stage that the government can never be trusted at face value. Government should always be questioned and made to prove what it says as truth. This applies to any government worldwide, now and into the future. After reading all this, do you still trust the government with your health and safety? Do you want to live under a tyrannical government with the impunity to lie, torture, and experiment on its citizens?

In 1990, the National Institutes of Health (NIH) funded the Human Genome Project (HGP), which started working on mapping the entire human genome found within our DNA -identifying each genome's functionality. In April 2003, roughly 85% of the human genome had been mapped out and identified. By January 2022, it was announced that 100% of the human genome had been mapped. In 2004, Dean Hamer, a Harvard Medical School Ph.D. graduate and geneticist, published his book *The God Gene: How Faith Is Hard-Wired Into Our Genes*, where he details his belief that the vesicular monoamine transporter 2 (VMAT2) protein, produced through the solute carrier family 18 member 2 (SLC18A2) gene, controlled humanity's spirituality connection. Hamer considered SLC18A2 as the "God" gene affecting mood, movement, and motivation.

On February 7th, 2013, the New England Journal of Medicine published the study *Brain Dopamine–Serotonin Vesicular Transport Disease and Its Treatment,* which found that the VMAT2 protein is essential for mood stabilization, autonomic nervous system regulation -e.g., heart and respiratory rates, digestion, and sexual arousal- and motor control (N Engl J Med. 2013 Feb 7;368(6):543-50.). If the SLC18A2 gene is confirmed as the God gene, what would stop the government from purposely attacking the gene, making us easier to manipulate and control?

Regarding COVID19 and the vaccines created for COVID19, are we sure we aren't being experimented on? The government does not have an issue with lying to the American public, nor does it have a problem experimenting on the American people without informed consent or with manufactured engineered consent. Government is still only a tool or action of control that select groups of individuals, and secret organizations, are wielding. If we cannot trust individuals to live their lives freely and control themselves, how can we trust others to rule over everyone, including ourselves? If the idea that government always leads to tyranny holds, why should we trust something tyrannical in nature with educating children without question?

"The conscious and intelligent manipulation of the organized habits and opinions of the masses is an important element in democratic society. Those who manipulate this unseen mechanism of society constitute an invisible government which is the true ruling power of our country. We are governed, our minds are molded, our tastes formed, our ideas suggested, largely by men we have never heard of. This is a logical result of the way in which our democratic society is organized. Vast numbers of human beings must cooperate in this manner if they are to live together as a smoothly functioning society." – Edward L. Bernays, *Propaganda*, 1928

During the Middle Ages, the Classical Trivium evolved into what we consider Classical Education today, which grew out of Christianity's influence on the world, helping to shape the future of Western culture. The Classical Trivium became a tool by rulers and monarchs to control the minds of the masses, effectively turning people into literacy slaves who were competent enough to do work and labor but not competent enough to think for themselves. This was achieved by only giving approved grammar and teaching how to understand and process that approved grammar. As early as the late 18th century, the U.S. started to adopt and use the Prussian Education system to instill blind obedience, which began with compulsory education.

In 1902, early adopters and advocates of this system in the U.S. created the private organization General Education Board to support higher education and medical schools, creating national education standards through funding by John D. Rockefeller. The General Education Board would receive over $180 million from the Rockefeller family and would eventually be incorporated into the Rockefeller Foundation. The Rockefeller Foundation started the same year the Federal Reserve began, 1913. The Rockefeller Foundation helped fund eugenics research for the Nazis and supported Harvard University's International Seminars, which also received funding from the CIA. The Rockefeller Foundation also established and endowed the School of Hygiene and Public Health at Johns Hopkins University and Harvard University. Multiple books have been written on the corruption and immoral and unethical actions that the Rockefeller Foundation has been behind and taken over the past century.

As time continued, the federal government gained greater control with the first major federal education reform, the *Elementary and Secondary Education Act of 1965* (ESEA), enacted as part of the War on Poverty push, which had the opposite effect and led to more poverty. This educational Act has gone through several modifications, including the *No Child Left Behind Act of 2001* (NCLB), which was an utter failure, and the *Every Student Succeeds Act of 2015*, which shifted accountability from the federal government to the states but kept many of the NCLB standards that had failed for so many years. This is moving responsibility, accountability, and blame to the States. All public schools receive federal and state funding and rely on this funding to operate yearly. These schools must follow government standards and rhetoric, or funding can and will be pulled. These standards include vaccination schedules, health standards, and nutritional standards, which are heavily influenced by a select group of individuals, government agents, corporations, and organizations. There is an incentive for public schools to teach blind obedience at the behest of the government.

Can we trust the education we have been forced and compelled to learn by the government from kindergarten through 12th grade, and in higher education, we paid to learn? How much of that education was scripted and shaped with the desire to control and manipulate us into acting a specific way? Can we be sure that what we hold to be true is not falsities being pushed as truth which leads us to fear, uncertainty, and doubt?

"A government big enough to give you everything you want is a government big enough to take from you everything you have." – Gerald R. Ford, *Presidential address to a joint session of Congress*, August 12th, 1974

Propaganda

"There are invisible rulers who control the destinies of millions. It is not generally realized to what extent the words and actions of our most influential public men are dictated by shrewd persons operating behind the scenes." – Edward L. Bernays, *Propaganda*, 1928

Can we recognize propaganda when it is being displayed and used against us? To recognize propaganda and its purpose, we must understand its definition, theme, and context. Propaganda comes from the idea of propagating the Catholic faith. Still, it encompasses "any movement or organization to propagate some practice or ideology" and "dissemination of information intended to promote a political point of view" (Online Etymology Dictionary). However, this theme and context can be seen in practice going back to Greek times.

The Greeks had theaters putting on dramas, sharing written books -a big deal then- festivals, games, and a central focused court of law that allowed an avenue of propaganda to be disseminated. Even though propaganda has existed for thousands of years, there is a difference between manipulation and persuasion, between being lied to and being informed of the truth to make an educated decision. Propaganda will always come with censorship, a way to silence dissenting voices. Remember, Plato had enough evidence to recognize that government had a lifecycle that ended in Tyranny, which was thousands of years ago. When wealth and riches are at stake, there is no depth a human might not drop to for a chance to obtain them.

All governments throughout history have used propaganda to push agendas and to shape public opinion to further government control. Nazi Germany used propaganda to find support and justification for targeting and slaughtering Jews during the Holocaust. We know from Operation Paperclip that Nazi ideology, sympathizers, and perpetrators were brought to the U.S. to continue experimentations and its ideological efforts -which continue to this day. In February 2021, the Conservative Political Action Conference (CPAC) in Orlando, Florida, built a stage resembling the Odal Rune symbol worn by Nazi soldiers. On December 18th, 2022 -the eve of the Jewish holiday Hanukkah- the New York Times published a cross-word puzzle that resembled the Nazi swastika symbol -originally an ancient religious symbol signifying divinity and spirituality before being used by the Nazis. Symbolism -rooted deeply in religious and spiritual connotations- is used in many aspects of propaganda, even if the masses are unaware of its purpose and use within the propaganda.

The U.S. government had used propaganda to blame Russia for interfering with the 2016 elections when leaks of factual information came to light that showcased the massive amounts of corruption, collusion, and election fraud in the U.S. government and election process within the Democratic National Committee (DNC) when Hilary Clinton colluded with the DNC to steal the nomination from Bernie Sanders. In 2012, the Republican National Committee (RNC) colluded to steal the presidential nomination from Ron Paul and handed it to Mitt Romney. In 2012, I had friends in Tampa, Florida, for the Republican National Convention who witnessed the fraud and collusion that kept Ron Paul from securing the GOP presidential nomination. The U.S. election system cannot be trusted to be the honest and open election process we are promised when significant power and resources are used to secure votes.

The Panic of 1907 was influenced by the New York Times pushing Fear, Uncertainty, and Doubt (FUD) as speculation started to rise over a potential scandal when the then-president of the Knickerbocker Trust Company, Charles T. Barney, tried to corner the copper stock market, leading to a bank run when the scheme failed, and the stock plummeted. Frederick G. Eldridge, who chartered the Knickerbocker Trust Company in 1884, was a friend and classmate of J. P. Morgan. In 1896, J. P. Morgan provided Adolph Simon Ochs, who owned the Chattanooga Times, the financing to secure the purchase of the struggling New York Times, which provided J. P. Morgan influence over the stories published in their papers. This push and influence helped cause the banking run leading to the failure of the Trust industry -only in New York. J. P. Morgan "saved" the day when he bailed out the industry using his money while convincing other bankers to do the same. The following year -following the Panic of 1907- John D. Rockefeller, Jr. established and led the commission looking into the panic and proposed the solution of creating the Federal Reserve System, moving the entire wealth and control of the U.S. monetary system into the hands of private bankers.

On December 23rd, 1913, the Federal Reserve Act was signed into law creating the Federal Reserve System, a group of 12 Reserve Banks -private corporations- in charge of the monetary policies of the U.S. The creation of the Federal Reserve System was helped by mainstream media of the time pushing propaganda. Each Reserve Bank owns stock in the Federal Reserve System, which isn't publicly traded. These stocks come with dividend payments, which are paid through the interest the government pays to the Federal Reserve System for printing and maintaining the U.S. monetary supply of the U.S. dollar. This debt system requires debt to be created for each dollar printed. The government collects taxes from taxpayers and uses these funds to pay the required interest payments on the created debt to the banks. All new money printed increases the interest payments to be paid to the Federal Reserve System.

"If the American people ever allow private banks to control the issue of their currency, first by inflation, then by deflation, the banks...will deprive the people of all property until their children wake-up homeless on the continent their fathers conquered." – Thomas Jefferson, *Debate over Bank Bill*, 1809

Between 1936 and 1941, Chase Bank worked directly with the Nazis helping them raise over $20 million in foreign exchange from Jews who had fled the Nazis. Chase Bank was paid $500,000 for its services. During this time, J. P. Morgan & Co. illegally seized bank accounts and safe-deposit assets of Jews during the Nazi occupation of France, which it refused to return to the rightful owners or their heirs. Both banks merged in 2000 to form JPMorgan Chase. Propaganda was heavily used to obfuscate the theft of wealth from Jews that directly benefited the Nazis and lined the pockets of bankers. Do you think these banks became ethical and moral since WWII? Is it possible that the banks, and those running them, are still affiliated with the Nazis and have not improved their unethical and immoral business practices?

During the Vietnam War, public opinion in support of the war was lost due to the media doing its job by reporting on what the war was like; how brutal and mentally breaking it could be. The government learned its lesson; much of what the media showed of the Global War on Terror was scripted rhetoric. Mainstream media is owned by six major corporations and subsidiaries, which are public corporations, with the largest shareholders being some of the largest investment firms worldwide, e.g., Blackrock, Inc. and Vanguard, Inc. These investment firms wield tens of trillions in assets and power alone. Mainstream media has become little more than a mouthpiece for officially approved rhetoric. Anything outside approved rhetoric is quickly quieted, taken out, vilified, and or discredited.

"It is part of the general pattern of misguided policy that our country is now geared to an arms economy which was bred in an artificially induced psychosis of war hysteria and nurtured upon an incessant propaganda of fear. While such an economy may produce a sense of seeming prosperity for the moment, it rests on an illusionary foundation of complete unreliability and renders among our political leaders almost a greater fear of peace than is their fear of war." – Douglas MacArthur, General of the Army, *Speech to the Michigan legislature*, May 15th, 1952

Hypnosis has been shown in studies to be successful in treating pain, anxiety, and cognitive-behavioral issues. If hypnotism can be used to heal, it can be used to hurt -a double-edged sword. The CIA used hypnosis for manipulation and control during MKUltra and in many projects since then, with many experiments bordering torture or extreme levels of torture to achieve the desired controlled results. Imagine all the experiments that have never seen the light of day because many exist. In the decades since MKUltra, the government has only perfected its propaganda campaign and ability to sway public opinion.

If we can hypnotize someone, they become easier to manipulate and control. If we are unaware of the propaganda and effort to hypnotize us, we can be hypnotized without ever knowing it. Hypnosis can create highly relaxed states of consciousness, making the subject more malleable to suggestion and influence. The Church of Scientology uses loaded language and changes definitions to words, causing recruits to become confused -easier to manipulate and control. This same practice can be seen in mainstream media. You can find video compilations showcasing news anchors at various news stations around the U.S. repeating word for word the same story and message, scripted rhetoric used to elicit a specific response in the masses.

This hypnosis isn't only through loaded language but is also through physical means, like consistent enforcement of mask use. On March 18th, 2022, the New York Post posted the article *Why masks make you more attractive: study*, which attempts to explain that by wearing a mask, we could potentially increase our attractiveness, making wearing a mask an appealing option outside of any actual medical benefit. In the Mask chapter, you will see why this type of thing is propaganda and being used for other purposes.

Edward Bernays, a nephew to the famed neurologist and psychoanalyst Sigmund Freud, laid the groundwork for today's propaganda campaign. Bernays wrote the book *Propaganda* (1929), which laid out the psyche of the masses and how manipulation of the desired response could be achieved through targeted propaganda campaigns. Bernays suggested that the engineered consent of the masses would be needed to extend the life of democracy before devolving into tyranny. Engineered consent is not informed consent and should not be treated as such, even though government views it as the same. Bernays found that propaganda was increasingly effective when the motives of the masses were understood. Eliciting strong emotional responses, achieved through fear, intimidation, threats, or rewards, resulted in faster and more dedicated responses.

Motivation is very important when trying to understand an individual or the masses. One theory describing motivation is the Self-Determination theory, which focuses on conditions supporting autonomy, competence, and relatedness as motivation factors. We have a psychological need for autonomy -free will over our actions- and voluntary compliance or non-compliance. Competence is another psychological need that often finds its need satisfied by conforming to what is socially acceptable and accepting what is socially held as truth. It is a need that requires the satisfaction of information to be true. However, if appropriate knowledge to the contrary of social conformity is gained, then psychological strife is achieved; by the conflict of opposing information and relatedness. Relatedness is also tied to social conformity and can cause psychological strife when multiple groups form an "us versus them" attitude in any given situation. When all these motivation factors are targeted during propaganda, it can be easier to hypnotize the individual and masses to the message and rhetoric being pushed.

The psychology around mask-wearing touches on all of the motivational factors described in Self-Determination theory and have been used to divide and conquer the masses during the COVID19 pandemic. Remember, at the start of the pandemic, the Centers for Disease Control and Prevention (CDC) and Dr. Anthony Fauci - current director of the National Institute of Allergy and Infectious Diseases (NIAID) under the NIH- openly and repeatedly said properly rated respirators were not needed by the masses, later changing their tune -but with a focus on cloth-mask-wearing. Citing only statistical modeling, the CDC and Dr. Fauci had no real studies showing masks, especially cloth masks, did anything to stop COVID19 or any other infectious disease or virus. Cloth is rarely used in a medical setting, except for things like clean sheets and bedding, until this pandemic; are we to believe the magical properties of cloth were only just discovered? We will go into detail on this topic in the Mask chapter.

The government has entire divisions dedicated to psyop missions and goals focusing on targeting citizen's motivation factors stateside and in other countries worldwide. Some of these government groups don't have initials and aren't on official classified books or servers - missions undertaken or completed are stored in highly-classified and secured vaults and remain off top-secret servers. These groups are found within the Department of Defense (DoD), NSA, CIA, and FBI. These unnamed groups can operate with impunity worldwide while only answering to a few unelected government employees -e.g., Directors of agencies. We can be sure some of their efforts are being used against us to convince and sway us into willingly giving up our freedoms and rights for a promise of security, safety, and health.

A perfect example of an avenue to push propaganda and maintain approved government rhetoric in the media is the establishment of the Corporation for Public Broadcasting (CPB) -a taxpayer-funded private non-profit corporation- through the Public Broadcasting Act of 1967, signed into law by President Lyndon B. Johnson. A nine-member board of directors runs the CPB -vacant positions are appointed by the President of the U.S.- who sets policies and guidelines and establishes programming priorities for over 1,500 radio stations and local TV stations across the U.S. CPB helped create the Public Broadcasting Service (PBS) and formed the National Public Radio (NPR). These organizations are massive propaganda machines used to steer the true political narrative, even if it is not readily apparent to the public.

The Bill and Melinda Gates Foundation (Gates Foundation) has donated over $300 million to fund various media projects -including CPB, PBS, and NPR. By November 2021, the Gates Foundation donated $2.4 million to CPB, $500 thousand to PBS, and $24.6 million to NPR. These donations have been used to push propaganda in mainstream media for issues that Gates has an interest in -including financial interests. Can this propaganda and intent by Gates be trusted? How much have we been influenced by the propaganda pushed by Gates through these mainstream media outlets?

On June 7th, 1991, President George H. W. Bush -former Director of the CIA- appointed Richard W. Carlson -father of famed talk show host Tucker Carlson and previous Director of the U.S. Information Agency- to Ambassador to Seychelles. In March 1992, CPB announced that Richard Carlson was chosen as president and chief executive officer, and he maintained this position for five years. Shortly after Tucker Carlson graduated in 1991 from Trinity College in Hartford, Connecticut, he attempted to join the CIA as an intelligence operative. Carlson's application was officially "rejected," which was when he decided to follow in his father's journalism footsteps. Carlson has been a host of his shows for MSNBC -*Tucker*- and Fox News -*Tucker Carlson Tonight*- and is currently the most-viewed host on primetime television. Carlson also previously worked for Cable News Network (CNN) and PBS while being registered as a Democrat -from 2006 to 2020- but advocates for President Trump while promoting some conspiracy theories. Could Carlson be a CIA asset where he is tasked with being controlled opposition, helping drive a needed narrative?

Intelligence gathering is a significant function and requirement to achieve successful psyop missions. SIGINT is gathering intelligence through capturing signals and communication, electronic and analog. U.S. Signals Intelligence Directive (USSID) SP0018 *Legal Compliance and U.S. Persons Minimization Procedures* and SP0019 *NSA/CSS Signals Intelligence Directorate - Oversight and Compliance Policy* are some of the legal requirements that intelligence agencies focused on SIGINT should be following that govern how data on U.S. citizens is collected, stored and analyzed -if at all. USSID SP0018 intends to "ensure that the missions and functions of the United State SIGINT System (USSS) are conducted in a manner that safeguards the constitutional rights of U.S. persons."

At lower levels within these intelligence agencies, following these policies and guidelines is heavily enforced, but as with all laws, there are ways to get around them. One way the CIA gets around laws designed to keep the CIA from spying on U.S. citizens is by using unnamed groups and partner foreign intelligence agencies who share data that has been collected with the CIA and other U.S. intelligence agencies. U.S. intelligence agencies do not have to monitor U.S. citizens directly to gather data and information on a subject when stopped officially by U.S. law.

In September 2020, the Defense Department awarded, for a second time, Microsoft Corporation its Joint Enterprise Defense Infrastructure (JEDI) cloud contract to facilitate infrastructure for a war cloud bringing together intelligence agencies, warfighters, and customer agencies to work together handling all levels of intelligence classifications, including Top Secret. In November 2020, it was reported that the CIA awarded its Commercial Cloud Enterprise (C2E) 15-year contract, worth tens of billions, to Amazon Inc. (Amazon Web Services), Microsoft, Google LLC (formerly Google, Inc.), Oracle Corporation, and IBM Corporation. The C2E contract was created to have these corporations -major corporations that have massive influence in the world of technology- complete specific tasks and orders issued by the CIA on behalf of itself and 16 other intelligence agencies, e.g., NSA or FBI. This contract will expand the capabilities of each intelligence agency within cloud computing at various classification levels.

"We are only puppets, our strings are being pulled by unknown forces." – Karl Georg Büchner, *Danton's Death*, 1835

In December 2008, the CIA released a study *What Analysts Need to Understand: The King's Intelligence Studies Program* showcasing how important and beneficial it was to "use universities as a means of intelligence training." This study lists the Department of War Studies at King's College London as one such program at a university that provided a "space in which analysts from every part of the community can explore with each other the interplay of ideas about their profession." The King's College London has entered into multiple secret contracts with the U.K. government to provide undisclosed services for various Western intelligence agencies.

The Department of War Studies trains and produces intelligence operatives, many top journalists worldwide, social media managers at international corporations, and Fact Checkers -those who "combat" misinformation by providing a side of a debate. Educating thousands of students, many Department of War Studies graduates have gone on to become highly influential staff members at The Facebook, Inc. (now Meta Platforms, Inc.), TikTok Pte. Ltd., Twitter, Inc., and Google, commanding vast amounts of influence over what we see and hear on social media.

Operation Earnest Voice, first used in 2011, was developed through a private contractor as a psychological weapon by U.S. Central Command, which allowed government agents to create and control sockpuppet accounts on social media platforms and websites to help promote U.S. government rhetoric or to oppose ideas and organizations. Initially, this operation was only limited to foreign networks and countries. These sockpuppet accounts could be set up with detailed histories and backgrounds from any geographic location. If we know how to look, we can spot these types of accounts operating throughout social media platforms that are being used against the masses in the U.S. and worldwide.

The IDF cyber intelligence unit 8200, a spy organization unit for Mossad -Israeli intelligence- focuses on amassing information on individuals for blackmailing and extortion and has had hundreds of former agents hired by corporations like Google, Meta, Microsoft, and Amazon. Former defense ministry director general and commander of IDF 8200, Pinchas Bukhris, was the director of Reporty Homeland Security, which Jeffrey Epstein had invested in. In 2022, it was reported by Mint Press News that at least 99 of these agents are currently working for Google, and at least 166 former agents are working for Microsoft. We should generally assume that all major social media corporations and platforms have intelligence agents -foreign and domestic- actively working at and monitoring the data on these platforms.

Social media corporations use Fact Checkers to censor dissenting viewpoints contrary to the official government rhetoric. Fact Checkers have gotten so bad that even purely satirical sites, like The

Babylon Bee, had their social media accounts suspended for spreading misinformation and fake news. The Babylon Bee is satirical, purposely posting "fake news that we can trust," so at no point should what they post be taken seriously, which is the point of their site. Yet, Fact Checkers and social media corporations deemed them to be spreading "misinformation," so their accounts were suspended.

FactCheck.org, its projects, initiatives, and coverage, are funded through the Annenberg Public Policy Center of the Annenberg School for Communication at the University of Pennsylvania, the Flora Family Foundation, Facebook, and Google. The Annenberg Foundation was started by Walter Annenberg, who owned the Philadelphia Inquirer, TV Guide, and Seventeen magazine and was appointed the U.S. ambassador to the United Kingdom by Richard Nixon. Annenberg developed a close friendship with Queen Elizabeth II and other royal family members. The Flora Family Foundation is a leftist grantmaking foundation focusing on its Climate Protection Program and Gap Program. The Flora Family Foundation was established by William Hewlett, co-founder of the Hewlett-Packard Company.

PolitiFact.com -a non-profit fact-checking journalism project- was established in 2007 by the Tampa Bay Times and was acquired in February 2018 by the Poynter Institute. PolitiFact claims that it focuses on being independent and transparent -journalism you can trust. Currently, PolitiFact receives more than 5% of its funding from Facebook (Meta) and TikTok. In November 2015, the Gates Foundation provided a $382,997 grant to the Poynter Institute "to improve the accuracy in worldwide media of claims related to global health and development."

Can any of these Fact Checker organizations be trusted? Will they publish the truth, or do they have another purpose? Are they funded to tell the truth? At times, yes, they will provide the truth, but they will also post sophistry used to control the narrative, which will be used to silence opposing voices. If you look hard enough, each Fact Checker organization has serious conflicts of interest and a financial incentive to confirm the official rhetoric.

"We just don't know the long-term side effects of basically modifying people's DNA and RNA to directly encode in a person's DNA and RNA. Basically, the ability to produce those antibodies and whether that causes other mutations or other risks downstream." – Mark Zuckerberg, *leaked Project Veritas footage*, July 16th, 2020

Given the quote above, which was made in a private conversation, it is a wonder why Facebook would then set their COVID19 and Vaccine Policy Updates & Protections rules to flag or suspend someone who "claims that COVID-19 vaccine changes people's DNA." Some mechanisms exist that can cause messenger RNA (mRNA) to alter DNA -which we will discuss in the COVID19 Vaccines chapter. Can Zuckerberg be trusted when he funds Fact Checkers and has a financial incentive to push the official narrative?

Alejandro Mayorkas, currently the U.S. Secretary of Homeland Security -who heads the Department of Homeland Security (DHS)- has direct supervision of the "nerve center" of federally directed censorship which coordinates with all major Big Tech corporations. This censorship does not only include the censorship of COVID19 information for Dr. Fauci and the government but of politically connected topics. On June 15th, 2021, the Informed Consent Action Network (ICAN) received email communications -due to a FOIA request- between White House staff, pharmaceutical corporations, and Big Tech corporations, showing a coordinated effort to promote vaccine confidence and to help drive up liability-free vaccine injections.

To further highlight these coordinated efforts, since Elon Musk took over Twitter, he began to release evidence of the massive level of censorship that was taking place at Twitter. On December 16th, 2022, Musk started to release the Twitter Files. The Twitter Files provided evidence that the government colluded with Twitter for years to run a network of fake accounts that pushed scripted narratives. The released files also showed evidence that the FBI -for years- flagged individual and business accounts for Twitter to suspend or ban from its platform over "misinformation" dealing with the 2020 and 2022 elections, the Hunter Biden laptop story - confirmed true- and the COVID19 pandemic in a clear violation of the First Amendment of the U.S. Constitution. It was released that the FBI paid roughly $3.4 million to Twitter from October 2019 to early 2021 for time spent processing FBI requests around the censorship campaign.

U.S. Constitution - First Amendment

"Congress shall make no law respecting an establishment of religion, or prohibiting the free exercise thereof; or abridging the freedom of speech, or of the press; or the right of the people peaceably to assemble, and to petition the Government for a redress of grievances."

Since Musk's takeover of Twitter, approximately 44,000 Twitter accounts were removed in India alone that were being used to exploit children sexually. These things are occurring worldwide, with governments doing very little to stop the exploitation of children. The FBI has very likely focused more on stopping COVID19 "misinformation" than trying to stop pedophiles from victimizing and exploiting children on a continued basis. Could it be that the culture within the U.S. government, and governments worldwide, have the disposition to encourage child exploitation?

The FBI responded to a request for comment by The Epoch Times over the released Twitter files: *"the FBI regularly engages with the private sector entities to provide information specific to identified foreign malign influence actors' subversive, undeclared, cover, or criminal activities. Private sector entities independently make decisions about what, if any, action they take on their platforms and for their customers after the FBI has notified them*"; however, the evidence released shows that U.S. citizens -not only foreign actors- were regularly flagged for censorship. Twitter routinely followed the direction and guidance of the FBI regarding these targeted accounts.

"*To be totally frank, almost every conspiracy theory that people had about Twitter turned out to be true. Is there a conspiracy theory about Twitter that didn't turn out to be true? So far, they've all turned out to be true. If not more true than people thought.*" – Elon Musk, *All-In Podcast interview*, December 24th, 2022

The Hunter Biden Laptop story broke during October 2020 - October Surprise- before elections where Hunter Biden's father, now President Biden, was running against President Trump. There is a potential Hunter Biden lost up to three laptops before the 2020 election -one lost during a 2018 drug binge, one stolen by Russian drug dealers while on drugs to be used as blackmail, and one left abandoned in 2019 at a Delaware computer repair shop. Significant incriminating data was found on the abandoned Delaware laptop - videos, e.g., smoking crack and sleeping with sex workers- texts and email communication that would make him a gold mine for blackmailing. Some of the data on the abandoned laptop provided evidence of corruption in several cash-for-access operations in Ukraine and China. Hunter Biden was charging significant amounts for access to his father and the Obama Administration.

By having leverage on Hunter Biden, an individual, organization, or foreign state would have had leverage over then-Senator Joseph Biden, now President Biden. From an intelligence risk perspective, this potential security risk should have disqualified President Biden from any sensitive public office -including the presidency. Why did government agencies censor this story in clear violation of the First Amendment, causing the most significant influence over the 2020 elections?

On July 10th, 2022, a 4chan hacker broke into Hunter Biden's iCloud account, recovered deleted media, information, and other contents of his phone and iPad, and then dumped everything online. In this hacked material were more videos of Hunter Biden smoking crack and sleeping with sex workers and family members' phone numbers -including President Biden's number.

To add to the fuel of conspiracy theories, Hunter Biden had his father listed as "Pedo Peter" in the phone contact list. What confirmed this "Pedo Peter" contact as President Biden was a text sent to the contact that said, "I love you, pop." Some of the emails Hunter Biden sent his father in 2017 had the name "Peter Henderson" attached to them -meaning it was attached to the email account, not entered in the body of the email. Peter Henderson -a Tom Clancy's Jack Ryan series character- was a KGB mole who infiltrated the U.S. government. With everything we have covered to this point, the iCloud evidence is disturbing and should be questioned. Censorship by social media corporations of this story also took place using Fact Checkers to disprove the story as being nothing but misinformation.

In 2013, the National Defense Authorization Act (NDAA) added an amendment that negated the Smith-Mundt Act of 1948 and the Foreign Relations Authorization Act of 1987, effectively allowing the government to use taxpayer funds to aim directed propaganda at U.S. citizens. In 2016, it came to light that the Pentagon paid a PR firm over $500 million to create fake Al-Qaeda videos for secret Iraq propaganda from 2007 to 2011 to help sway public opinion to support the ongoing war effort. Other media corporations received funds from 2006 to 2008 to produce other propaganda.

Governments, like the U.S., Russia, China, and Ukraine, and secret organizations are now using another form of propaganda called

Deepfakes. Deepfakes are synthetic media videos, pictures, and audio created by technologies that use machine learning and artificial intelligence (AI) to produce fake media. These are altered and manipulated media used to deceive the viewer. On August 7th, 2020, a Massachusetts Institute of Technology (MIT) researcher created a fake moon landing speech by President Nixon to showcase the new technology. Deepcake is a company that uses an AI-powered content optimization web platform to provide a library of AI-generated replicas of A-list celebrities.

There now have been many fake videos of celebrities and politicians, including President Obama giving a public address and Russian President Putin declaring peace in Ukraine. Some of the recent deepfakes that can be seen online are taking celebrity faces - e.g., Arnold Schwarzenegger and Sylvester Stallone- and swapping their faces and voices into famous movie clips of movies they were never a part of. Deepfakes can allow individuals to appear to dance when they have no skill at dancing. But now governments are using deepfake technology to lie and manipulate citizens to help sway public opinion.

On February 14th, 2022, the journal Proceedings of the National Academy of Sciences of the United States of America (PNAS) published the study *AI-synthesized faces are indistinguishable from real faces and more trustworthy*, which found AI-generated content was being weaponized for "nonconsensual intimate imagery, financial fraud, and disinformation campaigns" and that many have trouble distinguishing between what is real and fake (Proc Natl Acad Sci U S A. 2022 Feb 22;119(8):e2120481119.).

"And if all others accepted the lie which the Party imposed—if all records told the same tale—then the lie passed into history and became truth. 'Who controls the past' ran the Party slogan, 'controls the future: who controls the present controls the past.'" – George Orwell, *1984*, June 8th, 1949

On April 27th, 2022, the U.S. government started the Disinformation Governance Board (DGB), an advisory board under DHS that focused on protecting national security by disseminating guidance and information to combat misinformation and disinformation. The DGB came about due to the push from the government to blame Russian manipulation during the 2016 presidential election -to obfuscate the truth of the DNC email leak that showcased major voting fraud taking place within the DNC- and the 2020 presidential election. The DGB was dissolved after four months due to significant negative pushback. The DGB was eerily similar to the Ministry of Truth in the book *1984* by George Orwell - a propaganda ministry focused on pushing lies and half-truths to manipulate and control the masses through formal brainwashing programs, linguistic trickery, and peer pressure. This manipulation included falsifying historical events and introducing Doublethink, accepting two conflicting beliefs as absolute truth. I have maintained for years that *1984* was not a work of fiction but a roadmap to what we see today.

Next time you see or hear TV or radio stations talking about COVID19, pay attention to who is paying for the air time. It is always sponsored by something, and it always costs money. TV and radio stations are not broadcasting these messages out of the desire to help in times of crisis. During the pandemic's peak, the government sponsored most of the air time as health updates or warnings to encourage everyone to get vaccinated. Sponsored by the government means paid for by the taxpayer. The round-the-clock broadcasting of this scripted rhetoric while using taxpayer funding -courtesy of Health Departments- to push fear, uncertainty, and doubt and convince everyone to get a "free" COVID19 vaccine is an effective propaganda tactic that will be used again.

Of course, these vaccines are far from free, which has resulted in tens of billions in profit for the for-profit pharmaceutical corporations and the significant devaluing of the U.S. dollar as trillions in new money have been printed to continue the COVID19 propaganda efforts under the guise of being required for our safety and protection. If they were truly free, these corporations wouldn't be making billions off them and would operate at a loss. Calling the vaccines free is pure sophistry.

Government propaganda is used to further the government's agendas which always come with more control and restrictions because that is the natural progress of the lifecycle of government. We need to understand propaganda and how propaganda is and has been used against us. If we can adequately identify propaganda used against us, then we will have the tools and knowledge to keep from being manipulated and controlled through expertly timed propaganda. This will better prepare us for the fast-approaching future and give us a greater chance at surviving the coming changes.

"A mixture of gullibility and cynicism had been an outstanding characteristic of mob mentality before it became an everyday phenomenon of masses. In an ever-changing, incomprehensible, world the masses had reached the point where they would, at the same time, believe everything and nothing, think that everything is possible and that nothing was true. The mixture in itself was remarkable enough, because it spelled the end of the illusion that gullibility was a weakness of unsuspecting primitive souls and cynism the vice of superior and refined minds. Mass propaganda discovered that its audience was ready at all times to believe the worst, no matter how absurd, and did not particularly object to being deceived because it held every statement to be a lie anyhow. The totalitarian mass leaders based their propaganda on the correct psychological assumption that, under such conditions, one could make people believe the most fantastic statements one day, and trust if the next day they were given irrefutable proof of their falsehood, they would take

refuge in cynicism; instead of deserting the leaders who had lied to them, they would protest that they had known all along the statement was a lie and would admire the leaders for their superior tactical cleverness. "' – Hannah Arendt, *The Origins of Totalitarianism*, 1951

The Great Reset

"The pandemic represents a rare but narrow window of opportunity to reflect, reimagine, and reset our world." – Klaus Schwab, *Time for a Great Reset*, June 3ʳᵈ, 2020

The World Economic Forum (WEF), initially called European Management Forum, was established in 1971 by Klaus Schwab as a non-profit foundation headquartered in Geneva, Switzerland, with a stated mission to "demonstrate entrepreneurship in the global public interest while upholding the highest standards of governance" (WEF Website). This mission statement promotes a system similar to state capitalism -cronyism- capitalism at the hands of government control. WEF views itself as an "independent, impartial and not tied to any special interests" organization with "moral and intellectual integrity at the heart of everything it does." Its view is that a globalized world is best managed by a self-appointed coalition of corporations, organizations, and governments and that global instability like the 2007-2008 financial crisis or the COVID19 pandemic is an opportunity to further its goals and missions, bringing in a Great Reset and new world order. Funding for the WEF comes from the over 1,000-member corporations' donations and membership fees. The WEF was formally recognized as an international body by the Swiss government.

On June 22ⁿᵈ, 2016, the WEF published *Does capitalism need some Marxism to survive the Fourth Industrial Revolution?*, which makes the case that some of the ideas made famous by Karl Marx -

Marxism- are needed to bring about a transformation -"Great Reset"- to capitalism. Transforming capitalism was always a target of Marx. Marx was a German philosopher in the 1800s who pushed socialist ideology and socialist revolutionary changes. Marx believed that societies developed by class conflict where the ruling class controlled the means of production. Marx criticized capitalism and made a case for classless communist societies where the working class owned the means of production. Marx wrote the *Communist Manifesto,* which was published in February 1848. Since this manifesto was published, communist governments formed and, over 100 years, led to the deaths of over 100 million people. Pain, suffering, and death closely follow any time any group forces communism and socialism.

During annual meetings, executive leadership from member corporations, politicians worldwide, academia representatives, royalty, and religious leaders are selected to present at breakout sessions to discuss various topics and issues. Thousands of participants from over a hundred countries, with hundreds of journalists, join in these meetings to increase global public interest using the highest standard of governance. Individuals like Gates and George Soros have spoken at these annual meetings. Do you believe this organization is independent and impartial? Nothing involving government is or stays independent and impartial for long, quickly devolving into political agendas and propaganda campaigns in the name of philanthropy and helping the world's quality of life.

"We set up a new world order after World War II. We're now in a different world than we were then. We need to ask, what can we be doing differently? The World Economic Forum has a big responsibility in that as well – to be pushing the reset button and looking at how to create well-being for people and for the Earth." – Jennifer Morgan, Executive Director of Greenpeace International, Agenda Contributor for the WEF, *How the world can 'reset' itself after COVID-19 – according to these experts,* June 3rd, 2020

Klaus Schwab, a German economist and engineer -born in Nazi Germany- founded the WEF and has held many positions on significant boards, including being a former member of the steering committee of the secretive Bilderberg Group. Schwab received a master's in Public Administration from the John F. Kennedy School of Government at Harvard University. Schwab founded the Young Global Leaders non-profit organization in 1993, headquartered in Geneva, Switzerland. Schwab has spoken that Russian President Vladimir Putin and Canadian Prime Minister Justin Trudeau were past Young Global Leaders members. Many Young Global Leaders members and alums are active in politics today worldwide. Schwab has published multiple books, including the *Fourth Industrial Revolution*, which focused on transhumanism, posthumanism, and cybernetics, changing global capitalism.

Schwab's father, Eugen Wilhelm Schwab, moved to Nazi Germany during the Third Reich to be the director of Escher Wyss & Cie. which helped supply the Nazi war effort with hydraulic systems and equipment, flamethrowers, and research and development for turbines which was used to attempt the creation of nuclear weapons for the Nazis. Schwab has repeatedly called for a Great Reset to the idea of capitalism and how people view capitalism. On July 9th, 2020, Schwab published the book *COVID-19: The Great Reset*, which outlines the changes needed to create a more inclusive and sustainable future. Remember, sophists twist words to mean new things to confuse and manipulate. How much of the horrors committed in the past by governments and tyrants were done for the "common good"?

"But we must rethink what we mean by 'capital' in its many iterations, whether financial, environmental, social, or human. Today's consumers do not want more and better goods and services for a reasonable price. Rather, they increasingly expect companies to contribute to social welfare and the common good. There is both a fundamental need and an increasingly widespread demand for a new

kind of 'capitalism.' " – Klaus Schwab, *Post COVID Capitalism*, October 12th, 2020

When thinking of capitalism, what comes to your mind? Capitalism, capital (property) + -ism (a system or practice) is a system or practice of trading property using root definitions. Property is one of our natural rights; we are all born with the right to produce and acquire property. The product of our labor is our property, capital, and natural right. We cannot be forced to provide labor to produce property for others, or that would be slavery. We can voluntarily provide labor to produce property for someone else in exchange for whatever we willingly agree to. Currency or another medium of exchange -e.g., barter and trade- can be used to trade property we possess (might be valued less due to it not filling a need) for the property of others that we value more due to it serving a greater need.

An example of free market capitalism, in its purest form and action, is where we raise chickens and trade eggs. With an abundance of eggs we don't need, we can trade with the butcher for select meats or another farmer for vegetables we didn't grow. We could also trade the eggs for gold or silver, which we could use to buy equipment or obtain additional resources to build and improve upon the land, getting greater value out of the property we own and maintain. At no point should these situations be controlled or restricted through force, intimidation, or engineered consent when no victims have been created -this is the basis of philosophy concerning voluntary action. When capitalism is governed and limited by the government -state capitalism- it becomes very corrupt because the government over the innocent is tyrannical and corrupt in nature so that it will bring out the worst of any system or practice -this includes socialism. Discussion of capitalism and socialism in their purest forms versus when controlled and restricted by the government requires a much larger conversation and debate than the focus of this chapter and book.

"The transformation of capitalism into socialism is to be accomplished through state capitalism" – Mao Zedong, *The Only Road for the Transformation of Capitalist Industry and Commerce,* September 7th, 1953

Here are two examples of socialism being misused by the government to cause millions of deaths and suffering to countless lives. Russian-backed state socialism -under Joseph Stalin- in Ukraine during 1932 and 1933 was called the Holodomor -"to kill by starvation"- which ended with 4 to 12 million people dying. Mao Zedong, a ruthless ruler from 1949 to 1976 who was a strict Marxist-Leninist pushing socialist theories and ideas, launched multiple campaigns and movements during his time as a ruler that resulted in tens of millions of dead. One campaign -the Great Leap Forward-lasted only four years and led to 40 to 80 million dying from starvation and persecution. What if those pushing this new Great Reset have ulterior motives and the public message being told to us is only sophistry to usher in a new era of global tyranny, which only few will enjoy and flourish in? History often repeats itself, especially when the masses don't understand the language's history and meanings, and context during those times.

"You'll own nothing. And you'll be happy. What you want you'll rent, and it'll be delivered by drone." – World Economic Forum, Social Media Video, *Eight Predictions by 2030,* November 12th, 2016

What does this "Great Reset" of capitalism look like? How do these plans from a very politicized organization work with other groups moving into the future? Should we trust and accept Klaus Schwab and his push for a "Great Reset" of capitalism?

WEF maintains that there are three types of capitalism -ignoring free market capitalism. First, there is Shareholder Capitalism which Western corporations mainly use with the primary focus of maximizing profits for shareholders. Second is State Capitalism, which has the government maintaining the economy's direction and prominence in markets. All global markets are State Capitalism due to the over-abundance of regulation and control that governments maintain. The new type of capitalism Schwab and WEF are pushing is Stakeholder Capitalism which focuses on private corporations as being the gatekeepers and trustees of society and the economy; that these corporations will pay their fair share of taxes, have zero tolerance for corruption, uphold human rights through global supply chains, advocate competitive level playing fields, and usher Stakeholder Capitalism into the future through technological advancements and social equity programs.

When they say private corporations, they also mean those who are publicly traded -far from private- with most far from being able to stand on any moral high ground. As we have seen with Twitter recently, public corporations can be taken private and run by private institutional investors -including large asset firms. Should we trust a publicly traded or private corporation with anonymous shareholders -owners- dictating the moral and ethical actions and culture behind the business and society? How do we guarantee that they are producing safe products for the benefit of society and the future of humanity? We can't, so trust should never be granted to these globalist mega-corporations.

This push by the WEF will turn corporations into governments that will still be controlled by a select few and still violate natural rights across the board. We will then become slaves to the corporations under which we are forced to work. What difference would that be from now? These corporations would have a monopoly on violence like governments now.

Did you know that ten publicly traded corporations control most of everything we eat within the U.S.? These ten significant corporations are Nestle, General Mills, Coca-Cola, PepsiCo, Unilever, Danone, Mars, Mondelez International, Kellogg's, and

Associated British Foods. Dozens of commonly found foods at U.S. grocery stores -produced by these corporations- were banned in dozens of other countries for adverse effects they can cause. Should these corporations be trusted with dictating everything about our lives? Should these corporations have a monopoly on violence over us?

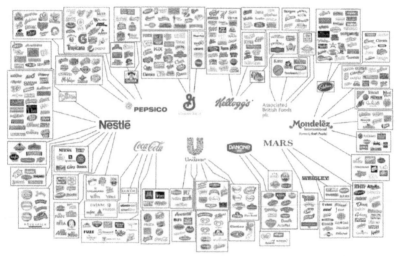

Oxfam International graphic (2014)

Did you know these publicly traded corporations are partially owned, maintained, and controlled by massive trillion-dollar investment firms? These investment firms, like BlackRock and The Vanguard Group -the two most prominent investment firms in the world- influence the boards and decisions that affect our daily lives through thousands of corporations. This control includes social media corporations like Twitter (before going private) and Facebook, mainstream media corporations like News Corp (e.g., New York Post, Wall Street Journal, Dow Jones & Company, and Sky News), and 21st Century Fox, Inc. (now owned by Walt Disney Co.), entertainment corporations like Walt Disney, service providers like

Amazon and Microsoft, central banks like JPMorgan Chase & Co and Bank of America, weapons and military corporations like Lockheed Martin Corporation, Northrop Grumman Corporation, and The Boeing Company, and pharmaceutical corporations like Pfizer, Inc. and Moderna, Inc.

As of 2021, BlackRock had $10 trillion in assets under its management and control, and Vanguard Group had $8 trillion under its management and control. BlackRock and Vanguard Group members have spoken at multiple WEF annual meetings and hold significant sway worldwide. This level of control and deception that we have legitimate choices should concern everyone. We are being fed scripted narratives at every turn by a select few. How can we be sure that what we think of as truth wasn't completely corrupted by these groups?

After the 2008 U.S. housing financial crisis, real estate investments from trusts, private equity investment firms, insurance companies/corporations, and pension funds started buying up properties and single-family homes across the U.S. to be used as rental properties. In 2019, the number of homes purchased by these corporations and institutional investors (Wall Street) significantly increased. Close to 100 thousand residential real estates were purchased by these corporations and institutional investors in the third quarter of 2021 alone, nearly 18% of all home sales. Billions of dollars have been poured into single-family homes over the past few years, with most being turned into rental properties. This is another step towards the Great Reset, where property ownership will become scarce. Most will and are starting to be outpriced of homes, keeping them from becoming property owners and forcing them to rent from these corporations and institutional investors.

Think of Amazon or Microsoft, or these massive investment firms, completely owning a city or state, setting laws and policies, and directly enforcing those laws and policies through the threat of death due to their monopoly on violence; "If you don't develop this code and feature by X date then you will be in violation of Quality of Work Policy #404, which will result in immediate termination from life and your body will be recycled pursuant to Recycling Waste Policy #187". "Sorry, it's corporate policy! I wouldn't do this if it weren't policy! So long, and thanks for all of the fish!".

This whole thing is similar to what we see today with the U.S. government; U.S. Code Title 28 > Part VI > Chapter 176 > Subchapter A > 3002 – Definitions; defines the "United States" to mean a Federal Corporation. Tax cattle would be an appropriate term for U.S. workers; I mean citizens. Corporations have for years been pushing for more and more constitutional affirmed rights. This is a slippery slope due to corporations and businesses not being individuals, even though they are made up of individuals. These sophist acts of giving corporations rights as individuals allow criminals running the corporations to have a type of qualified immunity protecting them against criminal charges, like the government. How many corporations have paid billions in legal restitution fines with no individuals seeing the inside of a prison or worse?

Electronic voting has grown since the early 2000s, and with its growing use comes concerns about reliability, tracking, and security. With each election cycle in the U.S., there are reports of hundreds to thousands of electronic votes accidentally being flipped to different candidates than what was selected and hackers -individuals or state-sponsored- attempting to break in to enact changes and steal information. Not only are the software and hardware bugs and external threats a concern, but so is the intent of those who own the corporations facilitating the electronic voting.

In the U.S., three corporations provide electronic voting machines and software facilitating voting for over 90% of eligible voters; Election Systems & Software (ES&S), Dominion Voting Systems, and Hart InterCivi. Each of these corporations is owned or invested by private equity firms that do not disclose who owns the corporations. ES&S is a subsidiary of McCarthy Group, LLC., Dominion Voting Systems has investments by Staple Street Capital Group, LLC, and Hart InterCivi was invested by H.I.G Capital, LLC until July 2020. Due to being listed as private corporations, information about actual ownership is kept from the public.

In December 2019, as the idea of election voting fraud was being pushed in multiple states, several Democratic Senators in Congress sent letters to each of the private firms requesting information on who owns the corporations that were hidden from public view. The response by the private firms was not released to the public. Can these private firms and corporations be trusted to facilitate voting in the U.S.? How sure can we be that what we are told is the absolute truth? Did the politicians purposely not disclose information that was provided?

To make things worse, governors like Governor Inslee of Washington State started pushing new legislation that would make it a misdemeanor for individuals to spread "unfounded" allegations of voter fraud -those individuals who claim voting fraud are labeled "conspiracy theorists." In May 2019, the FBI official labeled conspiracy theorists as domestic terrorists. Do you see the pattern and progress the government is pushing us down? Any disagreement with official government rhetoric is viewed as terrorism, which is ironic due to the actual definition of terrorism being a government's action against its populace.

The Great Reset to Stakeholder Capitalism will directly affect our livelihoods and should be a significant concern for our future. It is a growing movement backed by many of the political elites, corporation leaders, activists, and government officials to reset capitalism with a "progressive" form of modern socialism that includes government-provided universal basic income, universal healthcare, and tax increases across the board to help fight social issues deemed to be an emergency. Many aspects that are pushed might sound great on paper, but the reality is often much harsher than how it was described. The lives that could be lost during this Great Reset, if past trends of government-forced socialist movements hold, would be catastrophic for the global population and a significant reduction in the freedoms and rights we all should share.

"The difference of this fourth industrial revolution is, it doesn't change what you are doing, it changes you, if you take a genetic editing, just as an example, it's you who are changed, and of course this has a big impact on your identity." – Klaus Schwab, *Interview with Charlie Rose*, 2015

President Biden pushed the campaign slogan "Build Back Better" after taking office, similar to the "Great Reset." President Biden's Build Back Better campaign focuses on universal education, universal healthcare, and increasing taxes. Prime Minister Justin Trudeau of Canada explained at the annual WEF meeting on June 20th, 2020, that the world needed a reset. Prime Minister Trudeau said, "building back better means getting support to the most vulnerable while maintaining our momentum on reaching the 2030 Agenda for Sustainable Development and the SDGs (Sustainable Development Goals)." The UNFPA, which focuses on population growth reduction, was a prominent founding member of the U.N. Development Group, focusing on the U.N. SDGs.

Prime Minister Trudeau also said that in Canada, individuals have a right to own firearms for hunting or sport shooting, but no one in Canada can use a firearm for self-defense. A criminal could attack with the intent of murdering them, and if they attempted to defend themselves using a firearm, they could be viewed as a criminal and face prosecution. Governments around the world want all of us to be disarmed and compliant. Prime Minister Boris Johnson pushed "Build Back Better" during a speech on September 29th, 2020, which pushed many socialist ideas and greater government control. "Build Back Better" is a propaganda slogan showing several governments' coordinated efforts to push a singular idea and movement. Do you think this is for our benefit? Do you still believe that it is not possible that a group of individuals -acting nefariously across multiple countries- are working in a coordinated effort to bring about significant change to our daily lives?

In 1992, the United Nations Department of Economic and Social Affairs, during an Earth Summit in Brazil, was able to get more than 178 countries to agree to adopt Agenda 21, which was a "comprehensive plan of action to be taken globally, nationally and locally by organizations of the United Nations System, Governments, and Major Groups in every area in which human impacts on the environment" (SDGs UN website). Agenda 21 focused on Social and Economic Dimensions, Conservation and Management of Resources for Development, Strengthening the Role of Major Groups, and Means of Implementation. How many times have conspiracy theorists and others been vilified and laughed at when they brought up Agenda 21? It is a real thing that can be researched and proven true.

The full text for the UN Agenda 21 can be found here:
https://web.archive.org/web/20210318013442/https://sdgs.un.org/sit
es/default/files/publications/Agenda21.pdf

In 2015, Agenda 2030 for Sustainable Development, with 17 SDGs, was adopted by the General Assembly: 1. No Poverty, 2. Zero Hunger, 3. Good Health and Well-being, 4. Quality Education, 5. Gender Equality, 6. Clean Water and Sanitation, 7. Affordable and Clean Energy, 8. Decent Work and Economic Growth, 9. Industry, Innovation, and Infrastructure, 10. Reduced Inequalities, 11. Sustainable Cities and Communities, 12. Responsible Consumption and Production, 13. Climate Action, 14. Life Below Water, 15. Life

On Land, 16. Peace, Justice, and Strong Institutions, 17. Partnerships. All of this sounds great on paper when viewed individually, but when taken with context and theme of everything connected with Agenda 2030 and those pushing it, can we trust what we are publicly told?

One of the goals is the Immunization Agenda 2030, which "envisions a world where everyone, everywhere, at every age, fully benefits from vaccines to improve health and well-being. It aims to maintain hard-won gains in immunization, recover from the disruptions caused by COVID-19, and achieve even more – by leaving no one behind, in any situation or at any stage of life." (WHO, *Immunization Agenda 2030: A Global Strategy to Leave No One Behind*). Should we trust this immunization agenda with our health and safety? How could we possibly get to a world where everyone worldwide at every age is fully vaccinated? It would probably need several increasingly severe pandemics to reach this seemingly unattainable goal. Could these pandemics be manufactured to make sure these goals can be attained? Absolutely.

In 2016, U.S.-based ID2020, a non-profit and non-government tax-exempt 501(c)(3) organization, was officially created as a public and private syndicate in service to the U.N. 2030 SDGs with a primary focus of bringing digital IDs for billions of "undocumented" individuals worldwide. ID2020 is looking to build a global model for funding, researching, designing, and implementing a score of digital ID solutions and technologies. ID2020 views a digital ID as a vital requirement for social services, the ability to exercise rights, vote, and participation in modern society and economies.

In September 2018, ID2020, in partnership with the United Nations High Commissioner for Refugees (UNHCR), formally drafted *The Alliance Manifesto*, which describes ten principles as a guide to a future centered around global digital identity. These ten principles and guides focus on identity being a fundamental and universal human right, being able to verify and protect digital identities, getting ID access to those with no digital identities, and allowing for this system to be used globally without the worry of national borders and how to work with industries to bring about these changes. ID2020 has partnered with corporations like Microsoft, Accenture, Global Alliance for Vaccines and Immunizations (GAVI), Rockefeller Foundation, and Cisco Systems to help bring about these desired changes. In the U.S., Congress enacted the Real ID Act of 2005, 109-13 119 Stat. 302, which began to bring the U.S. into compliance with the goals of the U.N. 2030 SDGs.

A digital ID isn't the only aspect of moving to a traceable digital format. On November 15th, 2022, the Federal Reserve Bank of New York, in partnership with Citigroup Inc., HSBC Holdings Plc., Mastercard Inc., and Wells Fargo & Co., started a 12-week pilot program focused on the creation of a central banking digital currency (CBDC). Like with most cryptocurrencies, this newly created digital currency will be trackable, traceable, and completely controllable by the government. There is a reasonable assumption that an individual's access to their funds could be cut off for any number of reasons at any time. The government will significantly control our daily lives when the CBDC is combined with our digital IDs. There should be little doubt that the government would use this control to oppress and silence dissenting views to force compliance and obedience.

On December 7th, 2022, Nigeria, through the Central Bank of Nigeria, announced that starting in January 2023, ATM cash withdrawals were being limited to 20,000 nairas ($45) daily, and in addition to a weekly over-the-counter cash withdrawal limit at the banks is being set to 100,000 nairas ($225) for individuals and 500,000 nairas ($1,124) for businesses in the government's bid to push the economy into using a cashless digital currency. This is the type of response and action we can expect in the U.S. as the government pushes harder for a digital currency.

What happens if our digital ID, and our financial resources stored in CBDC, become restricted or suspended when it is fully integrated into everything? E.g., China's social credit scoring system locking people out of their assets for doing something the government deems socially unacceptable. What if our max carbon dioxide (CO_2) footprint allotted for the month is reached, and our digital ID, with access to our money and everything, is shut down? This is a dangerous slippery slope as it takes us down a path of complete and total monitoring of every individual in the world by a select few with little room for any disobedience in the face of tyranny.

On June 4th, 2021, the WEF released *Investing in Forests: The Business Case*, which focused on nature loss and climate change and the investment in forest conservation and restoration by corporations transitioning its business practices and policies into a "nature-positive, net-zero economy." A net-zero economy is an idea that an economy has net-zero greenhouse gas emissions and footprint, which is helped by buying and selling CO_2 credits to fight climate change and improve biodiversity. In 2013, the ten largest corporations that produce most of what we find in grocery stores emitted 263.7 million tons of greenhouse gas emissions, which, when put together and compared to entire countries, these corporations would rank 25th on a list of most polluting countries. On top of this, the U.S. military is the world's largest polluter. It produces more pollutants than 100 countries' pollutant production combined. Yet, we are told and encouraged to believe that our CO_2 footprint and locally procured meat are the problems and drivers of climate change.

Under the Great Reset, the WEF is advocating for a Great Food Transformation and a Great Energy Transformation to protect the planet and environment by changing "what we eat, how we produce it, and how it gets to us." The supposed reasoning behind these pushed transformations is climate change, specifically the researched 2019 report released by the U.N.'s Intergovernmental Panel on Climate Change (IPCC), which indicated "that by 2050, reforms of crop and livestock activities and agroforestry could mitigate up to a third of all greenhouse-gas emissions equal to the sum of the current annual CO_2 emissions of the U.S. and India." Do you see the hypocrisy in these polluters by telling us that we are the problem and must suffer and be restricted for the benefit and safety of the environment and the future of humanity? Of course, this will be at the same time they continue to pollute way beyond anything we could do in our lifetime.

The WEF formed the organization 1T.org with the stated mission:

"Trees and forests are a critical part of the solution to the climate crisis and biodiversity collapse. That's why we aim to mobilize, connect, and empower the global reforestation community to conserve, restore and grow one trillion trees by 2030. We are part of the World Economic Forum's work to accelerate nature-based solutions in support of the UN Decade on Ecosystem Restoration (2021-2030), supported by funding from Marc and Lynne Benioff."

There are roughly three trillion trees worldwide, so to conserve, restore, and grow one trillion trees in nine years is a lofty goal, and on the surface, it sounds like a great thing to do. Who doesn't want to protect the environment by giving our children a livable world where humanity is in balance with nature? But is this idea that grand as to benefit all and all that they claim to be?

One of the authors of this report is Nicole Schwab, daughter of Klaus Schwab. Nicole has a master's in Public Policy from the John F. Kennedy School of Government at Harvard University and a master's in Natural Sciences from Cambridge University. Nicole has worked with the World Bank, the Ministry of Health of Bolivia, and Young Global Leaders. Harvard University has had direct ties and a strong relationship with the CIA, e.g., funding projects and recruiting, since the 1940s and 1950s.

The *Investing in Forests: The Business Case* report focuses on corporations needing to invest in forests using existing assets to help fight nature and climate crises while creating short, medium, and long-term value, profitability, and growth. The number of corporations committed to the WEF's plan and goals has doubled from 2020 to 2021 -e.g., Amazon, Nestle, Rabobank, and Google- with 210 million hectares of land pledged to be restored by governments. This momentum, "build back better" -wording used in the report- is being used to accelerate global nature and climate action. For our benefit, supposedly.

The WEF states that their goals can be achieved by corporations working together to "seize the full environmental, social and market opportunities associated with forest conservation and restoration while mitigating emerging risks" through the use of shared guidelines, broader decarbonization, certifications, sustainability strategies, and the implementation of monitoring tools. Reading further into the report, it is explained that the monitoring tools will be through geospatial mapping, satellite and drone data, sensory and data processing, and regular and rigorous surveillance and tracking of things like canopy cover worldwide. It is not a far stretch to see that this massive global surveillance system is being set up to be used on free and innocent individuals worldwide to control and manipulate. This is the very idea of Big Brother monitoring everything you do. Will they allow you to cut down trees on your property? What extent of control will be enacted following the successful implementation of this surveillance system? What repercussions will they seek for violating their policies and guidelines?

The report showcases corporations like Google, which has begun collaborating with World Resources Institute to launch Global Forest Watch. The Global Forest Watch is an online monitoring platform tracking deforestation, "Forest Monitoring Designed for Action" uses high-resolution satellite monitoring systems, which will be integrated with other surveillance and tracking systems worldwide. How many corporate surveillance, monitoring, and tracking systems are needed to protect the world's forests? Can we be sure these won't be used against us as a way to enact more significant control over the masses?

Nestle is an international food and drinks processing corporation based out of Vevey, Switzerland, with more than 270,000 employees. Nestle signed on to the WEF's Invest in Forests campaign and has pledged to distribute 2.8 million shade trees by 2022 in Cote d'Ivoire and Ghana. Nestle, in partnership with the government of Cote d'Ivoire, is investing 2.7 million to restore degraded forest areas within the Cavally forest reserve by promoting sustainable cocoa production. In 2021, eight individuals sued Nestle over human rights abuse. They claim they were used, along with thousands of other children, as child slave labor working on cocoa farms in the Ivory Coast to help support Nestle cocoa supply chains. A lower court decision allowed the lawsuit to continue. Still, that decision was reversed by the Supreme Court mainly due to the plaintiff's failure to establish a connection to the alleged abuse of rights happening in U.S. jurisdiction. Nestle adamantly denies these allegations.

Pachama, another corporation partnered with WEF, is "a technology start-up, is combining satellite, drone and lidar scans of forests with machine-learning algorithms to assess the carbon storage potential of forests and detect any changes in canopy cover." Pachama is funded by Breakthrough Energy Ventures, which Gates founded in 2015. Breakthrough Energy Ventures has billions in funding thanks to its 28-high net-worth group members from ten countries. Some Breakthrough Energy Ventures group members include Jeff Bezos, Michael Bloomberg, Richard Branson, Jack Ma, George Soros, and Mark Zuckerberg.

In 2020, the Gates Foundation announced a new initiative called Bill & Melinda Gates Agricultural Innovations, or Gates Ag One, to "enable the advancement of resilient, yield-enhancing seeds and traits globally and facilitate the introduction of those breakthroughs into specific crops essential to smallholder farmers." Gates has repeatedly pushed Genetically Modified Organisms (GMO) seeds from Monsanto to be used in agriculture. Gates is now the largest individual farm owner in the U.S., dictating what types of seeds and food are grown worldwide. Gates-produced GMO potatoes, onions, and corn are now used by Mcdonald's in their fast food restaurants. How long until we are all eating what Gates grows? Are you sure you aren't already doing so?

Gates has openly stated that he wants everyone to eat 100% synthetic beef, which he has heavily invested in researching and developing plant-based and lab-grown meats. We can see that more and more fast-food restaurants are implementing and selling these products. This is occurring as government partnerships, like G20, dined on expensive wagyu beef while pushing the idea that we all need to get bugs or heavily processed plant-based and lab-grown synthetic meat -meat substitutes- to combat Climate Change. How sure can we be that these new products are healthy or provide the nutrients needed to stay healthy?

On September 21st, 2022, the journal of Nutrients published the study *Nutritional Composition and Estimated Iron and Zinc Bioavailability of Meat Substitutes Available on the Swedish Market*, which found -after analyzing 44 meat substitutes on the Swedish market- a "very low estimated iron and zinc bioavailability of meat substitutes, caused by the very high phytate content in products based on soy, pea and wheat protein" (Nutrients. 2022 Sep 21;14(19):3903.). Some of the best sources of iron come from meat - red meat is a very rich bioavailable source of iron. As we will discuss further in this book, being nutrient deficient directly influences our health and susceptibility to diseases like COVID19. On November 16th, 2022, the FDA announced that the lab-grown meat from Upside Foods was safe for human consumption -safe and effective. Investors in Upside Foods include but are not limited to Gates, Richard Branson, Tyson Foods, Cargill, and Kimbal Musk -brother to Elon Musk. Do these foods provide the nutritional value that we are being promised?

Most of the world's governments and corporations are working together in a coordinated effort to enact global changes that directly affect our lives, yet, trying to explain all of this to the general public is viewed as a crazy crackpot conspiracy not grounded in reality. The truth of our objective reality doesn't require everyone to believe in it. All of these goals and missions that have been planned for years, decades, or longer by the elite, political and industrial, have started to come together quickly thanks to the COVID19 pandemic and the economic hardship caused by the response governments have taken in the name of protecting us from COVID19. What if COVID19 was a live-fire exercise and is only the initial step in the Broken Window fallacy process to convince the masses to accept the massive changes coming?

"How will this expanded role of governments manifest itself? A significant element of new "bigger" government is already in place with the vastly increased and quasi-immediate government control of the economy. As detailed in Chapter 1, public economic intervention has happened very quickly and on an unprecedented scale. In April 2020, just as the pandemic began to engulf the world, governments across the globe had announced stimulus programmes amounting to several trillion dollars, as if eight or nine Marshall Plans had been put into place almost simultaneously to support the basic needs of the poorest people, preserve jobs whenever possible and help businesses to survive." – Klaus Schwab, *COVID-19: The Great Reset*, July 9th, 2020

Mainstream Science!™

"The Principle of Uncertainty is a bad name. In science, or outside of it, we are not uncertain; our knowledge is merely confined, within a certain tolerance. We should call it the Principle of Tolerance. And I propose that name in two senses. First, in the engineering sense: Science has progressed, step by step, the most successful enterprise in the ascent of man, because it has understood that the exchange of information between man and nature, and man and man, can only take place with a certain tolerance. But second, I also use the word, passionately, about the real world. All knowledge – all information between human beings – can only be exchanged within a play of tolerance. And that is true whether the exchange is in science, or in literature, or in religion, or in politics, or in any form of thought that aspires to dogma. It's a major tragedy of my lifetime and yours that scientists were refining, to the most exquisite precision, the Principle of Tolerance – and turning their backs on the fact that all around them, tolerance was crashing to the ground beyond repair. The Principle of Uncertainty or, in my phrase, the Principle of Tolerance, fixed once for all the realization that all knowledge is limited. It is an irony of history that at the very time when this was being worked out, there should rise, under Hitler in Germany and other tyrants elsewhere, a counter-conception: a principle of monstrous certainty. When the future looks back on the 1930's, it will think of them as a crucial confrontation of culture as I have been expounding it – the ascent of man against the throwback to the despots' belief that they have absolute certainty." – Jacob Bronowski, *The Ascent of Man,* 1973

Science is a never-ending process for determining the truth. Science is neither true nor false; it is a process for deciding what is true or false. Science is never settled and should never be considered settled. If someone is telling us that the science is settled (Science!^{TM}), they are telling us not to think and to have faith in whatever they are telling us. This is the opposite of science; asking questions ad nauseam. This is sophistry in action. Typically, when someone is telling us that the science is settled and evidence is provided to the contrary, they will laugh at the evidence and find anything wrong with it to say, "see, it's all wrong!" making it easier to ignore. These are fallacious arguments and rebuttals. These same people refuse to look at the evidence to their stance in the same detail and refuse to entertain the idea that they might be wrong with what they hold to be the truth. Mainstream science has become highly political and corrupt. It is up to us to determine what we believe is truth using all information available.

I hear it claimed a lot that someone must be a scientist or medical professional, or have multiple degrees in a discipline, to have any opinion on a topic, which is ridiculous. We can become knowledgeable in a subject without being a professional or degree holders from a university or institution. Medicine is called a practice for a reason. On May 3rd, 2016, the British Medical Journal (BMJ) published the study *Medical error—the third leading cause of death in the US*, which found that medical malpractice was the third leading cause of death in the U.S., at 250 thousand deaths annually (BMJ. 2016 May 3;353:i2139.). The study was conducted by John Hopkins researchers who stated that the CDC failed to classify medical malpractice errors on death certificates, resulting in a staggering statistic hidden from public view. No one should be condemned for challenging currently held mainstream beliefs in medicine and science with legitimate questions and concerns when the medical industry has such a high annual body count.

In 2020, the U.S. Department of Justice charged over 200 medical professionals across the U.S. with committing fraud and taking kickbacks from pharmaceutical corporations totaling hundreds of millions of dollars, pushing unnecessary and dangerous opioids on patients in their care and furthering the opioid epidemic going on in the U.S. (*2020 National Heath Care Fraud and Opioid Takedown*). On November 2nd, 2022, CVS Health Co. and Walgreen Co. announced that they had agreed to pay roughly $5 billion each to settle lawsuits nationwide for their roles in the opioid epidemic over the last two decades. On November 15th, 2022, Walmart, Inc. agreed to pay $3.1 billion to settle their lawsuits for their role in the opioid epidemic. No one in these corporations faced jail time for their criminal activities.

Academia publishes millions of articles annually, many being published as peer-reviewed research. Being peer-reviewed should mean that the research submitted is of high quality and credibility - the quality of being academically trusted as authentic- and of an unbiased truth. However, there is little evidence of the effectiveness of journals' peer-review systems. Peer review is a process where sometimes anonymous individuals -considered "peers"- review the work and if they can recreate the findings to confirm the research they do. This process can take up to a year or more at times. Recreation of the study isn't always possible, though, with some studies not being recreated and confirmed; only an opinionated analysis is provided.

Can these anonymous "peer" reviewers be trusted? Do the reviewers have a political agenda and bias that clouds their judgment? Were these reviewers paid to provide a specific review of a study (e.g., Pfizer study on a new drug or vaccine)? What if the editor doesn't like what the reviewers provided (e.g., not recommending publishing) and still publishes the study? Wouldn't that still technically classify the study as being peer-reviewed?

Hundreds of research paper retractions are made each year, after being peer-reviewed, due to being fake, heavily biased, having plagiarized ideas, and flawed methodologies. Attempting to review the raw data used by studies can be highly time-consuming, difficult to recreate, and potentially expensive, so it is understandable why there are so many issues with the peer-review process that academia uses today and why we cannot claim Science!^{TM} as being absolute truth; science is a process. As bad as this sounds, this is the only review process for these studies. It is up to us to determine if a study is accurate and to have the ability and opportunity to seek out information and data from all sources.

"And of course all the academics say we've got to have peer review. But I don't believe in peer review because I think it's very distorted and as I've said, it's simply a regression to the mean. I think peer review is hindering science. In fact, I think it has become a completely corrupt system. It's corrupt in many ways, in that scientists and academics have handed over to the editors of these journals the ability to make judgment on science and scientists. There are universities in America, and I've heard from many committees, that we won't consider people's publications in low impact factor journals. Now I mean, people are trying to do something, but I think it's not publish or perish, it's publish in the okay places [or perish]. And this has assembled a most ridiculous group of people. I wrote a column for many years in the nineties, in a journal called Current Biology. In one article, "Hard Cases", I campaigned against this [culture] because I think it is not only bad, it's corrupt. In other words it puts the judgment in the hands of people who really have no reason to exercise judgment at all. And that's all been done in the aid of commerce, because they are now giant organisations making money out of it." – Dr. Sydney Brenner, *King's Review magazine interview*, February 24th, 2014

The U.S. Supreme Court case *Daubert v. Merrell Dow Pharmaceuticals, Inc.*, 509 U.S. 579 (1993) set guidelines as to what could be admissible in a court case with one guideline saying studies should be peer-reviewed and published in a respected journal (how do you define "respected"?) to be admissible. However, the court also stated that peer-reviewed studies published in journals do not necessarily correlate with reliability as it only reduces the likelihood of considerable flaws and errors being found within the studies and possibly failing even there. We should always be allowed to question scientific studies because humans are fallible even when acting ethically and morally.

Over the years, groups of students and independent researchers, some from MIT, have submitted fake articles to dozens of publication journals, of which many were accepted and published, to determine the quality of the peer-review process and how biased the journals are with content and results. One such group of MIT students wrote a computer program, SCIgen (available for download), that created fake studies to be presented to scientific conferences that aggressively sought out academic papers to showcase at a conference while charging hefty fees to be showcased. This program continued to be used by others to submit fake papers and studies to respected journals worldwide. It was reported that more than 100 fake SCIgen papers were published in the U.S. Institute of Electrical and Electronic Engineers (IEEE).

In 2009, after receiving multiple emails to submit papers to The Open Information Science Journal, one graduate student had their computer-generated fake paper accepted for publication. Still, it would only be published after paying the $800 submission fee. There wasn't any peer-review process, even though the journal claimed to publish peer-reviewed papers. Some predatory journals seek any papers as long as the fee is paid. Only some of the most apparent papers that have errors or are entirely fabricated are caught and pulled from journals. The global retraction figures also include studies that journals pulled due to political pressure over what is being reported, regardless of truth, which happens more than you would think or hope. There is a significant issue with the peer-review process. Studies and papers should always be questioned and never taken at face value, especially pharmaceutical corporations and government-funded research. Still, we also cannot discount everything just because it goes against what we hold to be the truth.

Science, and academia, are not immune to the corruption of individuals, corporations, politics, and government, especially when most of the significant funding comes from taxpayers or corrupt and immoral individuals who weld significant resources and power. Epstein advocated eugenics and wanted to seed the human race with his DNA. One would hope that high-education institutions like MIT and Harvard University would distance themselves from someone like Epstein, but this isn't the case. MIT and Harvard University science departments and programs -with scientists worldwide- collaborated with Epstein on his projects, accepting millions in donations and funds. Epstein donated heavily to politicians, MIT, and Harvard University. Remember, Harvard University has been a CIA hub for decades. Gates and Mark Zuckerberg spent a few years at Harvard University. Scientists Epstein funded were also flown around on his pedophile jet. MIT Media Lab Director Joi Ito said in October 2014 in an email that Epstein had directed Gates to donate $2 million to the lab. Gates followed orders and provided the $2 million donation. Should we blindly believe in and trust the scientists that Epstein funded because they are scientists?

Merck & Co., Inc., the international pharmaceutical corporation, had a doctor hit list that they would vilify and attempt to get licenses pulled because the doctors would speak out against Merck's anti-inflammatory drug, Vioxx, which later was confirmed that it had caused close to 100 thousand heart attacks with tens of thousands dying from Vioxx -a product deemed safe and effective with full FDA approval. Vioxx was pulled from the market due to a voluntary recall by Merck. Vioxx doesn't enjoy the same liability-free protection that vaccines have, so there was enough legal incentive for Merck to pull Vioxx from the market when they couldn't hide the truth any longer. How many doctors were vilified because they questioned the safety of Vioxx?

It is common practice to target doctors to discredit their medical opinion when it goes against government rhetoric or prevents a corporation from potentially making billions. This practice occurred in the U.S. during the COVID19 pandemic. One such example is when Dr. Steven LaTulippe, an Oregon physician, had his medical license indefinitely suspended because he openly stated that he didn't wear masks at his clinic and didn't require his staff to either during the pandemic; in the Mask chapter, we will go over the science behind masks and respirators and their use. How many doctors were vilified and had their licenses pulled for standing against the government and corporate rhetoric?

Taxpayers fund most scientific research and studies through government grants. Other major funding comes from corporations - e.g., Pfizer- and non-profit organizations. Pfizer was fined in 2009 and ordered to pay $2.3 billion for the largest healthcare fraud in the history of the Department of Justice. Should we not question the validity and credibility of the studies Pfizer funds that help promote its products? Suppose the majority of funding for major studies is from the government or corporations incentivized to lie and manipulate the data. Can what is being pushed be trusted? The beauty of critical thinking is that we can entertain an idea without believing it to be the truth. How do we know if the data presented to us wasn't written in a sophist way intended to manipulate and control us into thinking a specific way?

For the past two decades, tens of billions of dollars, and countless hours of research, have been funneled into Alzheimer's disease research, trying to find treatments and solutions to the spike in individuals who now have Alzheimer's. Most of the more recent research has been based on the findings from the March 16th, 2006, journal of Nature study *A specific amyloid-β protein assembly in the brain impairs memory*, where the authors, primarily neuroscience professor Sylvain Lesné and neuroscientist Karen Ashe, linked Alzheimer's to extracellular accumulation of a 56-kDa soluble amyloid-β assembly (Aβ*56) -confirming a hypothesis that had been thought was the correct direction for years (Nature. 2006 Mar 16;440(7082):352-7).

Virtually all Alzheimer's drugs and treatments focused on Aβ*56 have failed and not provided the advancement that should have been made if the correlation and causation of Aβ*56 and Alzheimer's were accurate. In July 2022, Nature was informed of fraud in the 2006 study where hundreds of images were potentially tampered with, pushing the results incorrectly to link Aβ*56 to Alzheimer's. Nature listed an Editor's Note that an investigation is ongoing. This is only one case of potential fraud and misuse by professional scientists, with many more found throughout the history of the scientific community.

Climate change is a major politically charged hot topic issue that is being used en masse as reasons for greater government control. This control comes in various forms dictating our lives in every aspect -from the energy we use to what we eat. Our way of life is changing before our eyes -not a natural progression. Within the issue of Climate Change, everything that has been discussed so far - unethical and immoral behavior, corruption, lies, propaganda, etc.- can be found pushing a scripted narrative. The Science!™ behind Climate Change needs to be questioned, with potential alternative theories discussed and researched. That is the true process of science and the discovery of truth.

On July 17th, 2018, the Scientific Reports Journal published a study *Impact of Edible Cricket Consumption on Gut Microbiota in Healthy Adults, a Double-blind, Randomized Crossover Trial*, which stated "the current pressures on global food security, including climate change, population growth, and shifting dietary preferences, have ignited a search for more environmentally sustainable protein sources. Since livestock production is responsible for about 14.5% of total human-induced greenhouse gas (GHG) emissions, there is a mounting need for more efficient animal production systems." (Sci Rep. 2018 Jul 17;8(1):10762.).

This study is an example of a misleading or propagandized study. Taxpayer funds, totaling roughly $1.3 million, were used to determine if humans could eat crickets as an alternate source of protein instead of protein from cows, or other animals, to help combat climate change and to stop livestock greenhouse emissions "cow farts" from releasing so much CO2 in the air. Humanity has used insects as a viable food source at some point or another, so why is this study needed?

Another example of propaganda around climate change is Greta Thunberg -a young teenager pushing climate change action. She has addressed the U.N., governments, and corporations worldwide, calling for global transformations to combat climate change. This push using appeal to emotion and authority expects us to view her rhetoric as an authority on climate change while saying we cannot have an opinion on the subject if we are not scientists specializing in climate research. Thunberg, her parents, Public Relations (PR) handlers, and organizational crews handling logistics of PR operations have had massive CO2 footprints traveling back and forth worldwide over the years to help spread Thunberg's message. Will her travels be restricted since she and her team have significantly larger CO2 footprints than most individuals worldwide? Not if she continues pushing the approved rhetoric.

Don't you find it odd that the political voices that are the loudest on climate change tend to have multiple planes and vehicles traveling the world with an exponentially larger CO2 footprint than most? The 10% of wealthiest individuals worldwide cause over 40% of individual CO2 emissions globally, so if individuals were the actual cause, a lockdown measure -if they worked- should be aimed at those with the most significant footprint. This, of course, ignores that the U.S. government is the largest polluter in the world.

Throughout the COVID19 pandemic and towards the end of 2022, mainstream media and governments have pushed the rhetoric that weather changes -linked to Climate Change caused by humanity- are a cause of cardiac events indicating that the changing of the climate is driving the spike in cardiac events and sudden deaths that have been happening worldwide. One such example of science-driven propaganda being picked up by many mainstream media outlets is the December 12th, 2022, journal of Circulation published study *Associations Between Extreme Temperatures and Cardiovascular Cause-Specific Mortality: Results From 27 Countries*, which found that extreme hot and cold temperatures can cause cardiovascular-related events and deaths "especially under a changing climate" (Circulation. 2023 Jan 3;147(1):35-46.).

Now, while the overall premise is that changes in the climate and electrical environment can cause these types of events -it can- the Circulation study is being used to push propaganda to back a specific narrative. Looking at this study's funding sources, we can see that many government agencies and public universities worldwide helped fund the study -e.g., the U.S. Environmental Protection Agency (EPA) and the Harvard Chan National Institute of Environmental Health Sciences (NIEHS) Center for Environmental Health. Harvard University's Harvard Chan-NIEHS Center for Environmental Health -founded in 1962- is funded through NIH's second grant ever awarded (ES-000002). The NIH grant ES-000002 has been continuously renewed over the decades and, in 2019, was approved for five years of funding totaling $10.2 million. What if the narrative around the study is being used to hide the damages and deaths caused by the COVID19 vaccines -discussed in the VAERS chapter- while helping to continue the drive that humanity is responsible for climate change?

BlackRock's Climate Finance Partnership (CFP) aims to raise at least $500 million from institutional investors, organizations, and several governments to focus on climate infrastructure to reduce carbon emissions by investing significant capital into climate-related investments. BlackRock believes that the climate infrastructure market is expected to see high growth -profits- over the coming decades due to the expectation that 50% of global energy needs to be provided by renewable energy sources. Tens of millions of dollars are being spent to push the Climate Change narrative through news organizations like the Associated Press (AP), which requires hiring dozens of climate change journalists to report worldwide on the potential damages and the seriousness of climate change.

What might not be understood is that corporations like BlackRock are investing in the climate technologies that will help drive the progression away from coal and oil while funding the politicians who vote for regulations pushing economies to a more "green" infrastructure. These corporations are making billions by controlling the narrative of an issue and then selling the solution. Have you considered the negative environmental impact of creating lithium and cobalt batteries or seeking renewable energies? Sometimes the solution offered is worse than the issue we face.

"Unfortunately, Climate Science has become Political Science. It is tragic that some perhaps well-meaning but politically motivated scientists who should know better have whipped up a global frenzy about a phenomena which is statistically questionable at best." – Robert H. Austin, *Update: More Than 700 International Scientists Dissent Over Man-Made Global Warming Claims, U.S. Senate Committee on Environment & Public Works*, March 16th, 2009

What if we are being lied to about what is driving climate change? What if the Sun and galactic cosmic rays (GCR) drive real climate change -a natural process- through solar forcing and electromagnetic coupling between atmospheric layers? Is the narrative about CO2 driving Climate Change only a lie used to manipulate and control the masses? What if the electromagnetic particles, fields, and waves entering and leaving Earth are the real drivers behind the changes in weather patterns and climate? Humans can poison and destroy local flora and fauna environments that can devastate local areas and regions, but this doesn't mean we are driving climate change worldwide through CO2 emissions. We should be looking at reducing our local environmental impacts due to health concerns for the life living in those environments, but we need to focus on the correct mechanisms for the issues we face.

In the 1970s, scientists, governments, and mainstream media reported that we were heading towards a massive Global Cooling phase that would bring about a new Ice Age. This evolved into the 1990s Global Warming narrative, which was attributed to being driven by humanity. Many don't realize that the Sun's Grand Maximum cycle -maximum solar output- peaked in the mid-1990s, which is now heading into the next Grand Minimum after the current 11-year cycle -Solar Cycle 25- is due to be completed by 2030. Global Warming was considered paused in the early 2000s when the estimated temperatures of our global doom from the 1990s were not realized. Around this time, the narrative changed from Global Warming to Climate Change, which was still blamed on human activity. Climate Change is a loaded language since the climate has a documented history of wild changes even before humanity entered the picture. The climate will constantly change and should be expected even without humanity being involved. Nothing is static - there is a constant evolution of change.

The IPCC statistically attributes some of the Sun's energetic influence to human activity in its reports by viewing high-energy events and impacts as negligible on Earth. The increase in energy defaults to human activity if the Sun's energy output remains consistent or had a negative effect on energy levels during high-energy impacts. The Sun's activity and energy output continuously change through its documented maximum and minimum sun cycles, which can span hundreds of years -with some evidence indicating cycles spanning thousands of years. The Sun and GCR should be the first things we look at concerning weather and climate changes with the understanding that some cycles lag decades or longer behind energetic events until the effects are witnessed and felt.

Ben Davidson -of Space Weather News and Suspicious Observers- has authored a great book on solar forcing and how our Sun functions and plays a direct role on Earth called *Weatherman's Guide to the Sun* -currently in its third edition release. Davidson also releases a daily morning update on his YouTube channel reviewing the Sun's previous 24 hours of activity and the potential outcomes of that activity. I recommend you follow his work and keep watching the Sun for changes.

On April 9th, 2014, the journal of Environmental Research Letters published the study *Effect of solar variations on particle formation and cloud condensation nuclei,* which found that the maximum and minimum solar cycles had direct and indirect impacts on cloud seeding and cloud formation (Environ. Res. Lett. 9 045004). The study further explains that clouds play a crucial role in energy in the lower atmosphere and surface, influencing temperature changes. On September 18th, 2019, the Quarterly Journal of the Royal Meteorological Society published the study *Assessing North Atlantic winter climate response to geomagnetic activity and solar irradiance variability,* which found that winter climate weather is affected by geomagnetic activity and sunspot activity that can lag years after an energetic event (Q J R Meteorol Soc. 2019; 145: 3780– 3789). In November 2019, the journal of Astrophysics and Space Science published the study *High-latitude mesospheric intense turbulence associated with high-speed solar wind streams,* which found that energetic electrons from high-speed solar winds caused significant wind turbulence at high altitudes (Astrophys Space Sci 364, 210 (2019)).

We can track coronal mass ejection (CME) and solar energetic particles (SEP) from the Sun to technological disruptions and health issues on Earth. These events influence humanity's mental and physiological health. On January 9th and 10th, 2023, the Sun had several M-class and X-class flares and CMEs -not directly aimed at Earth- and starting on the evening of the 10th and leading into the morning of the 11th, the Federal Aviation Administration (FAA) had a Notice to Air Missions (NOTAM) U.S. wide system outage grounding thousands of flights the entire morning of the 11th. NOTAM provides flight conditions to pilots that affect the safety of travel. The FAA blamed the outage on a corrupted file in a database. Could it have been due to the solar activity seen on the 9th and 10th?

On February 22nd, 2015, the journal Proceedings of the Royal Society Biological Sciences published the study *Solar activity at birth predicted infant survival and women's fertility in historical Norway*, which showed that sunspot numbers and solar activity at the time of birth had a correlation and causation for the life span and health of an individual -the lower the activity, the more prolonged the span of life could be (Proc Biol Sci. 2015 Feb 22; 282(1801): 20142032.). There are more documented studies around this focus. There is a zero percent chance that the Sun's influence on life on Earth is negligible or non-changing. The Sun has been worshiped as far back as written human history and longer because of its importance.

"Students using astrophysical textbooks remain essentially ignorant of even the existence of plasma concepts, despite the fact that some of them have been known for half a century. The conclusion is that astrophysics is too important to be left in the hands of astrophysicists who have gotten their main knowledge from these textbooks. Earthbound and space telescope data must be treated by scientists who are familiar with laboratory and magnetospheric

physics and circuit theory, and of course with modern plasma theory." – Hannes Alfvén, *Dean of the Plasma Dissidents*, 1988

In recent discoveries and advancements, the SAFIRE project -run and conducted by plasma scientists- confirmed the Electric Sun model by creating a stable plasma reactor that replicated the atmosphere of the Sun in a laboratory. Mainstream science and governments willfully ignored this. Nuclear reactions were not needed to achieve the energy outputs recorded -which goes against currently held standard theories. The SAFIRE project generated 89 thousand degrees impinged at a single point using 182 watts of power in their plasma reactor, showing how the atmosphere of the Sun can reach millions of kelvins while the surface of the Sun is only a few thousand kelvins. Plasma cosmology goes against mainstream held beliefs, but that is what happens when scientific paradigms are upended and replaced by better-fitting theories.

What if the IPCC reports on Climate Change are produced to help hide that the intense and chaotic weather patterns we have started to experience worldwide are primarily due to a natural cyclical event that correlates with the Earth's poles flipping -geomagnetic reversal- not human-driven through $CO2$ emissions? On February 1st, 2014, the journal of Earth and Planetary Science Letters published the study *Dynamics of the earth magnetic field in the 10–75 kyr period comprising the Laschamp and Mono Lake excursions: New results from the French Chaîne des Puys in a global perspective*, which found that our current geomagnetic reversal is similar to the Laschamp Excursion -roughly 42 thousand years ago (Ear. Plan. Sci. Le. 2014; 387:184-197). The Laschamp Excursion magnetic field reversal lasted roughly 250 years, with the event having a direct role in leading to the extinction of the Neanderthals. Other reports indicate that a magnetic reversal can happen as quickly as the span of a human lifetime -roughly 100 years.

On September 1st and 2nd, 1859, the Carrington Event occurred after a large CME directly aimed at Earth struck, causing telegraph lines to catch fire and causing massive blackouts. Our current geomagnetic reversal started around this event and has begun to pick up speed over the past few decades exponentially. We are roughly 164 years into this reversal. There are documented cyclical patterns of events at play that matter -they can be predicted.

The South Pole is no longer over Antarctica and is racing to meet the North Pole someplace in the Indian Ocean. Earth's magnetic shield has significantly decreased in strength, leading to more significant solar geomagnetic storms, CMEs, and GCRs activity driving our chaotic weather patterns. At the current drop in strength, a complete reversal could be seen by 2035 to 2050. If a solar event the size of the Carrington Event hit us today -or even a strong solar event Earth could handle in the 1990s- technology would be wiped out. If this reversal goes the way of the Laschamp Excursion, we could see a significant population decline across all life on Earth without additional influences.

If true, what purpose could there be to hide something like this? Knowledge is power, and keeping it away from the masses keeps them at a disadvantage. One thing is for sure, the masses wouldn't be as accepting of the tyrannical changes we are witnessing and experiencing, nor of those causing them, if everyone assumed an impending unstoppable natural event of potentially biblical proportions was approaching -most likely in our lifetime. What would you do differently if you knew the "end of the world" was potentially 30 years or less away?

There is plenty of evidence suggesting that a natural 12-thousand-year cyclical event of biblical proportions is fast approaching -we'll call it an Age Ender, as Immanuel Velikovsky did. The 1950 book *Worlds in Collision* by Velikovsky provides worldwide evidence of past natural Age Enders affecting global cultures and societies, directly impacting spirituality, religious views, myths, and stories throughout written history. The CIA declassified a March 11th, 1966, publication by U.S. Air Force worker Chan Thomas called *The Adam and Eve Story* provided evidence of past worldwide cataclysmic events that corresponded with Earth's geomagnetic reversals. This shows the government -at least some in government- know that this potential event is possible and possibly coming very soon. The signs are there and point to it coming in our lifetime.

One strong theory by Davidson suggests that our solar system is preparing to pass through the Milky Way's galactic current sheet - similar to the solar system's heliospheric current sheet- which will trigger our Sun to micronova -shedding of its plasma- causing a tremendous upheaval ending our current age here on Earth. Davidson constantly provides scientific evidence and proof that his theory is highly plausible and more than likely true. The galactic current sheet trigger also explains why other planets in our solar system are also going through intense and chaotic weather pattern changes as Earth is -without human activity and influence. It is not a coincidence that Earth is going through massive changes like the other planets. It is all connected through electricity and magnetism -plasma cosmology. Watch the Sun and cosmic changes for signs as we move closer to this potential rare event. Do you think the government -those in the know- would officially confirm that an event of biblical propositions could be coming shortly unless it benefited them? They would keep everyone in the dark until the event occurred, giving them a greater chance of survival and control of what comes after. Think of the movie 2012 but with a different cause of the upheaval.

This would potentially explain why the U.S. government has spent many decades building underground cities and highway systems all over the U.S. Remember, Secretary of Defense Donald Rumsfeld announced on September 10th, 2001, -the day before 9/11- that the Pentagon couldn't account for $2.3 trillion. The financial and investigation evidence into the missing trillions were destroyed by the Pentagon attack on 9/11. Could some of the unaccounted-for trillions have been used to build these underground cities and highway systems? If the trillions had been taken out of the economy, there would have been a significant downturn easily identifiable. Could the underground construction be for housing those identified to be saved during the next Age Ender? They weren't built for the off chance nuclear attack was upon us -especially when a nuclear account wouldn't give anyone time to make it to one of these secretive underground facilities and centers. If all of this is true, then the WEF is using lies to justify ushering in a terrifying transformation into full-blown tyranny before this potential cyclical cataclysmic event occurs.

With these potential facts, why are innocent people driving to a local store to pick up groceries the real issue that needs to be targeted? Why are their gas stoves in need of being banned? Do you want to eat bugs or lab-grown overly processed meat because you -with your small CO_2 footprint- might be the driving force behind Climate Change? If you want to do "your part," then that is your natural right to choose, but leave those who don't want to join you alone. It is their right to decline to join you in your choices.

Another example of Science!^{TM} is that of the sugar industry. In April 2014, the JAMA Internal Medicine journal published the study *Added Sugar Intake and Cardiovascular Diseases Mortality Among US Adults*, which found that those who received roughly 17% to 21% of their daily calorie intake from processed added sugars had a 38% higher risk of cardiovascular disease (JAMA Intern Med. 2014;174(4):516-524.). In November 2016, the JAMA Internal Medicine journal published the study *Sugar Industry and Coronary Heart Disease Research: A Historical Analysis of Internal Industry Documents*, which called into question the validity and credibility of a 1967 research paper (JAMA Intern Med. 2016;176(11):1680-1685). In 1967 the New England Journal of Medicine published the study *Dietary fats, carbohydrates and atherosclerotic vascular disease*, which correlated fat and cholesterol as the cause of Coronary Heart

Disease (CHD) and reduced any causation or correlation to sugar (N Engl J Med. 1967 Aug 3;277(5):245-7 concl.).

In the 1960s, obesity was starting to tick up, and there were claims that it was caused by sugar being introduced into the food supply chain. The 1967 research paper was funded by the Sugar Research Foundation (SRF), -a trade association for the sugar industry- now called the Sugar Industry. The SRF started out focusing on public education and research for an industry that benefited from a positive view of sugar. The 1967 research paper was published by three Harvard University researchers -who had received numerous grants from the NIH and Harvard School of Public Health- who were paid roughly $50,000 in value -adjusted for inflation- to review a handpicked list of provided studies by the SRF. If you look at past photographs of beachgoers from the 1960s and 19070s and compare them to today, you will see a significant increase in obesity in society. This should not be normal.

"The most effective route to achieving optimal health is by channeling the intrinsic methods that the human body has developed during its hundreds of thousands years on Earth. Recommendations that drastically diverge from this pattern will likely lead to poorer health, which is indeed what has been witnessed over the past three decades." – Dr. Colin E. Champ, *Misguided Medicine, 2nd edition,* 2016

We are even being lied to statistically when blood tests are run to show our current levels for various physiological measurements that track a person's health. These measurements are provided to us as goals to be within the reference ranges -considered normal for the general population. The issue around these measurements is that if a population is overall unhealthy, what would be considered "normal" is unhealthy. In an unhealthy society -in which the U.S. is unhealthy-do you want to be in the normal unhealthy range or be in the legitimately healthy range?

The trend of targeting healthy fats and cholesterol while pushing us to normalize unhealthy physiological levels continues today. More heavily processed sugar, e.g., high-fructose corn syrup, continues to enter the food supply chain at every step with greater emphasis on processed foods. There is a clear correlation and causal relationship between the increase in obesity and Type 2 diabetes in the masses throughout the U.S. to the rise in sugar intake in foods and supply chains. In 2015, the New York Times published an article *Coca-Cola Funds Scientists Who Shift Blame for Obesity Away From Bad Diets*, showing how Coca-Cola hired scientists to help push the message of ignoring calorie intake and only focusing on exercise; or the lack of exercise being the sole cause of obesity. Soda has never been and will never be a healthy drink and has played a direct role in furthering the obesity epidemic that has only gotten worse.

These corporations are incentivized to lie and manipulate the masses into buying more of their products. Working out, building muscle, and exercising is vital to our health, but so is eating healthy. Imagine if Coca-Cola had a monopoly on violence to drive higher prices through threats, intimidation, and violence. This is a possible reality if we move towards Stakeholder Capitalism that is being pushed with the Great Reset.

Healthy debate has all but vanished from everywhere we look, and when attempted, contempt and harassment are not far behind. If anyone steps out of line from mainstream-held beliefs and approved government rhetoric, they get slapped down and experience loss of jobs, targeting and harassment, arrests, and persecution. Many doctors and nurses have lost their jobs and licenses for speaking against government rhetoric during the COVID19 pandemic. This is an antithesis to how science should be conducted; however, it is how medical tyranny is undertaken. Why is this our current reality? Why have the masses given up challenging authority without question, being completely obedient, when questioning everything in the universe is what has driven innovation and advancement throughout the ages?

In 1813, Congress passed the Vaccine Act, tasking government agents with regulating the supply and distribution of the smallpox vaccine, discovered in 1796. This was due to the high rate of individuals selling what the government deemed fraudulent, ineffective, and dangerous versions of the smallpox vaccine. Of course, in 1820, the Vaccine Act was repealed due to a smallpox outbreak in North Carolina caused by tainted smallpox vaccines. At this time, the United States Pharmacopeial Convention, a non-profit organization that still operates today, was founded and pulled together hundreds of delegates representing federal agencies, national and state associations, colleges, nursing, and pharmaceutical industries to set regulations and standards that are updated annually. These regulations and standards are considered official and are enforced by the FDA to this day.

In 1906, the Food and Drug Act was signed into law, granting the government regulatory authority and control of the food and drug industry in terms of fraudulent marketing, quality, strength, and chemical makeup. This authority was granted to the USDA Bureau of Chemistry. In 1927, the Bureau of Chemistry was reorganized into the Food, Drug, and Insecticide organization, and within a few years, was changed to the FDA. Even during this time, multiple groups and industries pushed to give the federal government greater power over our lives. This enforced authority has only grown in size and scope since its inception. Do you think the FDA, or those administrating the FDA, are immune to corruption?

The FDA has approved plenty of drugs and treatments that the manufacturer then pulled for the damages and deaths these products caused. Did you know that roughly 75% of the FDA's Drug Review Budget is covered by the for-profit pharmaceutical corporations the

FDA is tasked with investigating and reviewing? Conflicts of interest seem to matter no longer. Here is a small list of previous drugs that were once officially approved, considered safe and effective, and then pulled from the market:

Accutane (Isotretinoin) – On the market for 27 years (1982 to June 2009) and caused an increased risk of congenital disabilities, miscarriages, and premature births when used by pregnant women; inflammatory bowel disease and suicidal tendencies were also reported.

Baycol (Cerivastatin) – On the market for three years (1998 to August 2001) and caused rhabdomyolysis -breakdown of muscle fibers that results in myoglobin being released into the bloodstream-leading to kidney failure, 385 nonfatal cases, with most requiring hospitalization, and 52 deaths (31 in the US) worldwide. Twelve deaths were related to taking this drug in combination with gemfibrozil (Lopid).

Darvon & Darvocet (Propoxyphene) – On the market for 55 years (1955 to November 2010) and caused severe toxicity to the heart; between 1981 and 1999, there were over 2,110 deaths reported.

Duract (Bromfenac) – On the market for one year (1997 to 1998) and caused four deaths, with eight patients requiring liver transplants and 12 patients having severe liver damage.

Lotronex (Alosetron) – On the market for 0.8 years (February 2000 to November 2000) and caused 49 reported cases of ischemic colitis (inflammation and injury of the large intestine), 21 cases of severe constipation (10 requiring surgery), mesenteric ischemia (inflammation and injury of the small intestine), and five deaths.

Omniflox (Temafloxacin) – On the market for 0.3 years (January 1992 to June 1992) and caused reports of severely low blood sugar, hemolytic anemia, other blood cell abnormalities, kidney dysfunction -half of the cases required renal dialysis- allergic reactions, including some causing life-threatening respiratory distress, and three deaths.

Vioxx (Rofecoxib) – On the market for 5.3 years (May 1999 to September 2004) and caused an increased risk of heart attack and stroke linked to roughly 80 to 100 thousand heart attacks and tens of thousands of deaths. Merck spent close to $5 billion to settle lawsuits.

Other drugs beyond vaccines have been pulled for less than what some of the vaccines have caused -which we will cover in the VAERS chapter. These drugs did not come with liability protection as vaccines do; due to the National Childhood Vaccine Injury Act (NCVIA) of 1986. The government has regulated vaccine control and distribution since vaccines were discovered. All previous vaccines have taken 5 to 30 years to be approved by the FDA for official approval due to the safety standards set and required animal and human testing as well as experimentation. The new COVID19 vaccines were approved for licensure in less than two years from conception to official market approval, with market supply of the experimental versions to millions in less than a year. Does the speed at which these new experimental and traditional COVID19 vaccines hit the market inspire trust and confidence?

On average, 4,500 drugs and devices are recalled yearly, even though many items were FDA-approved first. Cigarettes and tobacco cause roughly 480,000 deaths annually, yet these dangerous products are regulated by the FDA -through the Family Smoking Prevention and Tobacco Control Act of 2009- and allowed to stay on the market. Facing thousands of lawsuits for damages and deaths caused by vaccines in the 1970s and 1980s, the for-profit pharmaceutical corporations lobbied Congress, spending millions then, to pass the

NCVIA of 1986, which shielded these corporations from any liability concerning vaccines.

Think about this with the currently rushed COVID19 vaccines; the COVID19 vaccines could kill 50% within three to five years of those who inject themselves with the new experimental medical procedures, and these for-profit corporations would face zero liability or criminal charges even if proven they lied about the data that was submitted to the FDA. What incentive do they have to tell the truth or to conduct legitimate studies when billions in profit, funded by taxpayers, are on the table?

"The more corrupt a society, the more numerous its laws." – Edward Abbey, *A Voice Crying in the Wilderness,* 1990

Did you know that between 2020 to the time of this writing, Pfizer and Moderna stocks were some of the most owned corporate stocks by Congress? Close to all 50 Congress members that financially disclosed they own stock in these corporations had a financial incentive to push Pfizer and Moderna COVID19 vaccines. Should we blindly accept what we are told and continue to inject away anything they tell us to?

These pharmaceutical corporations now spend hundreds of millions a year lobbying politicians. Pfizer spent $13 million for lobbying in 2020 alone. On average, Pfizer spends $2 to $3 billion a year on marketing paid to media outlets and platforms with a large user base. There is a large financial incentive to push the scripted narrative provided by Pfizer. Pfizer was fined in 2009 and ordered to pay $2.3 billion for the largest healthcare fraud in the history of the Department of Justice.

In 2019, the FDA Commissioner, Scott Gottlieb, resigned from his post and started working for Pfizer's board of directors. Pfizer's COVID19 vaccine was officially approved by the FDA for full licensure in record warp speed time by August 23rd, 2021 -20 months from when it was announced that COVID19 was formally discovered. The 2019 to 2021 FDA Commissioner, Stephen Hahn, resigned his post and joined the venture capital firm that launched Moderna, Flagship Pioneering, as their chief medical officer. Moderna submitted its application for full licensure of its COVID19 vaccine and received official approval on January 31st, 2022. Moderna board member Dr. Moncef Slaoui resigned from his post in May 2020 to become the Chief Scientist for President Trump's Operation Warp Speed which helped pave the way for his previous employer and other pharmaceutical corporations to make billions off taxpayers.

Should we trust everything Pfizer is saying without question? We should be paying attention to Pfizer's $36 billion in revenue from their COVID19 vaccine in 2021 as a potential incentive and motivator to lie and falsify data it shares with government officials and the public. Pfizer made even more in 2022 while looking to make close to these amounts in 2023. This revenue includes a 2021 $3.5 billion taxpayer-funded contract awarded by the U.S. Army to produce 500 million COVID19 vaccine doses. Why did the U.S. Army need that many doses, enough to inject close to the entire U.S. population multiple times, when the U.S. Army only has roughly one million personnel? The U.S. Army isn't giving each of their personnel 500 doses.

If vaccines are so safe and effective, why are they liability-free medical procedures when they can come with a risk of death? It is the responsibility of the manufacturer to initiate and conduct a recall if the product is defective and dangerous because they usually can face lawsuits for damages and deaths caused by their products, but if a product is liability-free, what incentive does the manufacturer have in recalling a defective and dangerous product? If any damages or deaths occur due to a vaccine, then the individual, or a representative of the injured party, must petition the government to seek restitution through a special court which is paid out using taxpayer funds shielding these for-profit corporations from losses.

Since the NCVIA was signed into law, over $4.6 billion in taxpayer funds has been paid out to settle vaccine injury claims protecting the bottom line of these for-profit corporations. This total was before the COVID19 vaccines were introduced to the market. Making a profit while facing no liability for damages and deaths is a slippery slope. It has many ethical and moral implications that those who claim to be champions of our safety and health ignore.

The mass vaccination campaign started in December 2020, hundreds of millions of doses of Pfizer and Moderna experimental mRNA COVID19 vaccines, as well as Johnson & Johnson (J&J) traditional experimental COVID19 vaccine, were given to roughly 221 million, 67%, of the U.S. population through engineered consent and a monopoly on violence. With the inclusion of all COVID19 vaccines worldwide, billions of doses have been given to billions of people in the largest human experiment in history.

Still, many are not questioning the massive conflict of interests or the flawed science being pushed as gospel by the government and mainstream media. The FDA took 108 days to review Pfizer's COVID19 vaccine application and approve it for full licensure. A FOIA request was submitted to have data found in Pfizer's application released to the public. The FDA petitioned the court to allow them to respond to the request over the course of up to 75 years, the year 2096, at 500 pages a month with hundreds of thousands of documents needing to be released. You read that correctly, up to 75 years before all of the information the FDA reviewed in 108 days would be released to the public. Why would the FDA request such a long timeframe to release documentation that only took 108 days to review and process? Could the agency be hiding something for nefarious purposes? Vaccines should always be a personal decision, never forced or mandated. This is only a small sample of reasons why we should question every step of the government, never take what it says at face value, nor trust it with our safety and health.

"I think people in power have a vested interest to oppose critical thinking." – Carl Sagan, *Science Friday interview*, May 1996

Engineered Consent

"As Albert Einstein once said to me: "Two things are infinite: the universe and human stupidity." But what is much more widespread than the actual stupidity is the playing stupid, turning off your ear, not listening, not seeing." – Frederick S. Perls, *Gestalt Therapy Verbatim*, 1969

What is consent? Consent is the voluntary acceptance and agreement in sentiment in a given situation. Consent is about truthful communication for activities between multiple individuals. For example, what makes sex, not rape? Consent. What makes taking someone's money or property not theft? Consent. This verbal or written affirmation of expressed agreement helps all parties understand and respect boundaries, keeping rights from being violated. When dealing with power dynamics, e.g., manager and employee or teacher and student, consent is not considered to be given freely. If pressure from intimidation, threats, or violence is used to gain consent -it is not considered given freely- meaning consent was not granted but engineered. Children cannot consent to adults, which is why parental authority exists. When consent is given freely, it is not a blanket thing that can be used in the future at any time; e.g., if someone agrees to have sex with another, that consent does not equate to a future encounter. Consent can be withdrawn at any point for any reason. Consent is not silence when discussing the potential violation of natural rights, even though the government considers silence as consent. Remaining silent due to the fear of being harassed, attacked, or violated is not consenting. Consent must be verbalized or written and acknowledged by all parties involved.

Informed consent, when it comes to medical decisions, is the fundamental principle for ethical decisions and practices. Informed consent requires that the individual be provided with all the truthful and essential information on risks, benefits, and other available alternatives. Informed consent is a fundamental need when conducting research and experimentation on test subjects. Full disclosure of the information is required so subjects can make informed decisions. There are no guarantees in a healthcare setting, so the informed consent process allows individuals to understand the risks undertaken with any treatment and decide for themselves. This decision needs to be free from lies, manipulation, threats, and coercion, or it is not voluntary or informed. Informed consent is viewed as a critical communication link between subjects and researchers. With informed consent -refusing to participate or discontinuing participation at any time- should not involve penalties nor loss of benefits that subjects are entitled to.

"The engineering of consent should be based theoretically and practically on the complete understanding of those whom it attempts to win over. But it is sometimes impossible to reach joint decisions based on an understanding of facts by all the people. The average American adult has only six years of schooling behind him. With pressing crises and decisions to be faced, a leader frequently cannot wait for the people to arrive at even general understanding. In certain cases, democratic leaders must play their part in leading the public through the engineering of consent to socially constructive goals and values. This role naturally imposes upon them the obligation to use the educational processes, as well as other available techniques, to bring about as complete an understanding as possible." – Edward Bernays, *The Engineering of Consent*, 1947

Engineered consent is the manufacturing of consent to get an individual to support ideas and programs they would disagree with if given all the information. Engineered consent is viewed as informed consent by the government and is used as justification for many terrible things the government has done throughout history. However, engineered consent is not informed consent because it uses manipulation and sophistry to get individuals to consent without providing an unbiased truth.

Through Edward Bernays' book *Propaganda* and *The Engineering of Consent*, fields of study like Consumer Behavior and Marketing have grown significantly in the understanding and ability to manipulate, control, and brainwash individuals and masses into acting and behaving in a specific manner. Consumer Behavior focuses on individuals' and groups' buying tendencies, preferences, attitudes, emotions, consumptions, wants, and needs of goods and services and how all of these are influenced by the various social sciences. Marketing is used to find target audiences and to reach them with the optimal message to manipulate and control or persuade individuals into buying goods and services. Governments use this scientific understanding to increase its control and power.

PR and Public and Policy Administration fields of study are heavily influenced by propaganda and those attempting to engineer consent from the public. PR focuses on disseminating information for an organization or individual to help maintain their public image -an image matters to the public. There are entire corporations and divisions within corporations dedicated to managing PR for an organization or individual. Public and Policy Administration is where individuals administer and champion the creation, management, and dissemination of policies and guidelines used by the government to maintain further control over the masses, covering areas like health, agriculture, education, and the military. These fields also apply to other public organizations and non-profits. If an individual cannot comprehend nor understand what is going on, they cannot give informed consent regardless of how engineered the consent was. Comprehension and understanding are foundational principles, themes, and contexts of the word consent. Sophistry twists these ideas and principles, gearing everything towards manipulation and control.

Everything the government has been doing by making COVID19 vaccines mandatory for employment, enacting travel restrictions, shutting down businesses from operating, arresting business owners who continued to operate, forcing businesses to deny services to those not vaccinated or wearing a mask, and offering monetary bonuses or lotteries to get a COVID19 vaccine violates the very definition of informed consent. It is an attempt by the government at engineering consent. How informed were you at the start of the COVID19 pandemic? How informed are you now? At the end of this book, ask yourself that question again.

There are many examples of propaganda to generate engineered consent to take the COVID19 vaccines, including corporations like Krispy Kreme offering free donuts for those who got the COVID19 vaccine. Krispy Kreme is owned by the JAB Holding Company, to which the founder had ties and supported Hitler and Nazism. Even children's entertainment shows like Sesame Street were promoting COVID19 vaccines through videos of Big Bird getting vaccinated. Musicians and bands were paid to create songs promoting COVID19 vaccines as being the cool thing to inject -peer pressure. Governments like Washington state started COVID19 booster incentive programs for its employees. For 2023, Washington state employees -pending legislative approval- would be provided a one-time $1,000 payment for proof that a COVID19 booster was injected -violating the idea and intent behind informed consent.

All COVID19 vaccines are still in the experimental trial phase until the end of 2023, when the experimental trials end, with final reports being submitted to the FDA in 2025. If the FDA was seeking up to 75 years to release the initial Pfizer mRNA COVID19 vaccine license application data to the public, how long will the request be to release the final reviewed material? Are you positive you haven't been lied to and that the COVID19 vaccines are safe and effective?

"People act like you have a choice. People don't feel like going to the stadium when they might get infected. You know, it's not the government who's saying OK, just ignore this disease, and people are deeply affected by seeing these deaths, by knowing they could be part of the transmission chain, and old people, their parents, their grandparents could be affected by this. And so you don't get to say, ignore what's going on here. There will be the ability, particularly in rich countries, to open up if things are done well over the next few months. But for the world at large, normalcy only returns when we've largely vaccinated the entire global population." – Bill Gates, *Financial Times interview*, April 2nd, 2020

Without proper informed consent, everything that has been done for COVID19 for the past two years has been illegal, unconstitutional, immoral, and unethical. Why do so many not view any of this as an issue? What we are seeing today is medical tyranny on an unprecedented scale. Why are the masses accepting medical tyranny at face value without questioning the potential ulterior motives? If we do not have faith in humanity to trust everyone without government, how can we trust the government -run by those we shouldn't have faith in- to control all of our lives? How much are we willing to accept until we say enough is enough and stand up for our rights and the rights of the innocent people around us?

"The picture of the world that's presented to the public has only the remotest relation to reality. The truth of the matter is buried under edifice after edifice of lies upon lies. It's all been a marvellous success from the point of view in deterring the threat of democracy, achieved under conditions of freedom, which is extremely interesting." – Noam

Chomsky, *Media Control: The Spectacular Achievements of Propaganda*, 1991

The Immune System

"A popular Government without popular information, or the means of acquiring it, is but a Prologue to a Farce or a Tragedy, or perhaps both. Knowledge will forever govern ignorance: And a people who mean to be their own Governors, must arm themselves with the power which knowledge gives." – James Madison, *letter to W.T. Barry*, August 4th, 1822

Organisms are biological living systems that have the properties for life, react to stimuli, reproduce, adapt, grow, and maintain balance by achieving homeostasis. Bacteria are small single-celled organisms and can be found everywhere we might look on Earth, from Antarctica to volcanic underwater vents. The root definition of bacteria means "stick, rod, staff, cudgel" because the first bacteria discovered looked rod-shaped (Online Etymology Dictionary). The human body comprises roughly 39 trillion bacteria cells and 30 trillion human cells, with some estimates saying microorganisms outnumber human cells 10 to 1. We are more bacteria than human, with many of these bacteria being a benefit to our survivability and health.

There are good bacteria -approximately 500 different species living in our gut alone- and harmful bacteria that can make us sick. The gut is an organ that directly affects and significantly impacts our health and immune system. In April 2019, an Arizona State University study published in the journal of Scientific Reports *Long-term benefit of Microbiota Transfer Therapy on autism symptoms and gut microbiota*, which showed that fecal matter transplants - Microbiota Transfer Therapy- had approximately a 50% reduction of autistic symptoms two years after the transplants (Sci Rep. 2019 Apr 9;9(1):5821.). This shows how important good gut bacteria and a healthy gut can be.

It is important to remember that we are, by a majority, more bacteria than humans because when prescribed antibiotics, all bacteria, good and bad, are targeted and can be killed off. It is counter-productive to our health if we kill off all good bacteria, further damaging our bodies. Antibiotic means "against life" (Online Etymology Dictionary). Why is it overly prescribed for everything if it is against life? Antibiotics should only be prescribed and used in rare cases when the body cannot fight off infections by other means and approaches. The overuse of antibiotics has driven the rise of antibiotic-resistant bacteria, causing another global crisis.

DNA is the genetic material found in the tree of life - Eukarya, Archaea, and Bacteria- that provides the blueprints and instructions for how cells should work and function -producing specific proteins. DNA cannot produce proteins directly. Cells require a way to get these instructions, so mRNA transports are used to get the DNA instructions to cells. mRNA is a single-stranded RNA -a nucleic acid- used in this protein production. mRNA is short-lived within the body, quickly broken down by the cells they instruct, and helps regulate the protein production rate based on the specific instructions they carry.

For centuries scientists have struggled to define what a virus is. Is it alive or not alive? After all, living and non-living things are complex combinations of atoms and molecules, which can be broken down into positive and negative electrical forces and frequencies. How do you define what a virus is?

The word virus has its roots in Latin: "poison, sap of plants, slimy liquid, a potent juice" (Online Etymology Dictionary). At its base, viruses are poisons that can affect all branches of the tree of life - depending on the virus. Viruses typically stay within a single branch dealing with infectability. Viruses had to be grouped in classifications for study to help define what a virus is. David Baltimore developed a virus classification scheme -the Baltimore Classification- which was used to help define and categorize what a virus is. This classification system identified seven class groups based on how a virus is transcribed and how it synthesizes mRNA. The seven classifications comprise DNA, RNA, and Reverse transcriptase (RT) viruses. In 1971, the International Committee for the Taxonomy of Viruses (ICTV) published its first report detailing 290 virus species, and its 2012 (9th) report detailing roughly 3,000 virus species.

In 1970, David Baltimore, Howard Temin, and Renato Dulbecco were made famous for discovering RT at the University of Wisconsin – Madison (UW-Madison). They went on to win the 1975 Nobel laureate in Physiology or Medicine for their discovery. RT is an enzyme that plays a specific role in regulating the flow of genetic information and is needed to modify DNA from RNA. The process of modifying DNA from RNA is called reverse transcription, where an RNA genome is converted into a DNA molecule that can be inserted into a subject's genome. The discovery of RT led to the discovery of retroviruses that uses RT to replicate -e.g., HIV. RT was initially thought to be only found in retroviruses. We will go into more detail about why RT is important when discussing mRNA COVID19 vaccines later in this book.

Viruses are poison, a potentially deadly infectious agent that typically consists of a nucleic acid molecule -DNA or RNA- usually in a protein coat -not always- that is generally too small to be seen by light microscopy -not always- cannot generate its energy, cannot translate the DNA sequences of its genes into proteins, and can multiply by taking control of the living cell it invades -it is the living cells that replicate viruses (Roossinck, Marilyn J. *Virus: An Illustrated Guide to 101 Incredible Microbes.* Ivy Press, 2016).

Viruses can range in many different sizes and shapes and are viewed as causing many kinds of symptoms. Viruses are not alive nor considered living entities. Viruses usually only become prominent when our natural cleansing processes -phagocytosis, bacterial, fungal, and parasitical- weaken or sterilize within our immune system. A virus uses a spike protein to attach to cells to help gain control of a host cell for further replication and growth. When surrounded by toxic pollution, poor air/water/food quality, nutritional imbalances -e.g., vitamin deficiencies- and overly prescribed medical treatments -antibiotics and medications- these critical living cleansing processes are weakened or sterilized.

Baltimore met Temin at the high-school Summer School Program at Jackson Laboratory funded by the NIH. In 1965, Dulbecco recruited Baltimore to work at the Salk Institute for Biological Studies -founded by Jonas Salk in 1960. Jonas Salk is the famed virologist who developed the first polio vaccine. In 1990, Baltimore was appointed as the 6th president of Rockefeller University in New York City. In 1997, Baltimore was appointed president of the California Institute of Technology (Caltech) where he set up a laboratory focused on gene therapies for HIV and cancer. The research there led to an Engineering Immunity program being started -funded by the Gates Foundation through the Grand Challenge Grant. The grant provided the funding for two gene therapy startups to get off the ground -Calimmune, Inc. (2006) and Immune Design Corp (2008). A third program within the Engineering Immunity program focused on developing an adeno-associated virus vector HIV vaccine -in clinical testing at NIH (Annu Rev Immunol. 2019 Apr 26;37:1-17.).

A protein is a biological polymer made up of amino acids. Polymers are DNA, RNA, and proteins that allow organisms to sustain life, grow, and reproduce. Amino acids are the foundational building blocks for life, with more than 500 types found in nature and 22 types appearing in our genetic code. A wide range of different kinds of proteins helps perform the functions in host cells, from structural to mechanical. There is still some debate on if life's first molecule was an RNA strand or a protein.

A spike protein (S Protein) is a glycoprotein, a membrane protein that helps with cell-to-cell interaction; a strand that extends from the surface of an enveloped virus which usually has a rod, club, or crown-like shape and appearance. The spike (S) protein is different from protein S, which functions as anticoagulation and is dependent on vitamin K produced in the liver. Being deficient in protein S can lead to thrombosis and blood clots that can potentially cause embolisms and death. The University of Kentucky College of Medicine reported that COVID19 could cause thrombosis by causing lung inflammation leading to a reduction in protein S levels that can last for weeks or months after COVID19 infection -long-COVID19; this study is still ongoing and has not been officially published.

"The greatness of human actions is measured by the inspiration that it brings. Blessed is he who carries within himself a God, an ideal of beauty and obeys it: an ideal of art, ideal of science, ideal of country, ideal virtues of the Gospel! These are the wellsprings of great thoughts and great actions. All reflections illuminate infinity."
– Louis Pasteur, *Discours de réception de Louis Pasteur*, April 27th, 1882

In the 1800s, a French chemist named Louis Pasteur made Germ theory famous. Germ theory is the leading standard for how diseases, symptoms, and infections occur worldwide, focusing on microorganisms -bacteria and viruses- as the driver of most diseases triggered by stress and critical issues. Germ theory focuses on treating the potential invader instead of focusing on the terrain and host system. This theory and view brought the advancements of antibiotics and vaccines, in which antibiotics destroy both good and bad bacteria and can lead to negative consequences, e.g., antibiotic-resistant pathogens. Vaccines primarily focus on a singular disease and pathogen. They have led to antibody-dependent enhancement (ADE), a phenomenon where vaccines can cause the enhancement of a virus's entry and replication in a host's cells.

Germ theory is limited with its singular focus on treating the disease instead of the entire system of the individual. It has been reported that Louis Pasteur's last words were, "Bernard is right, 'Le Meliu Interior' is everything, the bacteria nothing." Pasteur's friend, physiologist Claude Bernard, viewed the terrain of the human body - the entire system- as more critical than any pathogen that infects it. What if the government has been pushing the wrong theories on keeping ourselves healthy without the need for government or a long list of pharmaceutical drugs that make billions for corrupt for-profit corporations and politicians?

A healthy scientific debate should include discussions, experiments, and studies focusing on each theory and how they compare. It should be up to each individual to decide what is best for their health and safety. Instead, only one theory is pushed as the only truth in public schools, which drives the need for others to help keep us healthy. In today's society, if you step out of accepted public opinion, people tend to ostracize, segregate, harass, threaten, or commit violence against those seeking non-group thinking.

Our immune system is a highly complex system with skin and mucous membranes that play their part in granting immunity along with our lymphatic system. The lymphatic system is an extensive network of organs, tissues, and vessels that help transfer a fluid called lymph into our circulatory system. Lymph nodes around the neck, groin, chest, abdomen, and armpits help create immune system cells to fight infections while removing bacteria and cancer cells by filtering lymph fluid. Lymph fluid is made up of white blood cells that attack bacteria in the blood and chyle, fluid from the intestines that contains proteins and fats. The lymphatic system maintains fluid levels in our bodies, protects against foreign invaders, absorbs fat from our digestive tract, and transports and removes waste.

Skin and mucous membranes act as the first line of defense against external agents -bacteria and viruses- by capturing these pathogens in a dense mucous structure that creates barriers in our bodies. The mucous membranes are found within five systems in our bodies: the digestive system, respiratory system, urogenital system, inside of our eyelids, and inside of our ears. The mucous membranes can also absorb nutrients to be transferred to other areas of our bodies. This functionality is what allows topical creams to be absorbed into the bloodstream. These membranes remember past infections like the lymphatic system, making them highly important to our immune system.

To determine the degree of protection and immunity the immune system will provide, antibody levels -immunoglobulin- are tested and measured against a biological pathogen. There are five major antibody types: IgA, IgD, IgE, IgG, and IgM. A blood or mucous sample is added to infectious material and, through sophisticated machines, monitored to see if the antibody types will bind to the contagious material indicating protection and immunity. IgA antibodies are found in mucous membranes like the nose, respiratory airways, ears, eyes, saliva, tears, sweat, and vagina. IgD antibodies are found in blood serum and the tissues lining the chest and belly, which activate B cells -a type of white blood cell. IgE antibodies are only found in mammals within the mucous, skin, and lungs. They are involved during allergic reactions, e.g., asthma attacks, anaphylactic responses, or if an individual has been poisoned. IgE antibodies stay at high levels for individuals who suffer from allergies and react to fungus spores, pollen, and dander from animals. IgG antibodies are the most common in humans and can equal up to 75% of the antibodies produced. These antibodies are commonly found in blood circulation but can be found in all bodily fluids. IgG antibodies are the only type transferred through the placenta to protect a fetus from bacterial and viral infections. IgM antibodies can be found in blood and lymph fluid and are produced in response to an initial infection of a foreign invader. These antibodies range from 5% to 10% of the antibodies found and bind to infectious bacteria and viral antigens even when antibody levels are low or absent.

Vitamins, e.g., vitamin C (ascorbic acid), D, and K, and minerals, e.g., zinc, play an essential role in helping the immune system function properly, keeping us in homeostasis while maintaining the health of our organs. We will only focus on these few since they play significant roles in COVID19 infections. Our bodies do not produce these vitamins or minerals, so they must come from sunlight or the things we consume. Zinc is the second-most trace mineral in our bodies, behind iron, and is found in all cells. Our cells rely on a constant source of vitamin C to maintain healthy structures.

In December 1981, Dr. Robert F. Cathcart, through the journal of Medical Hypotheses, published his study *Vitamin C, Titrating To Bowel Tolerance, Anascorbemia, and Acute Induced Scurvy*, which found that the total amount of vitamin C that can be taken -orally or injected- depends and proportionately grows based on the stress and toxicity of a disease (Medical Hypotheses. 1981. 7:1359-1376.). Using the findings in his study, Dr. Cathcart developed the *Bowel Tolerance Theory of Vitamin C* model. Tolerances for daily oral vitamin C range from 4 to 15 grams for healthy individuals to 200+ grams for severe diseases, e.g., viral pneumonia or HIV.

When we are sick, our oral vitamin C intake can significantly increase. Appropriate doses of vitamin C change based on the immune system's health and the disease affecting the system. If diarrhea is a symptom after taking vitamin C, the max absorption rate is potentially reached. Vitamin C through an IV can have a 100-fold absorption rate than when taken orally, which has been shown to kill cancer cells. On October 1st, 1999, the Journal of Manipulative and Physiological Therapeutics published the study *The effectiveness of vitamin C in preventing and relieving the symptoms of virus-induced respiratory infections*, which found that cold and flu symptoms reduced by 85% after subjects were given a "megadose" of vitamin

C (J Manipulative Physiol Ther. 1999 Oct;22(8):530-3.). On January 31st, 2013, the Cochrane Database of Systematic Reviews published the updated study *Vitamin C for preventing and treating the common cold*, which found that vitamin C -when taken in large doses after cold symptoms began- reduced the severity and duration of the symptoms (Cochrane Database Syst Rev. 2013 Jan; 2013(1): CD000980.).

Our skin's reaction to sunlight produces vitamin D. Vitamin D can also be found in some fish and egg yolks and taken through supplements. Vitamin D is essential for maintaining healthy bones and calcium levels. The older we get, the less our kidneys can function properly, leading to an increased risk of vitamin D deficiency. Vitamin D deficiency can cause hypocalcemia -low calcium levels- autoimmune diseases, pulmonary diseases, cancers, depression, and heart disease, and can make a subject more susceptible to severe illnesses from colds and flu. On July 19th, 2007, The New England Journal of Medicine published the study *Vitamin D Deficiency*, which discussed how vitamin D deficiency was very common in the U.S. (N Engl J Med. 2007 Jul 19;357(3):266-81.).

Vitamin K is required to produce some types of proteins needed for blood clotting, which can lead to thrombosis and elastic fiber damage when vitamin K levels are reduced. Vitamin K can be found in green leafy vegetables or through supplements. Antibiotic medicines can potentially reduce vitamin K levels by killing good vitamin K-producing bacteria. Several studies have found that reduced vitamin K levels correlated to increased severity among COVID19 patients. On August 11th, 2020, the Scandinavian Journal of Clinical and Laboratory Investigation published the study *Vitamin K deficiency and covid-19*, which found that vitamin K deficiency can increase pro-inflammatory cytokines interleukin-6 resulting in more severe symptoms and morality rates (Scand J Clin Lab Invest. 2020 Nov;80(7):525-527.).

Vaccines only target the lymphatic system to generate a response, while natural infections generate skin and mucous membrane responses. This is one reason natural immunity is always better than immunity strictly through vaccination since natural immunity encompasses our entire immune system to give us a fighting chance. Why does the government only push injections that don't use our immune system holistically and efficiently to provide us with the best chance at fighting off diseases and infections?

"If she got the flu for 14 days, she is as protected as anybody can be, because the best vaccination is to get infected yourself." – Dr. Anthony Fauci, *C-SPAN Washington Journal discussing influenza*, October 11th, 2004

A peer-reviewed study published in the journal Vaccines, *Large-Scale Study of Antibody Titer Decay following BNT162b2 mRNA Vaccine or SARS-CoV-2 Infection*, which looked at COVID19 antibody levels over time comparing fully-vaccinated and unvaccinated -control- who had a prior natural infection and natural immunity (Vaccines. 2022; 10(1):64.). This study found that natural immunity provided superior protection for an extended period than through Pfizer's mRNA COVID19 vaccine. With natural immunity subjects, it was found that antibody levels decreased by less than 5% per month, while vaccinated subjects had antibody levels decrease up to 40% each subsequent month.

The public rhetoric from the government and mainstream media purposely ignores this critical issue. However, it does explain why in August 2021, President Biden and Dr. Fauci discussed requiring COVID19 boosters every five months. Within five months post-injection, antibody levels could be at 1% from the peak. With the ever-evolving COVID19 variants reaching herd immunity using vaccinations alone will never be an obtainable goal. Why is the idea of having natural immunity being looked down on by so many? How many injections are you willing to get until you say no more?

In 2000, the European Journal of Epidemiology published the study *Herd immunity and herd effect: new insights and definitions*, which defined herd immunity as "the proportion of subjects with immunity in a given population"; the definition of immunity covering natural and vaccine immunity (Eur J Epidemiol. 2000;16(7):601-6.). On June 9th, 2020, the World Health Organization (WHO) -a United Nations agency formed in 1948- defined herd immunity as "the indirect protection from an infectious disease that happens when a population is immune either through vaccination or immunity developed through previous infection." This definition includes natural immunity and vaccinated immunity to reach herd immunity. On November 13th, 2020, the WHO changed the definition of herd immunity to "a concept used for vaccination, in which a population can be protected from a certain virus if a threshold of vaccination is reached. Herd immunity is achieved by protecting people from a virus, not by exposing them to it." There is no mention of natural immunity in the new definition, which now focuses on protection, not providing actual immunity. Protection and immunity are two different terms that have different meanings.

Throughout history, natural immunity, and a healthy functioning immune system, have protected humanity through all sorts of diseases and contagions. Natural immunity has always been our primary defense against the continuation of any disease or infection. Even traditional vaccines leverage part of our immune systems to reach partial immunity. Why do governments and international organizations -like the WHO- ignore natural immunity and concentrate on for-profit liability-free experimental medical procedures when alternative treatments exist? Why are individuals being forced to vaccinate when they already have natural immunity, and it has been proven that COVID19 vaccines cannot and will not prevent infection or transmission?

"There are two levels of knowing a subject. There is the student who knows what the definition of a noun or a gene or a molecule is; then there is the student... who also knows how the definition was arrived at. There is the student who can answer a question; then there is the student who also knows what are the biases of the question. There is the student who can give you the facts; then there is the student who also knows what is meant by a fact. I am maintaining that, in all cases, it is the latter who has a "basic" education ; the former, a frivolous one." – Neil Postman, *Language Education in a Knowledge Context*, 1980

COVID19

"You [a disciple], shall I teach you about knowledge? What you know, you know, what you don't know, you don't know. This is true knowledge." – Confucius, *The Analects*, 475–221 BCE

COVID19, or SARS-CoV-2, is a class of coronavirus, a novel betacoronavirus from the subgenus Sarbecovirus, which all coronaviruses are considered to be a type of common cold virus associated with upper respiratory tract infections. COVID19 has a size range of .06 to .14 microns (μm). Coronaviruses account for 15% to 30% of the common colds tested for, with only six strains being able to affect humans, at least until now. The other type of common colds that make up the rest of the cases are Rhinoviruses, which can be broken down into more than 100 various strains that can affect humans by manipulating genes which brings an excessive immune response leading to cold symptoms. Influenza (flu viruses), type A, B, and C viruses, are similar to common cold viruses but are usually more severe with the symptoms that become present.

Coronavirus, corona (crown) + virus (poison), means crown poison and was coined due to a series of virus discoveries: upper-respiratory tract disease from chickens in North Dakota in 1931, a brain disease in mice discovered by a Harvard University pathologist in 1947, and a virus from a schoolboy in England who had common cold symptoms in 1961. Due to their solar corona-like (spikes) view on the virus surface, these viruses were collectively called coronaviruses. Coronaviruses have been discovered in pigs, dogs, cats, rodents, whales, birds, and bats and have been traced back to common ancestors hundreds of millions of years ago.

COVID19 was officially discovered in the capital of the Hubei province, Wuhan, China, in December 2019. This discovery was attributed to an open market that sold bats as a food resource. This open market is roughly 20 miles from the Wuhan Institute of Virology (WIV) Biosafety Level 4 (BSL-4) facility, which has been the center of attention, which has led many to believe that COVID19 came from a laboratory leak at this BSL-4 facility. On September 12th, 2022, the Chinese military entered the Wuhan BSL-4 facility and abruptly changed the leadership. Some intelligence reports indicated that the Chinese government potentially knew about the lab leak by that time.

Through investigation, the Chinese government said they had narrowed patient zero -the first individual to contract COVID19- to a pool of 266 potential patient zeros dating back to November 17th, 2019. In November 2019, three researchers at the Wuhan BSL-4 facility went to the hospital with an unknown illness similar to COVID19. The Chinese government also suggested that COVID19 was brought to China by U.S. military athletes during the World Military Games held in Wuhan, China, from October 18th to 27th, 2019. Reports have indicated that plenty of athletes were sick during the war games with symptoms resembling COVID19. On May 6th, 2020, The Sun suggested in a report *Fears coronavirus arrived in Europe in OCTOBER 'when French athletes at World Military Games in Wuhan brought it home'* that COVID19 hit Europe in October after the World Military Games when French athletes got sick and brought it back home two months before COVID19 was officially discovered.

On October 18th, 2019, *Event 201: A Global Pandemic Exercise -* a 3.5-hour pandemic tabletop exercise simulation into a coronavirus pandemic- was conducted by the Gates Foundation, WHO, Johns Hopkins Bloomberg School of Public Health – Center for Health

Security, and WEF, which called themselves the Pandemic Emergency Board. The event hosts included Avril Haines, the previous Deputy Director of the CIA. Significant discussions during this tabletop exercise focused on misinformation, combating fake news, and countering the anti-vaccine movement was discussed, and how a new vaccine would need to be created in record time. The goal of this simulation was to track a novel coronavirus transmitted from bats to pigs and then to humans starting in Brazil, leading to a pandemic that would kill tens of millions. The pathogen discussed in the simulation was modeled from the SARS virus. Convenient timing that this simulation took place as COVID19 started to make its appearance. Did they already know that the COVID19 virus had been leaked and was circulating in the wild?

After its official discovery, the Chinese government released the genetic data on COVID19 in January 2020, which the WHO used to issue guidance on travel, laboratory testing, and medical evaluation. On January 30th, 2020, the journal The Lancet published the study *Genomic characterisation and epidemiology of 2019 novel coronavirus: implications for virus origins and receptor binding*, which determined COVID19 was an 88% match with two bat-derived SARS viruses, bat-SL-CoVZC45 and bat-SL-CoVZXC21, a 79% match with the human virus SARS-CoV, and a 50% match to MERS-CoV (Middle East Respiratory Syndrome - Coronavirus) (Lancet. 2020 Feb 22;395(10224):565-574.).

Through additional investigation, scientists from the WIV concluded that COVID19 came from a horseshoe bat species, *Rhinolophus affinis*, located in the caves of Yunnan, China. They claim to have been able to determine this from a sample of feces collected in 2013 that had been "forgotten" until January 2020, when they retested samples, discovering that a sample contained the COVID19 virus. This sample was housed at the Wuhan BSL-4 facility. The similarity between COVID19, the two bat-derived viruses, and the sample from Yunnan caves is why the official rhetoric is pushing that COVID19 came from a bat eaten at an open market.

On January 31st, 2020, the preprint server BioRxiv published the study -authors have since withdrawn the non-peer-reviewed study for revision- *Uncanny similarity of unique inserts in the 2019-nCoV spike protein to HIV-1 gp120 and Gag*, which shows that there were four different "insertions in the spike glycoprotein (S) which are unique to the 2019-nCoV and are not present in other coronaviruses" and that "insert 1 (6 amino acid residues) and insert 2 (6 amino acid residues) in the spike glycoprotein of 2019-nCoV are 100% identical to the residues mapped to HIV-1 gp120." (Version 1. bioRxiv. Preprint. 2020 Jan 31.). This means that their conclusion for COVID19 is that it is most likely manufactured since the evolution and mutations of these inserts together could not have happened naturally in the wild. BioRxiv is supported by the Chan Zuckerberg Initiative (CZI) -owned by Mark Zuckerberg and his wife, Priscilla Chan- so they have sway if a study remains published.

On October 27th, 2022, an interim report commissioned by Senator Richard Burr, and released by the U.S. Senate Committee on Health, Education, Labor & Pensions (HELP) concluded that the COVID19 pandemic was "more likely than not, the result of a research-related incident" which means that government officials lied about the origins of COVID19 and Fact Checkers were complacent in helping push fake news -misinformation- and the government's official false narrative. Will anyone be held accountable for purposely lying to the public? Don't hold your breath.

"When I first saw the sequence of the furin cleavage site—as I've said, other beta coronaviruses don't have that site—it seemed to me a reasonable hypothesis that somebody had put it in there. Now, I don't know if that's true or not, but I do know that it's a hypothesis that must be taken seriously." – David Baltimore, *Caltech's David*

Baltimore discusses the debate over origins of SARS-CoV-2, Bulletin of the Atomic Scientists interview, June 23rd, 2021

In 2015 and 2016, Dr. Fauci registered several patents focused on the HIV gp120 (Patent numbers: 20160075786, 9441041, 20160333097, and 9896509). On February 14th, 2020, the journal of Emerging Microbes & Infections published the study *HIV-1 did not contribute to the 2019-nCoV genome,* which found that inserts 1 and 2 were 100% match while inserts 3 and 4 matched 42% to 88% between HIV and COVID19 (Emerg Microbes Infect. 2020; 9(1): 378–381.). Suppose the study from BioRxiv holds and the gp120 insert that was patented is in the COVID19 spike protein and COVID19 vaccines. In that case, there is a potential that Dr. Fauci could receive a large sum of money from royalties from each pharmaceutical corporation that developed a COVID19 vaccine using gp120. In 2020, several Gates and Dr. Fauci HIV vaccine trials switched focus to COVID19 vaccines. If they have similarities, then the switch would not be a difficult challenge.

On January 22nd, 2020, the Journal of Medical Virology published the study *Cross-species transmission of the newly identified coronavirus 2019-nCoV,* which indicated that COVID19 had a genetic structure most similar to bat coronaviruses but also had a codon usage bias most similar to snake coronaviruses (J Med Virol. 2020 Apr;92(4):433-440). Specifically, genetic coding that resembled the many-banded krait and Chinese cobra. A codon is a series of nucleotides that encode a specific amino acid within a polypeptide chain. Codon usage bias is the difference in the frequency codons appear in a DNA sequence. The study indicated that a bat and snake coronavirus recombined to produce the COVID19 virus.

How often did you hear about a potential link to snake coronaviruses when the government and media are discussing COVID19? This study and connection are why some claimed that

COVID19 is snake venom poisoning which could be ingested through government-controlled water supplies. A more likely scenario would be that snake coronaviruses were partially recombined with bat coronaviruses in gain-of-function (GoF) research leading to the similarities.

On August 24th, 2021, the Journal of Clinical Investigation published the study *Group IIA secreted phospholipase A2 is associated with the pathobiology leading to COVID-19 mortality*, which shows that an enzyme, secreted phospholipase A2 group IIA (sPLA2-IIA), plays a crucial role in COVID19 mortality rates (J Clin Invest. 2021 Oct 1;131(19):e149236.). This sPLA2-IIA enzyme has strong similarities to an enzyme in rattlesnake venom. sPLA2-IIA is found naturally in low levels in healthy individuals helping fight against bacterial infections by attacking microbial cell membranes. At high levels, sPLA2-IIA can attack vital organs leading to increased mortality rates by coagulating the blood supply, which happens during snake venom poisoning.

To determine coagulation -the clotting tendency of the blood- prothrombin time (PT) is measured. PT levels can also be elevated during diseases like HIV, inflammation, trauma, liver disease, heart disease, and pregnancy. On July 8th, 2021, -version 2 updated on October 14th, 2021- the F1000 Research -an open research publishing platform- published the study *Toxin-like peptides in plasma, urine and faecal samples from COVID-19 patients*, which found that toxin-like peptides that resembled toxic components of venoms were found in COVID19 patients (Version 2. F1000Res. 2021; 10: 550.). This further shows a potential connection to COVID19, snake coronaviruses, and venoms.

The NIH is the U.S. agency responsible for biomedical and public health research and was founded in 1887. The NIH comprises 27 institutes and centers focusing on various biomedical disciplines and responsibilities. In 2019, the Nature Index, which measures contributors of published papers, ranked NIH as the second largest contributor in the world behind Harvard University -with both having significant ties to intelligence agencies. The NIH helps funds tens of thousands of scientific studies each year and publishes the findings on the site for public access. Dr. Fauci is the current director of the NIAID -under the NIH- which he joined the NIAID in 1968 as a clinical associate and has been the director since 1984. Dr. Fauci's wife, Christine Grady, heads the NIH Department of Bioethics, focusing on bioethical issues within the NIH -meaning Dr. Fauci's wife ensures Dr. Fauci behaves ethically.

Dr. Fauci had a significant impact in the 1980s on HIV/AIDS research and policy making, which led to thousands protesting him due to the high cost of life and adverse events caused by the research and policies enacted by him and his agency. Dr. Fauci pushed those who tested positive for HIV but showed no symptoms and were otherwise healthy individuals to use the antiretroviral medication azidothymidine (AZT) as a preventive measure. In March 1995, the journal of Genetica published the study *The toxicity of azidothymidine (AZT) on human and animal cells in culture at concentrations used for antiviral therapy*, which found that the dosage of AZT prescribed as an HIV medication was highly toxic to human cells (Genetica. 1995;95(1-3):103-9.).

Some prominent HIV/AIDS activists called Dr. Fauci a mass murderer due to the deaths at the hands of his policies. In 1980, Congress passed the Dayh-Dole Act allowing Dr. Fauci and other scientists to patent drugs and other products produced with taxpayer funds and then license these drugs and products to pharmaceutical corporations enabling some to make millions off of royalties. This massive conflict of interest is a slippery slope that can and does breed corruption. What we see today with COVID19 is similar to how Dr. Fauci handled the HIV/AIDS epidemic.

Dr. Fauci was appointed as a primary member of President Trump's Coronavirus Task Force focusing on Operation Warp Speed, which aimed to facilitate the dangerously fast research, development, manufacturing, and distribution of COVID19 vaccines. Between 2010 and 2020, three key NIH executives received secret royalty payments, estimated to be roughly $350 million, that had not been disclosed to the public. This information was discovered by the non-profit government watchdog Open the Books through a FOIA request. Dr. Fauci received 23 of these payments and became a multimillionaire from taxpayers' funds during his time with the NIH.

In 2014, Dr. Fauci, through NIH grants, provided $3.7 million to the EcoHealth Alliance for GoF coronavirus research at the WIV. EcoHealth Alliance is a non-profit U.S. organization focused on emerging diseases. EcoHealth Alliance works with the WHO and U.N. Food and Agriculture Organization on infectious diseases. Dr. Peter Daszak, president of EcoHealth Alliance, was also a primary team member sent by the WHO to investigate the origins of COVID19. Dr. Daszak spoke at a forum on infectious diseases in 2016, in which he admitted that his colleagues in Wuhan, China, were sequencing and manipulating coronaviruses similar to the SARS sequence by altering their spike proteins until they could become pathogenic and lethal to humans.

Dr. Daszak admitted they had been researching bat coronaviruses for years in China, where they discovered over 100 new SARS-related coronaviruses, some being easily manipulated in a laboratory setting. The NIH paused direct funding for GoF research in October 2014, so it started using organizations like EcoHealth Alliance to continue the research indirectly. In 2017, the NIH announced that it was lifting the ban on GoF research, then proceeded to fund more GoF research for multiple infectious diseases. In March 2018, Dr. Daszak had a $14 million grant proposal to genetically manipulate bat coronaviruses rejected by the Defense Advanced Research Projects Agency (DARPA) due to needing to assess the risks within his proposed research appropriately.

On February 1st, 2020, Dr. Fauci sent off emails -released after a FOIA request- after being informed by several of his leading biologists that they believed the COVID19 virus was highly unlikely to be the product of natural selection. These carefully written emails detailed how the virus could not be from a laboratory leak and how he could be named as complicit in creating the virus. In April 2020, Dr. Fauci publicly supported a natural bat-to-human jump instead of the laboratory leak theory that mounting evidence suggested.

A paper created by those working with Dr. Fauci was published in the journal Nature Medicine, *The proximal origin of SARS-CoV-2*, pushing the naturally occurring theory attempting to cast doubt on any potential laboratory leak theory, even though several virologists working with Dr. Fauci suggested that COVID19 was more than likely a manufactured virus (Nat Med. 2020 Apr;26(4):450-452.). Dr. Daszak sent a personal email to Dr. Fauci thanking him for publicly rejecting the lab-leak theory with the hope that his voice "dispels the myths being spun around the virus' origins."

In 2021, evidence started being reported showing GoF research NIH and EcoHealth Alliance were performing. Senator Rand Paul, a physician, blasted Dr. Fauci over this GoF research during a congressional hearing, getting into arguments over the definition of GoF. On December 6th, 2022, Dr. Andrew Huff -a U.S. scientist and former VP of EcoHealth Alliance- released his book *The Truth About Wuhan* -detailing how COVID19 was a manufactured virus and not a natural spillover event that Dr. Fauci pushed. Dr. Huff further describes how Dr. Fauci, Dr. Daszak, EcoHealth Alliance, various partner organizations, and the governments of the U.S. and China coordinated in a massive collaboration to cover up the true origins of COVID19.

Dr. Ralph Baric -professor in the Department of Epidemiology and Department of Microbiology and Immunology at the University of North Carolina (UNC) Chapel Hill- worked directly with Dr. Shi Zhengli -Director of the Center for Emerging Infectious Diseases at the WIV- around GoF research for SARS-like coronaviruses. On November 9th, 2015, Dr. Baric and Dr. Zhengli -along with others-through the journal of Nature Medicine published the study *A SARS-like cluster of circulating bat coronaviruses shows potential for human emergence*, which details how they created a "chimeric virus encoding a novel, zoonotic CoV spike protein—from the RsSHC014-CoV sequence that was isolated from Chinese horseshoe bats" (Nat Med. 2015; 21(12): 1508-1513.). This alone shows that COVID19 was most likely a man-made virus that was developed partly using the research from Dr. Baric and Dr. Zhengli.

Through the government site USA Spending (usaspending.gov), we can find a $116 million-dollar contract that the DoD awarded to Black & Veatch Special Projects Crop -currently run by Randy Castro, a former Deputy Director of Defense Threat Reduction Agency, Corps of Engineers leader, and retired U.S. Army major general- (CONT_IDV_HDTRA108D0007_9700), which had a listed start date of September 20th, 2012, and ended on October 13th, 2020. Within this contract, a sub-awarded contract (19-6192) was awarded to Labyrinth Global Health Inc. on November 12th, 2019, totaling $369,511 for "SME manuscript documentation and COVID19 research." If COVID19 wasn't discovered until December 2019, how was Labyrinth Global Health Inc. awarded a government contract to research COVID19 a month before the official discovery of COVID19? Do you think this shouldn't be questioned?

Labyrinth Global Health Inc. was founded in 2019 by Karen Saylors. Karen Saylors spent a few years as Vice President of Field Research for Metabiota. Metabiota is viewed as helping "to push the boundaries of insuring catastrophic risks, preparing for infectious disease threats, and catalyzing public-private partnerships to protect global health security." The Place of Performance listed for the DoD contract with Black & Veatch Special Projects Corp is in Ukraine, the same country mainstream media and U.S. government swears didn't have U.S.-funded biological laboratories.

Since 2005, the DoD's Cooperative Threat Reduction Program – Biological Threat Reduction Program (BTRP) has partnered with the government of Ukraine to create public health facilities and biological laboratories to study pathogens that can become endemic. BTRP, which partners with the WHO and CDC, has provided roughly $200 million to Ukraine in setting up 46 Ukrainian biological laboratories, facilities, and diagnostic sites (*Fact Sheet: The Department of Defense's Cooperative Threat Reduction Program - Biological Threat Reduction Program Activities in Ukraine* – March 11th, 2022).

In March 2022, it was reported that Hunter Biden helped raise millions of dollars through Metabiota to fund biological laboratory projects in Ukraine. This is the same Metabiota that Karen Saylors worked for before being granted funds to research COVID19 a month before it was officially discovered. Metabiota has strong connections to EcoHealth Alliance and the WIV, which all partnered together in 2014 under EcoHealth Alliance's PREDICT project that focused on disease surveillance and response for infectious diseases like influenza, SARS, and Ebola. In addition to these connections, it was reported in early 2022 by NBC News and Breitbart that Hunter Biden received tens of millions from Chinese businessmen heavily connected to the Chinese government and intelligence agencies. These organizations and individuals potentially have had a direct role in the development and cover-up of COVID19, which has cost the lives of millions and has severely damaged worldwide economies. Why are we still listening to those connected to these organizations but have not answered for their involvement in the COVID19 pandemic?

Real Time RT-PCR

The Real Time Reverse Transcription Polymerase Chain Reaction (Real Time RT-PCR) test is the primary standardized test used worldwide to determine COVID19 case counts and active infectability. The government and Dr. Fauci considered the Real Time RT-PCR test the "gold standard" for testing COVID19. Most studies and discussions used this test as the basis of their work. Dr. Kary Mullis developed the PCR technique in 1986 and won the Nobel Prize in 1993 for his invention. Dr. Mullis had been a primary opponent of Dr. Fauci and the government's use of the PCR technique for years, which Dr. Fauci used to justify the restrictions and policies he set during the HIV/AIDS epidemic in the 1980s. Dr. Mullis repeatedly explained over the years that with the PCR technique, if done well, anyone can find almost anything in anybody. Dr. Mullis constantly spoke out against how Dr. Fauci and the government were misusing his invention.

"It's not even probable, let alone scientifically proven, that HIV causes AIDS. If there is evidence that HIV causes AIDS, there should be scientific documents which either singly or collectively demonstrate that fact, at least with a high probability. There are no such documents." – Dr. Kary Mullis, *Spin Magazine interview, Vol. 10 No. 4*, July 1994

With the PCR technique, someone can create a large quantity of something out of something minuscule. Dr. Mullis explained that given enough time and cycles, it was possible that anything could be found in anyone. The PCR technique is only designed to take something and make it measurable. At no point can the test determine infectability, or risk of symptoms, as that is not what it was designed for. Dr. Mullis has said that Dr. Fauci is not a scientist and did not understand medicine. Dr. Mullis died from pneumonia on August 7th, 2019, before COVID19 was officially discovered. I find the timing of Dr. Mullis' death suspicious since he would have been one of the most critical opponents of Dr. Fauci and the government during the COVID19 pandemic.

Since the start of COVID19, many people have been trying to shine a light on the fallacious statistics being pushed by the CDC and government using the Real Time RT-PCR test, with high cycle rates producing large numbers of false positives. In May 2020, Tanzania President John Magufuli had a goat and papaya sample sent in for testing, and both returned positive for COVID19. President Magufuli repeatedly downplayed the threat of COVID19 and even suspended Tanzania's head of testing over alleged testing errors. Less than a year after coming out with evidence that something was seriously wrong with the official COVID19 testing, President Mafufuli, who had grown into a prominent opponent of the testing and vaccines being pushed, died of a "heart condition." I find it highly suspicious that he died of a heart condition, especially since the CIA has had a secret heart attack gun since the 1970s, which has only been perfected since then.

To further highlight the issues around Real Time RT-PCR tests, on July 21st, 2021, the CDC issued a Laboratory Alert indicating changes to the Real Time RT-PCR testing due to the test failing an audit which showed that the test could not "facilitate detection and differentiation of SARS-CoV-2 and influenza viruses." Laboratories had until the end of 2021 to change to a different test. This failed audit calls into question all statistics and official numbers provided by the government since the start of the COVID19 pandemic. How can we trust any study or official government numbers concerning COVID19 when the primary test being used couldn't tell the difference between variations in all coronaviruses and influenza viruses?

Now the government has been sending hundreds of millions of at-home rapid antigen test kits to households across the U.S., and the FDA approved a breathalyzer that supposedly can detect COVID19 through an exhaled breath. The at-home testing kits are provided by China's Andon Health Co.'s unit iHealth Labs Inc., which received a roughly $1.3 billion contract through the U.S. Army Contracting Command to provide these kits. There is little guarantee that these new at-home tests are accurate or not already contaminated. All official numbers need to be called into question because there is no incentive for governments or for-profit pharmaceutical corporations to tell us the truth. Don't you find it interesting that these at-home testing kits were developed and sent out as laboratories had to stop using the Real Time RT-PCR test?

COVID19 Symptoms

COVID19 symptoms, which range in severity, can include dry cough, fever, loss of appetite, loss of smell, body aches, fatigue, shortness of breath, pneumonia, palpitation, arrhythmia, headaches, cognitive dysfunction, dizziness, insomnia, amnesia, myocarditis, pulmonary fibrosis, pulmonary heart disease, and death. This is not an all-encompassing list. Myocarditis can lead to cardiac arrest and death without respiratory distress and could happen years after the damage occurred in the heart. There were also reports that patients saw liver damage from COVID19. Those who recover can have lasting damage -Long COVID19- to their lungs, heart, liver, and brain. In Italy, autopsies showed that patients were dying from Thrombosis and Pulmonary Embolisms, blood clots, which were also being seen in the U.S. These blood clots can still kill a patient day to months after COVID19 symptoms have vanished.

In December 2020, the Journal of Neurobiology of Disease published the study -through Temple University- *The SARS-CoV-2 spike protein alters barrier function in 2D static and 3D microfluidic in-vitro models of the human blood–brain barrier*, which shows that the SARS-CoV-2 spike proteins trigger inflammatory responses in the brain which may contribute to altered brain function and damage (Neurobiol Dis. 2020 Dec;146:105131.). This damage was confirmed by examining cadavers, which provided some understanding of how the virus can cause mild to severe neurological symptoms that could manifest years after infection.

COVID19 can attack the heme, which gives myoglobin and hemoglobin the ability to bind oxygen when an iron atom is present, by removing the iron atom from the cell and allowing the iron atom to roam free in the bloodstream forming porphyrin. Too much porphyrin can lead to porphyria, which can also occur when someone is over-exposed to an excess of iron or has HIV. COVID19 has been reported to attack and damage T lymphocytes, a type of white blood cell that helps the immune system fight infection and cancers, compared to HIV. This is more anecdotal evidence that COVID19 was manufactured.

COVID19 causes hemoglobin levels to drop, reducing the oxygen in the blood and thereby increasing CO_2 levels carried to organs through the blood. When this happens, the lungs get poisoned and inflamed due to the inability of the lungs to exchange oxygen and CO_2, resulting in pulmonary nodules forming in the lungs that have a ground-glass opacity to them. Low oxygen levels can result in hypoxemia which can lead to additional organ damage or death. COVID19 can also lead to cytokine release syndrome -a cytokine storm- an overproduction of immune cells and activating compounds, inflammatory cytokines, into the lungs. This leads to lung inflammation and fluid buildup that causes respiratory distress, bacterial pneumonia, and possibly death.

On June 27th, 2020, the Journal of Medical Virology published a study *The cytokine storm and COVID-19*, which shows that COVID19 resulted in a high expression of tumor necrosis factor-α (TNFα) and interleukin-6 (IL-6) -specifically- but other interleukins and inflammatory proteins levels were also increased (J Med Virol. 2021;93:250–256). Interleukins are proteins and signal molecules which have critical roles within our immune system. Having underlying health conditions can make this whole situation even worse. A difficult challenge when trying to determine the cause of death is that COVID19 seems to cause other issues that can cause death. If someone dies from a heart attack and has COVID19, was it due to an underlying condition triggered by COVID19 or due to another cause?

COVID19 Mortality Rate

As of December 11th, 2022, there were roughly 101.2 million "confirmed" COVID19 cases in the U.S., 99.6 million closed cases - with 1.11 million deaths and 98.5 million having recovered- showing a mortality estimated rate of roughly 1.11%, or 11.13 deaths per 1,000 persons -crude mortality rate- across all age ranges and comorbidities using official numbers, assuming the official numbers are accurate. This can be further broken down by age range, which shows that those 49 and younger had a 0.4% mortality rate or less, with those nine and younger facing nearly zero numbers. Mortality rates are only a statistical analysis based on the data available, the truthfulness of the data, and the intent of the individual(s) putting the statistics together. To calculate a crude mortality rate, we take the total number of deaths, divide it by total infections, then multiply by 1,000 (deaths/total infections X 1000), which gives us the number of deaths per 1,000. This can also be multiplied by 10,000 to get the rate per 10,000 persons.

At the start of the COVID19 pandemic, official numbers of infections and deaths suggested the total mortality rate was closer to 20%. I called these numbers and statistics into question in an article I wrote in 2020 because it was not what we saw in reality. A 20% mortality rate should have led to massive deaths everywhere, leaving no individual spared from the grief of losing loved ones. This idea and fear of a 20% mortality rate virus and narrative is what the government and mainstream media pushed hard for two years, with the only solution being brand new liability-free injectable experimental products. Why would this feeling and fear be encouraged so strongly by the government and mainstream media, with the sole goal being to get the number vaccinated as possible?

If the 1.11% mortality rate is accurate, how will the masses react at an authentic 10% to 20% mortality rate virus? How many would be willing to give up their natural rights and accept being experimented on out of fear of a higher mortality rate disease? Do you remember the videos of Chinese citizens falling over in the middle of the streets and bleeding out in December 2019 and January 2020? We never saw those incidents happening here in the U.S., so were those videos more lies and propaganda pushed by China? Or did something else kill those individuals, and propaganda related the deaths to COVID19? This fear is being used to control the masses.

During the 2019 Cold and Flu season, from September 2019 to December 2019, the CDC reported roughly 65,000 influenza cases throughout the U.S., which was an average year. During January and February 2020, it was reported that influenza cases were spiking way above the yearly averages when numbers should have been dropping. This would indicate that many initial COVID19 cases were being misattributed to influenza. However, by the end of 2020, the CDC reported only 1,016 influenza cases for the same period as the previous year -magically, influenza had disappeared from the U.S. Do you believe this? Or is it more likely that the CDC attributed influenza cases to the COVID19 case counts?

Throughout 2020 and 2021, the government pushed the masses to get their influenza vaccine which they said would help protect against influenza and coronaviruses. However, in January 2020, the journal of Vaccines published the study *Influenza vaccination and respiratory virus interference among Department of Defense personnel during the 2017-2018 influenza season*, which showed that influenza vaccines could cause virus interference for coronaviruses (Vaccine. 2020 Jan 10;38(2):350-354.). This means that if someone gets the influenza vaccine, it could cause them to be at a higher risk of catching a coronavirus, like COVID19, with greater symptoms than before. The government knew about this study but ignored it and didn't let anyone know about the potential risks of getting the influenza vaccine. No studies have confirmed the safety of getting influenza and COVID19 vaccines together.

On May 20th, 2020, and updated on March 19th, 2021, the CDC released five planning scenarios to advance and advise public health preparedness and planning. These scenarios are based on predetermined possibilities using inputted parameter values for viral transmissibility, disease severity, and pre-symptomatic and asymptomatic contribution. Asymptomatic are those who never develop symptoms. In their worst-case scenario, the CDC estimated 291,780 deaths per 1 million infections, which is a 29.1% mortality rate. In their lowest death count scenario, the CDC estimated 27,956 deaths per 1 million infections, which is a 2.8% mortality rate. This is still an overestimation of what official numbers were suggesting. The CDC considered their best-case scenario -the scenario used most to shape policies and guidelines- as being 96,520 deaths per 1 million infections, which is a 9.7% mortality rate. In each scenario, most deaths (roughly 92%+) were attributed to the 65+ age group. Even using the worst-case scenario, those 17 and under were estimated to be 80 deaths per 1 million infections, which is a .008% mortality rate. With such a low mortality rate for those 17 and under, why is the government pushing to have that age group injected with a liability-free experimental product?

All of the CDC scenarios do not consider individual deficiencies -vitamin D, K, etc.- and established comorbidities as a significant role and assume that asymptomatic individuals play a crucial role in helping drive the COVID19 pandemic. The CDC views asymptomatic individuals as being 25% to 100% infectious and capable of transmitting COVID19 to others. When dealing with infectious diseases, these mortality estimates can only be rough guestimates since reality deals with symptomatic and asymptomatic carriers, those with significant deficiencies and comorbidities, and how the cause of death was determined. The official COVID19 statistical numbers do not include cases where individuals were asymptomatic and never tested and symptomatic people who recovered without seeking help from medical professionals.

During 2020, there were many reports from people calling into question the COVID19 deaths due to watching the death of a terminally ill loved one, e.g., stage 4 cancer, but then were classified officially as a COVID19 death because they tested positive for COVID19 at the time of death. How many passed away due to an underlying comorbidity but were formally listed as a COVID19 death and used as propaganda? In April 2020, Dr. Deborah Birx, the White House Coronavirus Response Coordinator, openly stated that all deaths involving someone who tested positive for COVID19 would be classified as a COVID19 death. This is pure sophistry and a manipulation of data that makes it seem like COVID19 is worse than it is.

In January 2020, New York faced a $6.1 billion-dollar budget deficit. New York Governor Andrew Cuomo said he was looking to cut $2.5 billion from Medicaid before the COVID19 pandemic began. In 2020, under the Federal Medicare Coronavirus Aid, Relief and Economic Security Act, for each COVID19 pneumonia case, Medicare paid out $13,000 per case -typically, pneumonia cases are $5,000- and up to $39,000 for each patient that was put on a ventilator. New York classified all presumed COVID19 cases as official resulting in larger payouts for the state. To make things worse, Governor Cuomo forced hospitals and healthcare facilities to send more than 6,300 COVID19 patients to vulnerable nursing homes during the early months of the pandemic in 2020 to help free up hospital beds, which led to New York having the highest number of COVID19 cases and death count in the U.S.

In April 2020, a study in New York using hospital data involving 5,700 COVID19 patient records found that 88% of those patients who were put on ventilators died -nearly 9 out of 10 patients. By mid-May 2020, New York had roughly 358 thousand "official" COVID19 cases, with approximately 28 thousand deaths. COVID19 became a financial windfall for the cash-strapped New York healthcare system. On September 1st, 2003, the journal of Lung Cellular and Molecular Physiology published the study *Differential effects of mechanical ventilatory strategy on lung injury and systemic organ inflammation in mice*, which found that mechanical ventilation could cause acute lung damage while increasing the production of TNFα and IL-6 levels (Am J Physiol Lung Cell Mol Physiol. 2003 Sep;285(3):L710-8.).

Ventilators force air into the lungs, but the lack of air in the lungs isn't what is causing the low oxygen levels in COVID19 patients; it is the inability of the body and lungs to convert oxygen into the cells and bloodstream that causes the low oxygen levels. Ventilators must be calibrated correctly for each patient; too much oxygen and air pressure will damage the lungs. This calibration would be a moving target for each patient as the COVID19 infection improves or worsens. Doctors and other medical professionals worldwide began to recognize the issues with ventilators and moved away from them as a treatment -except for the rare extreme cases. Putting a conscious COVID19 patient, who can still breathe on their own, into an induced coma and placing them on a ventilator could have been what killed many, not COVID19. It is a potential and massive ethical and moral violation when hospitals and doctors can push the use of ventilators which can directly affect their employers' wallets. Remember, medical malpractice accounted for roughly 250,000 documented deaths each year before COVID19.

In May 2020, the CDC quietly updated its website and downgraded roughly 30 thousand deaths that were no longer attributed to COVID19. Several states reported these inconstancies with official numbers and provided downgraded COVID19 case counts. In May 2020, Washington State acknowledged knowingly including deaths caused by gunshots in the State's COVID19 death count because the individuals had tested positive for COVID19 at the time of death. In July 2020, an individual in Florida was killed during a motorcycle accident but was officially listed as a COVID19 death due to testing positive at the time of death. How can we trust official numbers when everything was being attributed to COVID19 (influenza, other coronaviruses, cancers, accidents, etc.)?

The CDC has changed its reporting guidelines several times since the pandemic started. In May 2021, the CDC updated its guidelines to stop reporting on fully vaccinated people, those with two shots of Pfizer or Moderna or one shot of J&J -fully vaccinated definition changed to include boosters- who test positive for COVID19 unless it resulted in hospitalization or death. This update reduced the number of breakthrough cases reported even though the CDC still tracks unvaccinated individuals who test positive for COVID19 -even if the individuals are not hospitalized or die. This is more lying using statistics to show the unvaccinated as having COVID19 at a much higher rate than those fully vaccinated when the opposite is true. None of the official numbers released by the government can be trusted at face value and should be questioned at every step.

Doctors and scientists reported through mainstream media in 2020 that when a patient was re-infected by COVID19, showing no lifetime immunity, the mortality rate was much higher than with the first infection. These re-infection reports could be false positives due to the Real Time RT-PCR test not being able to distinguish between the genetic material of an active or inactive virus fragment. As with everything we have seen, can all of these reports during the COVID19 pandemic be trusted? Do COVID19 and its variants cause all of these symptoms, or were some of the symptoms propaganda to convince the masses that they were sicker than they were -a mass psychosis tactic- and to use them as excuses for future issues -e.g., vaccine adverse events being blamed on something else?

"But the one thing historically people need to realize that even if there is some asymptomatic transmission, in all the history of respiratory born viruses of any type asymptomatic transmission has never been the driver of outbreaks. The driver of outbreaks is always a symptomatic person. Even if there is a rare asymptomatic person that might transmit, an epidemic is not driven by asymptomatic carriers." – Dr. Anthony Fauci, *HHS brief on COVID19*, January 28th, 2020

In August 2020, the journal of Emerging Infectious Diseases published the study *Coronavirus Disease Outbreak in Call Center, South Korea*, which found "Of the 97 persons with confirmed COVID-19, only 4 (1.9%) remained asymptomatic within 14 days of quarantine, and none of their household contacts acquired secondary infections" (Emerg Infect Dis. 2020 Aug;26(8):1666-1670.). In August 2020, the journal of Respiratory Medicine published the study *A study on infectivity of asymptomatic SARS-CoV-2 carriers*, which found "no severe acute respiratory syndrome coronavirus 2 (SARS-CoV-2) infections were detected in 455 contacts by nucleic acid test" (Respir Med. 2020 Aug;169:106026.).

In December 2020, the BMJ published the study *Covid-19: Asymptomatic cases may not be infectious, Wuhan study indicates*, which found and identified, after screening 10 million Wuhan, China residents, "300 asymptomatic cases of covid-19, none of which was infectious" (BMJ 2020;371:m4695). In April 2021, the journal of Emerging Infectious Diseases published the study *Analysis of Asymptomatic and Presymptomatic Transmission in SARS-CoV-2 Outbreak, Germany, 2020*, which found "no transmission from asymptomatic case-patients" (Emerg Infect Dis. 2021 Apr;27(4):1159-1163.). These studies show that asymptomatic transmissions are not occurring with COVID19.

At this time, I have not found any studies confirming asymptomatic transmission. To further highlight this point, on

September 2nd, 2021, a FOIA request was sent to the CDC and Agency for Toxic Substances and Disease Registry (ATSDR) requesting "documents reflecting any documented case of an individual who: (1) never received a COVID-19 vaccine; (2) was infected with COVID-19 once, recovered, and then later became infected again; and (3) transmitted SARS-CoV-2 to another person when reinfected," in which the CDC responded with "a search of our records failed to reveal any documents pertaining to your request." Suppose the CDC and the government were even remotely correct on asymptomatic transmission being a factor in the COVID19 pandemic, they would be willing and able to produce the records at request, which should be apparent in multiple readily and quickly found studies. Every study I looked at that attempted to indicate that asymptomatic transmission is a cause for concern and a driver of the COVID19 pandemic uses words like "may" or "potential" without actual confirmation of asymptomatic transmissions. These are assumptions and not facts. Either asymptomatic transmissions can be proven, or they can't.

On March 5th, 2020, the New England Journal of Medicine published the study *Transmission of 2019-nCoV Infection from an Asymptomatic Contact in Germany*, which found that a pre-symptomatic individual, who became symptomatic, appears -loaded language- to have transmitted COVID19 to others during the incubation period, and that "asymptomatic persons are potential sources of 2019-nCoV infection may warrant a reassessment of transmission dynamics of the current outbreak" (N Engl J Med 2020; 382:970-971.). The subjects in this study were symptomatic -not asymptomatic- cases.

On June 17th, 2020, the International Journal of Infectious Diseases published the study *Asymptomatic patients as a source of COVID-19 infections: A systematic review and meta-analysis*, which looked at 506 patients from 34 studies and found "asymptomatic patients may be contagious and thus a potential source of transmission of COVID-19" (Int J Infect Dis. 2020 Sep;98:180-186.). There were no confirmed asymptomatic transmission cases in that study.

In December 2021, the journal JAMA Network Open published the study *Global Percentage of Asymptomatic SARS-CoV-2 Infections Among the Tested Population and Individuals with Confirmed COVID-19 Diagnosis A Systematic Review and Meta-analysis*, which reviewed 95 unique studies that covered 29.7 million individuals and found that "the pooled percentage of asymptomatic infections was 0.25% among the tested population and 40.50% among the population with confirmed COVID-19" and that this meta-analysis study "highlights the potential transmission risk of asymptomatic infections," not that it found evidence of actual asymptomatic transmission (JAMA Netw Open. 2021;4(12):e2137257.). These studies are being used to showcase asymptomatic transmission as a risk and danger. Yet, when the studies are examined, they do not show evidence or proof that asymptomatic transmission is occurring.

Asymptomatic transmission was the reason why the government pushed and forced -through threats and violence- everyone to wear masks in public. "My mask protects you, and your mask protects me!" with the assumption that anyone could be an asymptomatic carrier spreading COVID19. If symptomatic individuals are the drivers of epidemics and pandemics -not asymptomatic individuals- why are so much time and effort being spent addressing asymptomatic carriers? Why would the government lie to the masses about this?

"One of the [pieces of] information that we have pretty much confirmed now is that a significant number of individuals that are infected actually remain asymptomatic. That may be as many as 25%. That's important, because now you have individuals that may not have any symptoms that can contribute to transmission, and we have

learned that in fact they do contribute to transmission." – Dr. Robert Redfield, CDC Director, *National Public Radio affiliate WABE interview*, March 30th, 2020

One way to help determine the number of individuals infected by COVID19 is through antibody testing. Understanding the level of antibodies found in society helps provide a better statistic for the mortality rate. If a large portion of individuals remains asymptomatic, then the mortality rate is much lower than official numbers suggest. Early estimates in 2020 indicated that 25% to 80% of individuals who had COVID19 were completely unaware they even had it. Antibody tests from multiple cities, like Chicago and Los Angeles, showed a 30% to 50% positive COVID19 antibody rate of individuals with blood tests. This doesn't include those who never got tested. In June 2022, the WHO released that two-thirds of the world's population had high levels of COVID19 antibodies, which could have been through natural infection or vaccination.

Each of the individuals who tested positive for antibodies - assuming an actual positive test- have a natural immunity to COVID19, which even the Michigan government agreed that "natural infection almost always causes better immunity than vaccines" (Comparing Natural and Vaccine Immunity, 2015), and has further been confirmed for COVID19 through the study published in the journal of Vaccines; *Large-scale study of antibody titer decay following BNT162b2 mRNA vaccine or SARS-CoV-2 infection* - previously discussed. The significant decrease in antibodies -up to 40% a month- for COVID19 vaccines is why the government is pushing boosters.

In July 2020, the CDC acknowledged that the COVID19 antibody tests were faulty and that only half of those who tested positive had antibodies. It is possible that this was a lie to continue the narrative that vaccination is the only path forward. If most of the population already had a natural infection, the need for vaccinations would become significantly less. At what point does the government acknowledge herd immunity being reached or being an unattainable goal? Or was getting to herd immunity only a false narrative pushed by the government to convince the masses to inject themselves?

In July 2022, the Toronto Sun reported that the Canadian government announced that its citizens must get a COVID vaccine every nine months. The government will continue to add more required boosters so that we stay up-to-date on vaccines making this our new normal. Early in 2020, I wrote how the new COVID19 vaccines would become annual cold vaccines, eventually combined with the influenza vaccines becoming annual cold and flu vaccines. This prediction has turned out to be correct.

COVID19 Transmission

COVID19 spreads through respiratory droplets; tiny droplets with droplet nuclei size of five μm or less -aerosol particulates- make up the bulk of the droplets produced with each breath. Each breath we take can have up to 10 thousand of the smallest of these particulates. These tiny particulates can linger in the air for hours, with some studies showing them potentially staying in the air for months in a static environment with little to no airflow. Large respiratory droplets with droplet nuclei size of 5 μm and larger -spittle flying out as we speak- only travel a short distance before dropping to the ground. Large droplets are not the driver of the COVID19 pandemic.

In September 2020, the journal of Environmental Research published the study *Transmission of COVID-19 virus by droplets and aerosols: A critical review on the unresolved dichotomy* which found that "unlike larger droplets, aerosols may pose a greater risk of the spread of the COVID-19 disease among many susceptible hosts positioned far from the point of origin" (Environ Res. 2020 Sep; 188: 109819.).

Each environment and setting can change the survivability of COVID19 based on temperature, humidity, airflow and pressure, and how individuals interact within the environment. All mask studies that have shown why masks work do not take any of these items into account. COVID19 is roughly 0.125 μm in size -very small- invisible to the naked eye, and can easily pass through materials like cloth, e.g., a gnat moving through a chain-link fence.

In January 2021, the journal of Public Health published the study *Transmission of SARS CoV-2 virus through the ocular mucosa worth taking precautions*; after reviewing 172 studies from 16 countries, it found that "if healthcare workers and executives wore eye shields, there is a significant protection against being infected by this virus and other respiratory pathogens" (Vacunas. 2021 Jan-Apr;22(1):56-57.). Additionally, the study determined that when wearing eye protection, the transmission of COVID19 was about three times less likely than without eye protection. It has been known that the eyes can lead to infections. This is why we are told not to rub our eyes before washing our hands because our eyes are highly susceptible to absorbing bacteria and chemicals.

In November 2020, Moderna's Chief Medical Officer, Dr. Tal Zaks, told Axios in a TV interview that it had yet to be proven that the vaccines would stop COVID19 transmission. In December 2020, Pfizer CEO Albert Dourla explained in an interview that Pfizer's COVID19 vaccine does not prevent transmission. If transmissions are not stopped by vaccination, breakthrough infections -infections that happen after vaccination- would not be rare. In July 2021, the Health Ministry of Israel stated that the COVID19 vaccines are only 39% effective at stopping transmission.

Remember, the narrative throughout 2020 and 2021 was that vaccines would end the COVID19 pandemic and that breakthrough infections were extremely rare. In February 2021, the journal of the American Academy of Otolaryngology - Head and Neck Surgery published the study *COVID-19 Vaccines May Not Prevent Nasal*

SARS-CoV-2 Infection and Asymptomatic Transmission, which explained that COVID19 vaccines do not stop transmission due to not producing a local mucosal secretory response, meaning that patients fully vaccinated can still spread COVID19 through their upper respiratory tract (Otolaryngol Head Neck Surg. 2021 Feb;164(2):305-307.).

"Everybody talks about freedom about not to have a shot or have a test. Well guess what? How about patriotism? How about you make sure you're vaccinated, so you do not spread the disease to anybody else? What about that? What's the big deal? Those who aren't vaccinated are the ones that continue to spread the disease. And so, we should think of as a patriotic duty. [...] This is a pandemic of the unvaccinated. Not the vaccinated, the unvaccinated. That's the problem." – President Joseph Biden, *local news WHIO-TV in Ohio interview*, December 15th, 2021

If vaccines cannot stop transmission, then vaccines will never be able to stop COVID19, and viewing only vaccines as a solution is a fallacy. People have forgotten that we are responsible for our health. If we are in a high-risk category, we should take precautions to protect ourselves. It violates others' rights to force them to be responsible for our health and safety when it was never their job to be responsible and accountable for us. We are not responsible for the lives of those we might interact with outside or within the community. This is not how rights work. Suppose we are to take COVID19 seriously as a real threat. In that case, we should be taking a vastly different approach to protecting people and cleaning environments by having proper industry standards of control mechanisms in place, which don't include lockdowns or masks.

COVID19 Variants of Concern in the U.S.

The Nextstrain project, a 2015 collaboration of researchers from Seattle, Washington, and Basel, Switzerland, works together to provide real-time tracking of pathogen evolutions. Nextstrain has identified multiple variants mutated from the original COVID19 strain based on samples collected worldwide. Nextstrain received funding through NIH's Open Science Prize granted to the lead investigator. Nextstrain continues to update data showcasing the most prevalent COVID19 variant circulating worldwide. At the time of this writing, one Omicron sub-variant (22B) of the sub-variant (21L) is the most widespread COVID19 strain worldwide. However, new Omicron 22E and 22F have started to gain traction and spread. None of the available COVID19 vaccines cover these new Omicron variants.

The original COVID19 strain is no longer considered a threat and is not circulating worldwide. Yet, the government still lists all case counts under the COVID19 catchall heading, which is disingenuous when determining real statistics. Remember, all COVID19 vaccines were created to combat the original strain and pushed throughout 2021 and 2022, even though the original strain was no longer the primary strain circulating then. This shows that the vaccines were already ineffective at combatting COVID19 when they were approved for public use and would never be able to stop the pandemic, especially when the government is only using vaccines as a tool to combat the pandemic and constantly playing catchup.

The CDC has considered each of the following variants a cause for concern since the start of the COVID19 pandemic due to their transmission being "much faster" than the original strain. The naming convention of variants follows the Greek Alphabet.

The Alpha (B.1.1.7) variant was first identified in the United Kingdom in September 2020 and is viewed as roughly 50% more transmissible than the original virus. There is little to no evidence of a change in the severity compared to the original strain. Still, if each variant follows the same trajectory as other viruses when they mutate, each subsequent variant becomes less lethal than the previous one. The Beta (B.1.351) variant was first identified in South Africa in August 2020. The Delta (B.1.617.2) variant was first identified in India in December 2020. Some studies suggested a vaccine effective rate of 88% or less, depending on the vaccine and study -some reporting only 13%- for the Delta variant. The Delta variant was the main variant that the government and mainstream media focused on for most of 2021. Gamma (P.1) variant was first identified in Brazil and Japan in January 2021.

On August 30[th,] 2021, the WHO announced that a newly named variant, "mu" (B.1.621), was being tracked and that it had mutated enough to get past the antibodies that vaccines previously provided. Still, it has not been a focus in the mainstream media or government rhetoric. An additional South African variant was identified in May 2021 (C.1.2) and discovered in multiple countries worldwide. This variant also mutated and is "associated with increased transmissibility" -always with increased transmissibility- and the ability to evade the vaccine's protection. The Omicron (B.1.1.529) was first identified in South Africa and "may" spread more quickly than other variants due to its "numerous mutations." Now we must worry about subvariants of Omicron (BA.2, BA.3, BA.4, and BA.5), which are supposedly far more infectious than the original Omicron variant but not deadlier.

On June 22nd, 2022, The New England Journal of Medicine published the study *Neutralization Escape by SARS-CoV-2 Omicron Subvariants BA.2.12.1, BA.4, and BA.5*, which found that each subvariant escaped the antibody responses from the Pfizer COVID19 mRNA vaccine (N Engl J Med. 2022 Jul 7;387(1):86-88.). Little information is available on the mortality rate of these variants and if it is worse for symptoms and mortality rate than the original COVID19 virus.

There will be a constant evolution of these viruses, and there can always be another one that government can blame and distract us with to maintain control. Do you remember when the White House officially released a statement in December 2021 saying that the unvaccinated would face "a winter of severe illness and death" from Omicron? This prediction wasn't even remotely accurate -the government was spreading misinformation. Yet, the masses ignore that they are being lied to at every step, nor do they question the reasoning behind the lies. We have to deal with the ever-evolving COVID19 virus in the wild, and we still have to worry about GoF research into even deadlier variants.

On October 18th, 2022, researchers at Boston University's National Emerging Infectious Diseases Laboratories announced that they had created a new COVID19 variant by combining the Omicron variant with the original strain, producing an 80% mortality rate in the infected mice subjects. The researchers announced that this new strain was five times more infectious than the Omicron variant. They stated that their research was not GoF research because they made it less dangerous than Omicron or the original strain. However, an 80% mortality rate is excessively more dangerous than the original strain and all other variants combined based on mortality rate. This new strain comes with real risks if it gets out since no one would be immune to it, which, if it were released by accident or malice, it would mean a high rate of deaths would come from it. If it was released into the wild, you could be the pharmaceutical corporations, and the government would push everyone to inject a new poorly tested liability-free vaccine.

A theme among the current circulating identified variants is breakthrough infection; those fully vaccinated yet still catching the virus and having symptoms are expected. As time continues, it has been proven that breakthrough infections are a lot higher than we were told. The Omicron variants are only found in and are transmitted through the upper respiratory tract. This was determined by researchers from LKS Faculty of Medicine at the University of Hong Kong, who released their findings in the press release *HKUMed finds Omicron SARS-CoV-2 can infect faster and better than Delta in human bronchus but with less severe infection in lung*. It was also established that Omicron affected the vaccinated more than the unvaccinated. The Omicron variant is being primarily spread by the fully vaccinated -a true pandemic of the vaccinated, which is the opposite of what the government has been pushing.

This situation is similar to superbugs that are antibiotic-resistant due to the overuse of antibiotics. Noteworthy COVID19 breakthrough infections of those who are fully vaccinated and have had their booster shoots are House Majority Whip Jim Clyburn, Senator Elizabeth Warren, Governor Inslee, Governor Tim Walz, Governor Larry Hogan, Senator Nancy Pelosi, Dr. Fauci, Canada PM Trudeau, and many more. Granted, these breakthrough infections will be used as proof that everyone should be vaccinated and boosted. Are you positive that these individuals injected these new experimental vaccines, or are some lying to the public?

I find it highly suspicious that the AstraZeneca vaccine trials were conducted in the UK, South Africa, Brazil, and India, with highly transmissible viruses emerging from these locations that are now being tracked. It is possible that the AstraZeneca trials were causing the COVID19 virus to mutate -due to using a live-virus vaccine- and spread new variants that the government then followed. Many of these variants mutated before the initial push of COVID19 vaccines were available to the general public, so the initial vaccines were geared towards stopping the original strain of COVID19, making them ineffective at stopping the pandemic from the start.

The CDC has claimed that COVID19 vaccines do not create or cause variants of COVID19, that COVID19 vaccines help prevent new variants from emerging, and that high vaccination coverage in the population reduces the spread and prevents new variants from emerging; however, ICAN -through its attorneys- requested from the

CDC -from January to May 2022- evidence to back up their claims around new variants not being created by COVID19 vaccines. The CDC responded to the ICAN requests with "a search of our records failed to reveal any documents pertaining to your request." This shows that they have no studies or evidence to support the claim that COVID19 vaccines do not create new COVID19 variants. Since the CDC is making the claims -the burden of proof is on the CDC- there should be documented studies and evidence to support these claims. Is the CDC spreading misinformation?

We are no longer in a pandemic and have entered the endemic phase. This means COVID19 is something we will all need to learn to live with because it will constantly be with us leading into the future. This should be even more reason for everyone to stand against the government's push to force everyone to be vaccinated with a new, unproven medical procedure that targets older versions of COVID19 that are no longer a threat. If the current round of vaccines did not stop these variants, how can "defeating COVID19" be achieved when the target the government keeps trying to hit has already moved several times? It can't because that isn't the actual goal and purpose of these vaccines.

There is no stopping COVID19 when the only tool available to defend against it is vaccines. How many injections will you get back to "normal," 4, 10, 20? The goalposts have already moved several times and will continue to move in the future to suit the government rhetoric and narrative being pushed. The government only needs to announce a new variant or type of deadly virus to convince many to get another booster shot or a new mRNA vaccine developed in record time.

"The danger is becoming greater. As the arsenals of the superpowers grow in size and sophistication and as other

governments—perhaps even, in the future, dozens of governments— acquire these weapons, it may be only a matter of time before madness, desperation, greed or miscalculation lets loose the terrible force." – Jimmy Carter, *The Watchtower magazine*, August 15th, 1981

Government Restrictions

"rightful liberty is unobstructed action according to our will, within the limits drawn around us by the equal rights of others. I do not add 'within the limits of the law'; because law is often but the tyrant's will, and always so when it violates the right of an individual." – Thomas Jefferson, *letter to Isaac H. Tiffany*, April 4th, 1819

How do you define outbreak, and what does it mean to you when the government and mainstream media use that word? When I first thought about the word outbreak and what it means, my mind instantly wandered to Hollywood movies like *Outbreak* or *Crazies*, where the mortality rate of the virus is 20% or higher and quickly burned through a town, city, or country, causing untold destruction and chaos. Does anyone else get this sense from how the government and mainstream media present the numerous "outbreaks" that have occurred over the years leading up to the COVID19 pandemic?

In 2019, measles outbreaks were happening at what almost seemed like a daily and weekly occurrence, with the government and mainstream media blaming these outbreaks on "anti-vaxxers" or "vaccine hesitancy" -those who might oppose the current vaccine industry in some way due to a wide range of reasons. These individuals believe there are connections between vaccines and severe injuries and deaths -adverse events- that the government purposely tries to hide and ignore, or they are choosing to wait until more safety data comes out -non-experimental phases. Many were past champions of Science!™ until their children, relatives, or friends suffered undeniable extreme adverse events to a liability-free injectable product. They were mocked and ridiculed for attempting to connect the damages to the product. This stance against vaccines has become more steadfast as the government pushes harder to convince, intimidate, and force compliance through government restrictions and mandates. Any disagreement with this government rhetoric is met with hysterical laughter -laugh emojis online- harassment and violence. Many within society fear the truth and being wrong, so much so that they will spit on the truth while watching it die in a ditch to their cheer and glee.

The WHO defines an outbreak as the "occurrence of disease cases in excess of normal expectancy. The number of cases varies according to the disease-causing agent, and the size and type of previous and existing exposure to the agent." The root definition of outbreak is defined as an "eruption, a sudden and violent manifestation" (Online Etymology Dictionary). To the WHO and governments worldwide, an outbreak is any number of cases outside the expected results. If the government sets the expectation to zero, all cases will be considered an outbreak. This sophistry started to be heavily used before COVID19 when measles was the big scary thing.

"Of the density-dependent diseases, measles requires a population of about half a million to become endemic, and the others probably less; in other words, while no city in Greece could support smallpox, it could certainly have become established in Rome." – **Neville Morley**, *Metropolis and Hinterland: The City of Rome and the Italian Economy, 200 BC-AD 200*, December 19th, 2002

Do you remember that in 2017 and 2018, the "world is ending" attitude was reported in the U.S. because of measles "outbreaks"? Humanity has had to deal with measles for thousands of years - meaning it is endemic, never-ending- and we are still here. However, the masses have now been trained to be completely fearful of it as long as they are told to be fearful of it. In 2000, the CDC declared measles "eliminated (absence of continuous disease transmission for greater than 12 months)." Since the expectation for cases was set to zero, every single case of measles since 2000 was considered an outbreak. Let's take a quick look at the totals for several years in the early 2000s:

Measles Confirmed Cases, per the CDC

- 2000 – 86
- 2001 – 116
- 2002 – 44
- 2003 – 56
- 2004 – 37
- 2005 – 66

When was measles eradicated? Never, but now the government and mainstream media can claim an outbreak is occurring when only a single case has been confirmed -or even unconfirmed. The context around the term outbreak is critical to remember as we read and watch the news on COVID19 or any future infectious disease like monkeypox or bird flu. The word outbreak does not mean death and destruction, only that the assumed -doesn't have to be confirmed- case counts have increased beyond what is expected, which is zero. This is sophistry and is only used to trigger fear in the masses and make society easier to manipulate and control.

During the measles "emergency" in 2019, thousands of Los Angeles universities' students were forcibly quarantined on campus over concerns about measles outbreaks. These quarantined students were vaccinated against measles in their youth, yet they had their rights violated over something they supposedly had immunity against. Each outbreak location had only a few cases at most during each incident; of course, these outbreaks were attributed to the anti-vax movement and lack of herd immunity. Using this fear, several states started to remove personal, philosophical, and religious exemptions for vaccinations from laws, making it a requirement to be vaccinated to go out in public spaces. These are forced vaccinations through intimidation and threat of violence.

California removed most medical exemptions with 2019 SB 276 and started requiring medical exemptions given by a doctor to be reviewed by a government review board before approval. This step towards mandatory and forced vaccinations we see today is a dangerous precedent and a slippery slope that is the beginning stages of full-blown tyranny. The violations of our freedoms and liberties won't slow down anytime soon. There is no law too small that the government will not kill over it. Is it "our body, our choice" or "government's body, government's choice"?

"When are we gonna stop putting up with the idiots in this country and just say it's mandatory to get vaccinated? Fuck 'em. Fuck their freedom. I want my freedom to live. I want to get out of the house already. I want to go next door and play chess. I want to go take some pictures. This is bullshit." – Howard Stern, *Sirius XM Program*, September 7th, 2021

In March 2020, at the start of the COVID19 pandemic, we were told that the lockdowns and restrictions, stay-at-home orders, would only be for two weeks to help protect hospitals from being overrun with COVID19 cases and deaths. Between March and April 2020, 43 governors issued stay-at-home lockdown restrictions and mandates. These restrictions forced gyms to close and made going outside in the Sun and fresh air illegal. People who go to the gym often tend to live healthy lives, yet the government forced them to live unhealthy lives at a time when living healthy was of up-most importance.

The two-week narrative turned out to be a lie, with some states staying in lockdown restrictions for months based on purely made-up statistics on how deadly and dangerous COVID19 was. This narrative was helped by mainstream media showing hospitals as full of patients and death. Yet, most, if not all, were images and videos that were reused from other countries or videos and pictures from years earlier. This was propaganda used to manipulate and control the masses by instilling fear.

Many videos started surfacing in 2020 of people doing independent journalism and reporting by recording themselves walking through empty hospitals and waiting rooms. On top of this, countless TikTok and YouTube videos of hospital staff doing choreographed dances and routines started showing up all over, even though they were on the front lines of a pandemic and supposedly being overworked to death. Fact Checkers, the new Thought Police, started silencing and censoring anyone who spoke out on these inconstancies yet ignored the blatant lies being pushed by mainstream media.

Throughout the world, people in multiple countries have been arrested for defying government lockdown orders. Some governments, like the Philippines, issued shoot-and-kill orders for those who defied the lockdowns. Some were arrested for going to the beach and surfing alone because they dared to defy government orders. To be detained, police -policy enforcers- had to defy social distancing orders to make the arrests and then put the non-violent offender into a cell with others, further breaking social distancing orders. These arrests didn't just happen in foreign countries but also throughout the U.S. in multiple states.

There were reports in many U.S. states of business owners being arrested for defying government restrictions by keeping their places of business open. Even though the government was pushing to enforce restrictive mandates using the threat of jail or worse, the federal and state governments were letting thousands of prisoners out of jail and prison due to the danger of COVID19. This shows how tyrannical and hypocritical it was to arrest people for being outside.

Between March and April 2020, the following arrests are some that occurred due to violating the various states' stay-at-home mandates:

- A Pastor was arrested in Central, Louisiana, for holding church services
- A man was arrested in Charles County, Maryland, for hosting two parties at his home
- A man was arrested in Paterson, New Jersey, after being a victim of a gunshot
- Three men were arrested in Chicago, Illinois, who had gathered to remember a man who had been fatally shot the week prior
- Eight men were arrested in Monsey, New York, for having a gathering at a private residence
- A man was arrested in New York City, New York, for running a speakeasy
- A man was arrested in Malibu, California, after paddle boarding alone in the ocean
- Three men were arrested in Richmond, Rhode Island, for playing golf
- A pastor was arrested in Hillsborough County, Florida, for holding church services
- A homeless man was arrested in Orlando, Florida, because he violated the mandated curfew

On top of the stay-at-home orders, non-medical face mask mandates started in 2020. They lasted for over a year in many states through Executive orders due to the ongoing pandemic, which didn't reduce case counts as cases continued to increase after the restrictions were put into place. Initially, the CDC and the government said masks were unnecessary and recommended to the public not to use Personal Protective Equipment (PPE) respirators. Dr. Fauci even said store-bought face masks would not effectively protect against COVID19. This narrative quickly changed into states enforcing mask mandates through threats of violence and intimidation and the federal government forcing airlines to require masks while traveling. Many businesses had their business licenses and livelihoods threatened if they didn't enforce the government mask mandate. These were no private businesses making private business decisions, but businesses being forced to act as government enforcers or risk being shut down for good.

To make things worse, the government forced children to wear masks in school even though children were at the lowest risk of COVID19. Children from early childhood to high school rely on facial expressions and social interactions to develop mentally, which is vitally important to their growth and development; forcing children to wear masks caused delayed development and other issues in the name of potentially protecting themselves and their loved ones at home who might be susceptible to COVID19. Do you remember seeing the pictures of politicians not wearing masks surrounded by children forced to wear masks? Can a government with a history of sacrificing innocent children for the greater good, which never results in anything good, be trusted with the safety and protection of children?

In March 2020, Governor Inslee ordered the halt of elective surgeries and dental services to reserve critical equipment for healthcare workers. Other governors followed suit by enacting their version of restrictions. These tyrannical restrictions caused people to miss appointments scheduled to help maintain their health and catch deadly issues early on. Because of COVID19 restrictions, including the unethical push to vaccinate everyone, unvaccinated patients throughout the pandemic had life-saving medical procedures like critical kidney, liver, and heart transplants denied or were removed from transplant wait lists. How is that in their best interest when the risk of death for COVID19 was significantly lower than the risk of death from not having a transplant? How long until these procedures are denied because you didn't get your 5th booster shot or another vaccine the government approved for emergency use?

"If you're willing to walk among us unvaccinated, you are an enemy." – Gene Simmons, *TalkShopLive Interview*, November 11th, 2021

Due to the lockdown restrictions and the forced stoppage of medical procedures -the government deemed unnecessary- many hospitals and healthcare facilities started furloughing tens of thousands of healthcare workers for months in 2020. These furloughs caused a reduction in the workforce by individuals finding other careers and jobs. The U.S. Bureau of Labor Statistics reported that 1.4 million healthcare jobs were lost in April 2020, on top of the 43 thousand jobs lost in March 2020. This loss of healthcare workers continued as the government began to mandate vaccinations for the healthcare industry throughout 2021, when many healthcare workers around the U.S. refused to get vaccinated with an experimental mRNA product never seen in the market.

In New York, more than 30 thousand healthcare workers were terminated for refusing to vaccinate. There is a healthcare worker shortage happening all over the U.S. that has some direct correlation and causation to these lockdowns, and these shortages have only gotten worse as we move through 2022 and into 2023. Why are we ignoring many healthcare professionals who do not think the COVID19 vaccine is worth their job and livelihood? Are we not told that we need to trust and listen to healthcare professionals, or do we only need to trust and listen to those who confirm the government's rhetoric?

In June 2022, the Journal of Macroeconomics published the Federal Reserve study *Business Exit During the COVID-19 Pandemic: Non-Traditional Measures in Historical Context*, which determined that roughly 200,000 establishments and businesses - above the average yearly number- closed for good in the first year of the COVID19 pandemic (J Macroecon. 2022 Jun;72:103419.). These exits from the market continued to move through 2021, and we will see greater business closures as we face the next pandemic.

Due to the knee-jerk reaction by the government, not a virus, the unemployment rate in 2020 went from 3.5% to close to 15%, causing over 36 million individuals to file unemployment claims, severely damaging the economy that would take years to recover even if all of the mandates and restrictions were removed. Many unemployed workers stayed out of work and never returned, which can be seen by the exploding homeless population in every state, or these individuals moved into a different career path with job openings. As unemployment benefits end, statistics show that unemployed individuals, those actively seeking a job, are reduced even though the individuals might still be looking for jobs.

This loss of businesses will continue its trend throughout 2023. The loss of businesses was primarily due to government restrictions on opening and running during a pandemic, not a virus. Between March and April 2020, Ohio, Oregon, Colorado, California, Tennessee, New Jersey, West Virginia, Nevada, New York, and Rhode Island closed hundreds of businesses, suspending their business and liquor licenses, because they violated the stay-at-home orders which damaged hundreds of lives who depended on these businesses being open to support their livelihood.

Due to these tyrannical restrictions happening worldwide, roughly 150 million people did fall into extreme poverty by 2021, with food insecurities doubling to tripling in some areas. As this global issue rises, watch as governments -and those like Bill Gates- push harder for the forced adoption of lab-grown and heavily processed foods they control and produce.

Do you think this negative trend will stop if the government restricts more and more and forces mandatory vaccinations in the future? Things will get a lot worse. What do you think will happen when the next virus potentially burns economies worldwide down? Because there will be other viruses like monkeypox, smallpox, or bird flu that will have devastating effects. The plans for them have already been set into motion.

On December 19th, 2020, the American Institute for Economic Research (AIER) published the article *Lockdowns Do Not Control the Coronavirus: The Evidence*, which reviewed 35 studies that focused on the lockdown restrictions and any potential correlation to virus control. This research found that evidence supporting lockdowns is very "thin," with most data supporting lockdowns coming from computer-generated forecasts and untested models. Remember, science is a process it is not true or false and should constantly be reviewing old and new data to find the truth of a subject. The article summarizes the 35 studies showing how ineffective the lockdowns are at controlling, slowing down, or stopping COVID19. Were the lockdowns for our safety and protection, or were they used to convince people to inject the COVID19 vaccines?

"My main concern is that we're not going to reach herd immunity because of vaccine hesitancy. And I know that's hard for a lot of people to believe, who desperately want the vaccine right now, and they're thinking, "oh, it's just a small percentage of people who are actually anti-vaxxers," and that's true, there's the anti-science, anti-vaxxer contingent. But there are many more people, millions of people who for whatever reason have concerns about the vaccine, who just don't know what's in it for them. And we need to make it clear to them that the vaccine is the ticket back to pre-pandemic life. And the window to do that is really narrowing. You were mentioning about how all these states are reopening. They're reopening at 100%. And we have a very narrow window to tie reopening policy to vaccination status. Because otherwise, if everything is reopened, then what's the carrot going to be? How are we going to incentivize people to actually get the vaccine? So that's why I think the CDC and Biden administration needs to come out a lot bolder and say, "If you are vaccinated, you can do all these things. Here are all these freedoms

you have." Because otherwise, people are going to go out and enjoy these freedoms anyway, and I fear a situation of coming into the Fall where we never reach herd immunity, and then we get hit by the next surge of COVID-19 in the fall. Something we could have prevented, if we just got people vaccinated now." – Dr. Leana Wen, *CNN Interview*, March 10th, 2021

Another negative aspect of the government lockdowns and restrictions is what they did to the mental health of many citizens. In August 2021, the journal of European Child & Adolescent Psychiatry published *The impact of COVID-19 lockdown on child and adolescent mental health: systematic review*, which found that anxiety and depression symptoms increased significantly due to government lockdowns and restrictions, especially among children (Eur Child Adolesc Psychiatry. 2021 Aug 18: 1–27). Suicide attempts in teenagers and young adults increased by up to 51% between February – March 2021, per the CDC, compared to the same period in 2019.

Mental illness helplines reported a 65% increase in calls and emails since the pandemic started. The increase in suicides and overdose deaths, above yearly averages, in children, teenagers, and young adults -those under 25- have totaled individually more than the deaths of COVID19 for the same age range and same time range COVID19 has been around. There was a 77% increase in suicidal ideation and self-harm among children. This means that government action is costlier to the youth of the U.S. and the world than any virus could be, yet we are still expected to blindly trust the government for the safety and protection of everyone.

Fentanyl overdoses have become the leading cause of death in adults between 18 and 45 years of age, partially due to the government restrictions from COVID19. Yet, an unlimited amount of effort is being focused on COVID19 and liability-free COVID19 vaccinations. The government focuses on the Broken Window

Fallacy through a DoD-funded study at the University of Houston that looked into developing a new liability-free fentanyl vaccine to combat the manufactured fentanyl crisis.

On October 26th, 2022, the researchers, through the journal of Pharmaceutics, published the study *An Immunconjugate Vaccine Alters Distribution and Reduces the Antinociceptive, Behavioral and Physiological Effects of Fentanyl in Male and Female Rats*, which described how their newly created fentanyl vaccine could alter the behavioral and physiological effects of fentanyl in rats, with human trials starting soon (Pharmaceutics. 2022 Oct 26;14(11):2290.). This will soon see human trials and will more likely than not find its way to the market, netting large profits for the corporations making it.

Do we only care and think about the children, elderly, or healthcare workers when it suits our biases? The lockdowns and restrictions are more dangerous to the youth, the economy, and our livelihoods than COVID19 has been or will ever be. Yet, we are constantly told that this damage and destruction is necessary to help support hospitals from being overrun, protect the world's citizens, and achieve the Great Reset.

Since the pandemic's start, mainstream media has pushed the narrative that ICU beds are dangerously close to being full again; "two weeks!". As I mentioned previously, the U.S. healthcare workforce has significantly declined, reducing the number of available ICU staffing beds.

This formula determines ICU occupancy:
(Number of ICU beds occupied during the 7-day period / ICU staffed beds during the 7-day period) x 100 = Percent ICU Occupancy

Suppose a hospital has ten ICU beds staffed, and eight are currently filled. In that case, when the hospital terminates some staff and reduces the number of staffed beds available to eight, their ICU

Occupancy rate jumps from 80% to 100% without seeing an actual increase in patients. However, the media and the government use the 20% increase to generate more fear by saying COVID19 patients are overrunning hospitals. These are manipulative statistics, and the usage of those manipulations to support lying to the public. Do you remember the different military field hospitals set up in 2020 to help overrun hospitals but never saw COVID19 patients like it was only a training exercise?

A New York Brooklyn field hospital that cost $21 million to construct shut down shortly after opening due to seeing zero patients. The Army's Washington Seattle field hospital closed after three days of being open without seeing or treating any COVID19 patients. The University of Kentucky's $7 million-dollar field hospital was closed after never seeing any COVID19 patients nor being used for anything else. Joint Base Cape Cod in Michigan closed its COVID19 field hospital without seeing a single patient. This has been the scenario for most, if not all, hastily built field hospitals in the U.S.

If COVID19 was such an issue for hospitals, why did these field hospitals go unused? This shows that the models being used to predict the level of suspected COVID19 patients are vastly overreported, and the healthcare system was never close to being overrun. How much money has the government wasted in setting up these field hospitals only to take them down without being touched? Maybe there was another purpose to setting these up and taking them down. Were they only training exercises to be used in future scenarios?

If hospital usage was that big of an issue, these field hospitals should have stayed open to take care of the overflow of COVID19 patients. Restricting and controlling citizens, shutting down businesses, and damaging local economics because a private or public hospital might become overrun with COVID19 patients when efficient and effective alternatives exist are criminal and ineffective. Everything done for our protection and safety was in words only. Government should be a greater cause for concern than any virus.

This issue is further expanded due to healthcare professionals being terminated for refusing to get the COVID19 vaccines. The healthcare worker shortage worsens as these individuals are removed from their jobs. These frontline heroes were praised since the start for working directly with COVID19 patients, so why were they being terminated and vilified after more than a year because they didn't want to take an injection when it wasn't needed before? Since the pandemic started, these individuals have had no issues with conducting their duties and responsibilities, and they weren't vaccinated then, so why push to force vaccinations on them?

"I think it is a major over sight on the part of Biden administration to not issue this yesterday. And we have to talk about the reason. The reason isn't so much that we need to keep train travel and plane travel even safer. They are pretty safe. Although I definitely think that having a vaccine requirement would make it even safer and probably encourage many people who are vaccinated or who have young kids and want to protect them, maybe it will help to encourage those people to start traveling again. But there is an even bigger reason too, which I think we need to make it clear that there are privileges associated with being an American. That if you wish to have these privileges, you need to get vaccinated. Travel, and having the right to travel in our state, it's not a constitutional right as far as I know to board a plane, and so saying that you want to stay unvaccinated, that is your choice, but if you want to travel, you better go get that vaccine." – Dr. Leana Wen, *CNN Interview*, September 10th, 2021

During the 2021-2022 Cold and Flu season, the government circled back to these tyrannical restrictions, adding in vaccine mandates because of the case counts of Delta and Omicron COVID19 variants, and will do so again during the next pandemic. This is getting people used to being in a constant lockdown, blindly injecting anything the government says, and viewing restrictions as a normal way of life that can be called upon for any reason, including climate change. An example of this can be seen in China as they continue to lockdown major cities using their Zero COVID19 policies. The idea and desire to enact future city-wide lockdowns to help fight climate change have already been proposed, with steps already being made to enact the next stage of tyranny.

State and federal governments started pushing mandatory vaccinations for employment and to be out in public spaces through threats of violence and intimidation. By October 2021, 6 states announced and mandated COVID19 vaccines for healthcare workers and state employees or face termination: Colorado, Maine, New York, Oregon, Rhode Island, and Washington. By the end of September 2021, 11 states and the federal government mandated COVID19 vaccines to state and federal employees, contractors, and healthcare workers or faced with constant testing. The mandates caused thousands of businesses to either force employees to vaccinate, terminate disobedient employees, or require constant COVID19 testing.

Toward the end of 2021, the Occupational Safety and Health Administration (OSHA) under the U.S. Department of Labor, issued two vaccine mandate orders: a vaccine or test emergency temporary standard (ETS) for all federal contractors and employers with 100 employees or more and a Department of Health and Human Services (HHS) - Centers for Medicare & Medicaid Services (CMS) Interim Final Rule (IFR) vaccine mandate for healthcare workers -current memo #QSO-22-07-ALL-Revised 4/05/22 which exempted 25 states from the order. On November 17th, 2022, 22 state attorney generals petitioned the Biden administration and HHS CMS under the Administrative Procedures Act to repeal the IFR vaccine mandate for healthcare workers.

The U.S. Supreme Court struck down the ETS mandate on January 13th, 2022 -*NFIB v. OSHA*, 590 U.S. ___ (2020)- as being unconstitutional as it was written, but the U.S. Supreme Court allowed the CMS mandate to remain in effect (*Biden v. Missouri*, 590 U.S. ___ (2020)). An appeal to the ETS stay was ruled in favor of the federal government, making the ETS mandate enforceable; however, this was appealed, and again, a stay was granted for the ETS mandate. The court battle for this is still ongoing, but with how things are, I suspect it will be approved and enforced soon -definitely during the next pandemic.

Since the U.S. federal vaccine mandate that President Biden implemented was an Executive Order, it only applied to the executive branch, meaning that the legislative branch, Congress, and their staff, do not fall under the vaccine mandate for federal employees. This also means the entire judicial branch, Supreme Court, and other courts and their staff was exempt from the vaccine mandate. This should be viewed as a concern since tens of millions were being required to vaccinate or face termination, and those who make laws that we must follow, and those who run the justice system, are free from worry. This is a conflict of interest that only feeds an already corrupt system.

On August 23rd, 2021, the FDA approved the first COVID19 vaccine developed by Pfizer for licensure (COMIRNATY) not under the Emergency Use Authorization (BNT162b2) to be officially approved for use by the public since these vaccines were released to the public. Many of these states had already started publicly pushing these mandates before the official approval for licensure, which means that these states were mandating truly experimental injectable liability-free products. This is a clear violation of informed consent. To make matters worse, it took months before COMIRNATY saw distribution, so everyone was still taking the truly experimental Emergency Use Act (EUA) BNT162b2 vaccine. Mandating experimental injectable medical procedures or facing termination that could ruin livelihoods is a massive violation of ethics and moral principles, yet it is accepted by many.

Due to a FOIA request, it was reported in August 2021 that Governor Inslee of Washington State -in emails from July 2021- looked to make religious vaccine exemptions "as narrow as possible" for the vaccine mandate that he enforced due to his emergency declaration granting him what some would view as a form of dictatorship. This can be viewed as a conflict of interest due to his daughter-in-law, Emily Inslee, working as a Senior Program Officer on the Philanthropic Partnerships Team for the Gates Foundation.

Governor Inslee enacted these emergency powers until October 31st, 2022, yet his vaccine mandate for state employees and healthcare workers remained in place. Governor Inslee's vaccine mandate only requires the original vaccine series, not boosters, even though the original vaccine series focused on the original strain of COVID19 - not in circulation- and not any of the new variants of concern. The mandate also removed the option of weekly testing for all state workers and healthcare personnel. For 2023, Washington state employees -pending legislative approval- would be provided a one-time $1,000 payment for proof that a COVID19 booster was injected.

The mandate started a month before the FDA issued its approval for licensure of the Pfizer COVID19 vaccine. Governor Inslee was already mandating vaccines at a time when they were officially still an experimental medical procedure under the EUA. Even past Governor Inslee's deadlines to start COVID19 vaccine injections, the licensed Pfizer product was not even available for people to get, so only the official experimental medical procedures were available.

Why was there a discussion on mandating a medical procedure with the risk of death for healthcare and state workers when the medical procedure available was still only approved under the EUA for high-risk individuals? Maybe it is due to Governor Inslee's connections and ties, including family ties, to some of the major players in this political theater being played out. Washington State isn't the only state to push this tyranny. Should we trust these governments who only drive citizens to a single focused liability-free product shown not to provide lasting lifetime immunity?

To be approved under the EUA, the known and potential benefits of the product must outweigh the known and potential risks of the product, and no adequate, approved, and available alternative to the product for diagnosing, preventing, or treating the disease or condition should exist. Since the experimental trials for the COVID19 vaccines are still ongoing until the end of 2023 and beyond, the true risk still needs to be discovered. On top of this, several alternatives have been shown to combat COVID19. Based on these facts, the COVID19 vaccines should not have been approved under the EUA nor licensed. We should never blindly trust in governors' actions, especially when they tend to act tyrannically.

On April 24th, 2020, the WHO issued guidance for "immunity passports," stating that there was not enough evidence on the effectiveness of antibody immunity to prevent infection and transmissions from moving forward with implementing immunity or health passports, health code apps, or vaccine passports as others have called it. However, throughout 2021 the Biden administration, working with private corporations and officials involved with the international vaccine effort, began to work on developing a standard of handling health and vaccine credentials that would allow citizens to prove that they have been vaccinated against COVID19 or anything else government decides to add as a requirement.

The government focused on forcing businesses to require customers to show proof of their vaccination status using paper certificates provided during their vaccination. This was getting people used to "showing their papers," which is eerily similar to when Nazis required Jews to carry identification papers. During this process, many reports of people faking these paper certificates were used to showcase the need for a centralized digital certificate that could be tracked and monitored by the government.

Soon, this new government-created software application and new tyrannical restrictions will be implemented throughout the U.S. as the next pandemic burns its way through societies worldwide. The COVID19 Credentials Initiative (CCI) was developed to bring to market a digital certificate that lets individuals prove, or request proof from others, that they have been vaccinated or recovered from COVID19. This initiative includes partnerships with hundreds of individuals and corporations worldwide.

On November 16th, 2022, the U.S., in collaboration with G20 -19 other countries- issued a declaration that promoted the creation of global digital health networks, "immunity passports," and the development of actionable policies to help prevent and respond to future pandemics. There is immense pressure to force the U.S. and everyone worldwide into this restrictive system. One example is Montana's House Bill 702 -signed into law May 7th, 2021- which sought to "prohibit discrimination based on vaccination status [any vaccine] or having an immunity passport." On December 9th, 2022, U.S. District Court Judge Donald Molloy -appointed by President Bill Clinton- ruled that the law was unconstitutional and violated federal law. Legal challenges are still ongoing for that case.

"Love the idea of covid vaccine passports for everywhere: flights, restaurants, clubs, football, gyms, shops etc. It's time covid-denying, anti-vaxxer loonies had their bullshit bluff called & bar themselves from going anywhere that responsible citizens go." – Piers Morgan, *Twitter*, February 14th, 2021

These vaccine passport efforts and pushes using digital technology and documentation are possible through the Real ID Act of 2005, which was to become fully implemented and enforced throughout the U.S. by May 3rd, 2023 -multiple extensions have been granted over the years. However, due to the COVID19 pandemic, the deadline was extended to May 7th, 2025. Remember, the Real ID Act of 2005 aligned the U.S. with the ID2020 and U.N. 2030 SDGs efforts. Vaccine passports come in physical vaccine certificates, digital forms, certifications, and QR codes within various apps that countries have started implementing. These digital vaccine passports and regulations around their enforcement include thermal facial-recognition cameras, temperature checkpoints, and location tracking.

Over 100 countries, multiple universities, and dozens of corporations, organizations, and initiatives, worldwide have worked on and implemented some form of a vaccine passport, with many only accepting vaccination status as proof and ignoring natural immunity. The idea and goal of these vaccine passports are to facilitate safe and free movement between countries; however, some of the worst atrocities committed in the history of humanity were in the name of safety and protection of our rights and freedoms. How sure can we be that this is for our safety and protection? If the government protects us from everything, who or what protects us from the government?

As an example, we only need to look at China, where in June 2022, a planned protest by hundreds of individuals wishing to seek access to their frozen bank funds, totaling at least $178 million, had their health code apps turned red, so they were restricted from traveling to the planned protest. This is not the first nor last time these passports and apps will be used to stamp out dissent and instill obedience. The direction we are going is a very steep, slippery slope that will only end in disaster and greater tyranny and restrictions for the innocent people of the world. If you think what we have witnessed so far is horrifying, imagine how governments worldwide will react when the next pandemic starts -which looks significantly worse.

"Tyranny naturally arises out of democracy, and the most aggravated form of tyranny and slavery out of the most extreme form of liberty." – Plato, *The Republic Book VIII* (Socrates), ~375BCE

COVID19 Vaccines

"The ultimate measure of a man is not where he stands in moments of comfort and convenience, but where he stands at times of challenge and controversy." – Martin Luther King, Jr., *Sermon*, August 1958

Vaccinations and the idea of vaccines came from the Latin word *vaccinus* "from cows" (Online Etymology Dictionary). In 1796, after many centuries of recorded smallpox outbreaks, Edward Jenner experimented on an eight-year-old boy by infecting the child with cowpox and then exposing the child to smallpox to study the results. This was unethical testing on a child who could not give voluntary informed consent. Still, many advancements in science have been made by crossing moral and ethical lines that should not be crossed. Typically, inoculation would be done through a scratch and open wound, not through an injection. Smallpox has been found on Egyptian mummies dating from 1570 BC and is assumed to circulate throughout humanity beyond recorded history -up to 10,000 BC. This shows that even with something like smallpox, which has a higher mortality rate than viruses like measles or coronaviruses, it will not wipe out humanity even without modern vaccines.

Jenner was the first person to successfully confirm that cowpox - a less severe infectious disease with a lower mortality rate- could provide protection and immunization against the more contagious and dangerous smallpox infection. This type of inoculation granted natural immunity to both cowpox and smallpox. With the success of this study, Jenner's work is viewed by many as the foundation of immunology. This type of simplistic inoculation, using one virus infection to fight against a different kind of virus infection, is no longer done as the vaccines today are injected into a subject and contain other types of genetic material and chemicals that come with real risks beyond a viral infection.

These traditional vaccines are considered routine medical procedures -attempt to mimic natural immunity inoculation- and, in some cases, are successful but come with real risks -including death. Modern vaccines are not very profitable since they should only take one or two injections for a disease to no longer be an issue, which is not how pharmaceutical corporations make their money. This is why pharmaceutical corporations rely on government subsidies to turn significant profits and why vaccines should never be considered free since taxpayers foot the bill for the vaccines.

In 2012, the CDC defined vaccination as an "injection of a killed or weakened infectious organism in order to prevent the disease" and a vaccine as "a product that produces immunity therefore protecting the body from the disease. Vaccines are administered through needle injections, by mouth and by aerosol." In 2021, the CDC quietly changed the definition of vaccination from "produce immunity" to "produce protection." The CDC currently defines vaccination as "the act of introducing a vaccine into the body to produce protection from a specific disease." The CDC currently defines vaccines as "a suspension of live (usually attenuated) or inactivated microorganisms (e.g., bacteria or viruses) or fractions thereof administered to induce immunity and prevent infectious diseases and their sequelae. Some vaccines contain highly defined antigens (e.g., the polysaccharide of Haemophilus influenzae type b or the surface antigen of hepatitis B); others have antigens that are complex or incompletely defined (e.g., Bordetella pertussis antigens or live attenuated viruses)."

This slight change in vaccination wording significantly changes the actual definition. Immunity keeps an individual from being symptomatic and infectious. Protection only means to protect someone from the severity of the infection, potentially lessening the symptoms that they might have. Someone can still be infectious while being protected, making them a potential risk to others. This is sophistry. Do the COVID19 vaccines meet the older definition of what vaccines should be, or do they only meet the new standard? If the COVID19 vaccines can only meet the new standard, should we continue to classify them as vaccines?

In August 2021, St. Louis County in Missouri defined a "Fully Vaccinated Person" as a "person who 14 days prior received a second dose of a 2-dose series or 14 days prior received one dose of a single dose vaccine. A person is not fully vaccinated until this time period of 14 days from the last date of the required dose has lapsed. Additionally, after 3 months from the last dose, a person is no longer considered to be a Fully Vaccinated Person."

Read that again. Someone can only be considered fully vaccinated 14 days after their single dose or second injection of a two-dose series vaccine and within three months from their last dose in a series. Outside of this small window, an individual is considered unvaccinated. How many injections are you willing to chase to be considered "fully vaccinated"? How many more billions in taxpayer funds do you feel comfortable with the government handing over to these for-profit pharmaceutical corporations while forcing you to inject their products? This entire situation should throw up massive red flags for everyone. This is a slippery slope, and we are moving full steam ahead over a cliff as a society.

If the COVID19 vaccines do not keep people from catching or transmitting COVID19, then it does not fit the definition of a vaccine by eliciting immunity and preventing infection. Influenza vaccines fall under the same concept and fail to meet the standard of immunity, meaning they are not actual vaccines using the previous definition. Cold and Flu "vaccines" are only potential immunity boosters if they work as advertised. President Biden and Dr. Fauci discussed in August 2021 about requiring COVID19 boosters every five months since antibodies drop significantly the further you get away from the last injection. In July 2022, Canada started to require its citizens to get COVID19 vaccine boosters every nine months, further showing that lifetime immunity is impossible and that these vaccines can't even provide immunity for a year.

By 1955, the first polio vaccine -poliomyelitis- had passed through clinical trials and was approved for widespread usage in children. Jonas Salk was attributed to the creation of this polio vaccine produced by the Cutter Institute, which had announced the success of the polio vaccine trial. No long-term studies were done before its widespread use. This advancement in medicine was hailed as a modern marvel, viewed as completely safe and effective, and was quickly injected into roughly 120,000 children.

This incident, known as the Cutter Incident, became the worst pharmaceutical disaster in U.S. history, which caused approximately 40,000 children to develop poliomyelitis -polio- permanently damaging and killing some. This polio vaccine was contaminated by the polyomavirus simian virus (SV40). SV40 is a DNA virus that can induce brain and bone cancers, mesothelioma -tumors in tissue- and lymphomas -cancers in the immune system. How often do you hear the government and mainstream media use the terms "safe and effective," yet evidence tends to show the opposite as time progresses?

In the early 1980s, pharmaceutical corporations and manufacturers who created vaccines faced a never-ending list of claims, lawsuits, and tort litigation over the injuries and deaths that their vaccines were causing in children and adults. After extensive lobbying by these pharmaceutical corporations, the federal government enacted the NCVIA in 1986, which removed most civil and criminal liability from the billion-dollar for-profit pharmaceutical corporations, leaving taxpayers on the hook for restitution when damages and deaths were attributed to vaccines. Do you think this is an unethical and immoral situation with high corruption?

The liability protection provided by the NCVIA was challenged in the U.S. Supreme Court under the court case *Bruesewitz v. Wyeth, LLC*, 562 U.S. 223 (2011), which the Supreme Court sided with Wyeth -acquired by Pfizer in 2009- finding that the NCVIA does provide liability protection to vaccine manufacturers even if a vaccine is found to have a defective design formula and inadequate directions or warnings when other safer vaccine formulas are available and known. The NCVIA requires citizens to petition the federal government through a specialized court that was set up by the U.S. Department of Health and Human Services, the National Vaccine Injury Compensation Program (NVICP), for vaccine injury restitution which requires a heavy burden of evidence and proof while stretching trials out for years.

Remember, the consensus of medical professionals -those taught in approved government rhetoric- is that vaccines do not cause injuries or death and should not be questioned. Most of these medical professionals are not toxicologists nor virologists -with limited study and research into potential adverse events- and mostly attribute reactions to other causes leading to significantly underreported cases of adverse events. Those who do speak out are vilified, potentially losing their government-approved medical licenses.

The NVICP compensation for deaths has a $250,000 maximum payout but has no maximum limit for injuries sustained from vaccines. Two of the largest payouts for damages have been $32 million and $38 million, which took decades to settle the claims - totals included lawyer fees. As of the end of 2019, the NVICP has paid out over $4.2 billion of taxpayer money to settle restitution lawsuits, protecting billion-dollar corporations from liability. Federal funds pay for roughly 95% of all publicly funded vaccinations.

"The history of medical research and human experimentation reveals both great successes and horrible abuses. Plagues like smallpox were rampant and capable of wiping out entire cities. People were desperate for relief and would try anything that could help ward off the horrible plagues, even experimenting. English aristocrat Lady Mary Wortley Montague introduced the idea of variolation to the gentry in 1715. In variolation, ooze from the sores of smallpox victims with mild cases was scratched into the skin. During the French the Indian War, General George Washington was convinced that his most formidable for was smallpox and he subjected his men to forced variolation to stop its spread. Many of the soldiers had only mil reactions, but some became seriously ill and died. The European press, especially among the antivaccine society, bitterly criticized Washington for forcing his men into possible harm without their consent, Hessian soldiers, who fought alongside the British, were captured and imprisoned in Frederick, Maryland, where they may have been subjected to variolation experimentation—a safety precaution before Washington would order to the procedure for his own army. When British physician Edward Jenner (1749-1823) introduced the use of cowpox sores to make a vaccine against smallpox, he was subjected to the same criticism. In the 1700s principles of individualism, self-determination, and consent of the governed formed the establishment of the United States. Ethicists all this idea the principle of "respect for persons." Therefore, informed consent is a human right and an outgrowth of life, liberty and the pursuit of happiness." – Evelyn B. Kelly, *Stem Cells*, 2007*

Traditional modern vaccines have been in place and used for decades, but the number of vaccines children require to get injected with continues to increase yearly. Those born in earlier decades did not fall under the requirements as children today and would not be considered fully vaccinated to today's standards. When a child turns 18, they will have been required to inject 14 vaccines. This schedule doesn't include COVID19 vaccines, but on October 20th, 2022, the CDC voted 15-0 to add COVID19 vaccines to the Children's Immunization Schedule for six months and up starting in 2023.

Many states, if not all, will soon require public school children to be vaccinated with one of the primary COVID19 vaccines series -not reformulated boosters- which focuses on the original strain of COVID19 that is all but absent from circulation. As time progresses, it has been realized that adults require booster shots for some of these vaccines past age 18 -like MMR- showing that these vaccines do not provide lifetime immunity. If a vaccine is supposed to provide lifetime immunity, why does it require boosters?

Here are lists of the vaccine schedules by year and vaccine schedules by age:

- **Late 1940s**: Smallpox, Diphtheria-Tetanus-Pertussis (DTP)
- **Late 1960s**: Smallpox, Diphtheria-Tetanus-Pertussis (DTP), Polio (OPV), Measles, Mumps, Rubella
- **1994-1995**: Diphtheria-Tetanus-Pertussis (DTP), Polio (OPV), Measles-Mumps-Rubella (MMR), Hib, Hepatitis B
- **2010-2019**: Diphtheria-Tetanus-Acellular Pertussis (DTaP), Polio (IPV), Measles-Mumps-Rubella (MMR), Hib, Hepatitis A, Hepatitis B, Varicella (VAR – Chickenpox), Pneumococcal, Influenza, Rotavirus (RV1 or RV5)
- **2022**: Diphtheria-Tetanus-Acellular Pertussis (DTaP), Tetanus-Diphtheria-Acellular Pertussis (Tdap), Polio (IPV), Measles-Mumps-Rubella (MMR), Hib, Hepatitis A, Hepatitis B, Varicella (VAR – Chickenpox), Pneumococcal, Influenza, Rotavirus (RV1 or RV5), Pneumococcal conjugate (PCV13), Human papillomavirus (HPV), Meningococcal

In 2022, the following are the vaccine requirements for children:

- **Birth to 15 months**: HepB – 3 doses, RV1 – 2 or RV5 – 3 doses, DTaP – 4 doses, Hib – 4 doses, PCV13 – 4 doses, IPV

- 3 doses, Influenza – 1 or 2 doses (annually), MMR – 1 dose, VAR – 1 dose, HepA – 2 doses
- **18 months to 18 years old**: DTaP – 1 dose, IPV – 1 dose, Influenza – 1 or 2 doses (annually), MMR – 1 dose, VAR – 1 dose, Tdap – 1 dose, HPV – 2 or 3 doses, Meningococcal – 2 doses

There have been no studies looking into all vaccinations combined, nor do studies use non-vaccinated children as a control. At most, studies conducted by pharmaceutical corporations might include three different vaccines, but none cover the entire list holistically. When studies are conducted, they use the healthiest children and adults possible and remove outliers as complications happen. Typically, the control group in a vaccine study is given another vaccine instead of an inert placebo, like a saline solution, which completely alters the data and results.

HHS's publication on the childhood vaccine schedule shows that the only vaccine to have a placebo control group is Merck's HPV Gardasil-9 vaccine. HHS has stated that "Inert placebo controls are not required to understand the safety profile of a new vaccine, and are thus not required. In some cases, inclusions of placebo control groups are considered unethical." On top of this, often, the control group is later given the vaccine being studied, removing any semblance of a control group for long-term studies. There are other types of vaccines, but those additional vaccines are only given at the discretion of healthcare professionals. With those excluded, children are looking at up to 71 doses of vaccines by age 18. Do you honestly believe this constant increase in injections isn't causing long-term issues?

Each traditional vaccine is produced slightly differently, but each contains a long list of other chemicals and heavy metals that are far from safe and effective for everyone. Many ingredients are constantly changing, making it challenging to determine which specific ingredient could cause adverse events. Remember, injecting chemicals has a different absorption rate and process than ingesting or absorption through skin contact. One way that adverse events are hidden is through lot numbers -batches of vaccines made simultaneously- sent to multiple locations worldwide, reducing the likelihood of adverse events being linked to a vaccine.

On December 14th, 2022, a Consumer Reports investigation was released, which found high levels of lead and cadmium -dangerous heavy metals- in dark chocolate from Hershey's, Trader Joe's, and others that, when exposed to small amounts over long periods can lead to significant health problems -developmental problems, lower IQ, Alzheimer's, and dementia. If chocolate eaten -orally taken- for decades could lead to these severe health issues, what serious health issues could arise from injecting heavy metals found in "safe and effective" vaccines?

Western culture, compared to third-world countries that do not follow these vaccine schedules, has been facing several epidemics which have spiked in alarming numbers, e.g., peanut allergies, autism, and Sudden Infant Death Syndrome (SIDS) rates. Roughly 2 million children are now estimated to have a peanut allergy. As of 2022, children's autism rates have increased to 1 in 30 children compared to the 1 in 10,000 seen in the 1980s. Autism can run in families but can also form in children that have no family history of autism.

On November 4th, 2017, the journal of Clinical Nutrition ESPEN published a study *Evidence the U.S. autism epidemic initiated by acetaminophen (Tylenol) is aggravated by oral antibiotic amoxicillin/clavulanate (Augmentin) and now exponentially by herbicide glyphosate (Roundup)*, showing that Tylenol, Augmentin, and Glyphosate all play a part in the ongoing autism epidemic (Clin Nutr ESPEN. 2018 Feb;23:171-183.). Suppose these constantly used products, which we are told are safe and effective, can cause autism. Why, then, should we assume "save and effective" liability-free vaccines that are injected do not cause autism or any other harm?

SIDS typically occurs in the same window as most injections infants get during their initial wellness checks. In the federal court case *Boatmon v. Secretary of Health and Human Services*, 13-611 (Fed. Cl. 2017), it was proven that the infant J.B. passed away from SIDS due to vaccines, which occurred a day after receiving the DTaP, IPV, HiB, PCV, and Rotavirus vaccines. All of these vaccines were given at one time which is standard practice for many vaccines. J.B. died of asphyxia, which is the cause of most SIDS cases. Most of these cases are attributed to parents causing asphyxia by letting a child sleep with them and accidentally suffocating them or other unknown causes. How many "accidental" deaths that occurred shortly after wellness checkups were caused by the vaccines given?

When we are told vaccines are safe and effective, most refuse to acknowledge and view vaccinations as a potential cause of adverse events and risks. Can other factors besides vaccines influence the increase in these epidemic rates? Absolutely. Can vaccines be ignored entirely because we are told they are safe and effective for everyone? No. There is a correlation between the increase in vaccines required and these increased epidemic rates.

Here is a small list of potentially harmful ingredients within traditional vaccines that are injected into children and adults at an ever-increasing rate:

- **Formaldehyde** - is a carcinogenic -cancerous- and highly toxic organic compound mainly used in industrial resins and adhesives. Formaldehyde is found naturally in nature and within the human body -in small amounts- as part of our natural metabolic process. However, too much of it is extremely dangerous to our health. Formaldehyde is used to inactivate viruses and detoxify bacterial toxins and is found in the final products injected. It is only used in vaccines that do not contain a live virus, e.g., DTaP, Hep A, Hep B, Influenza, IPV, and Meningococcal.

- **Aluminum Salts** - an adjuvant used to stimulate intense immune responses and can be found in most vaccines. Chapter 21 of the U.S. Code of Federal Regulations (610.15[a]) limits the amount of aluminum in biological products to 0.85 mg/dose. Vaccines in the U.S. typically range from 0.85-0.125 mg/dose. Reaction to these adjuvants depends on the injected individual and can vary from benign to fatal. Aluminum from the adjuvant can make its way to the brain, assisting in a buildup of aluminum toxicity which can cause Alzheimer's and dementia decades later.
- **Polysorbate 80** - is a synthetic drug associated with an increased risk of systemic hypersensitivity reactions, an immunologic response to an antigen or allergen. It can be found in Influenza, DTaP, Hep B, HPV, and Meningococcus vaccines.
- **MRC-5** - is a cell culture line developed from the lung tissue of a 14-week-old aborted Caucasian male fetus in September 1966. MRC-5 is used to culture live-virus vaccines and contains human DNA in the final product. A constant replication and continuation of the cells have maintained this cell line. However, this cell line does not have genetic testing conducted to confirm that cancer-causing genic mutations have not occurred. MRC-5 can be found in VAR, MMR, Hep A, DTaP, OPV, and HiB.
- **WI-38** - is a cell culture line developed from the lung tissue of a three-month-gestational fetus aborted in 1963. Similar to MRC-5, it is used to culture live-virus vaccines and contains human DNA in the final product. WI-38 can be found in VAR and MMR.
- **Monosodium glutamate (MSG)** - is a flavor enhancer used in a wide range of products in U.S. markets. It stabilizes the vaccine making it more resistant to heat, light, and humidity. MSG can potentially disrupt neurons in the brain and have adverse effects on behavior. It has been shown to induce

obesity, impair glucose tolerance, and cause damage to the liver. MSG can be found in Influenza, MMR, and VAR.

- **Thimerosal** - is a mercury-based compound -ethylmercury- with antiseptic and antifungal properties. It can be very toxic if inhaled, ingested, injected, or in contact with skin. It is used as a preservative in some vaccines. It was more widely used in vaccines until 1999 when Public Health Service agencies, the American Academy of Pediatrics, and vaccine manufacturers agreed to stop using it in childhood vaccines due to neurodevelopmental disorders like Guillain-Barré syndrome (GBS) being caused. It is mainly still used in Influenza -one reason the Influenza vaccines are still highly associated with GBS.

Besides the potential danger with the chemicals within the vaccines, some vaccines can cause an individual to be a carrier and spread infectious diseases due to some of the vaccines coming with live attenuated viruses that can cause shedding. On September 8th, 2008, the journal of Vaccine published the study *Shedding and immunogenicity of live attenuated influenza vaccine virus in subjects 5–49 years of age*, which found that 17% to 44% of subjects, depending on age, shed the vaccine-derived influenza virus after vaccination with a live virus (Vaccine. 2008 Sep 8;26(38):4940-6.). Is it possible that heavy flu seasons are encouraged through individuals getting an influenza vaccine and then shedding and spreading influenza to some of those around them, causing more harm than good?

Another example of this shedding phenomenon can be seen in the polio emergency in New York that was announced on September 9th, 2022, where multiple counties -Rockland County, Orange County, and Sullivan County- reported finding vaccine-derived polio in their water systems. On July 22nd, 2022, ABC News published the article *What to know about vaccine-derived polio after rare case found in New York* linking the polio virus found in Rockland County to the oral polio vaccine that is still given in countries overseas. In 2000, the U.S. stopped licensing OPV -which contains a live attenuated poliovirus- due to the shedding it can cause. If we research further, we will find that the reach of wild polio has been significantly reduced worldwide and replaced with the vaccine-derived poliovirus in the wild. All live-virus vaccines, including COVID19 vaccines that use a live attenuated virus, can cause shedding.

COVID19 vaccines are a mixture of traditional vaccines -using a live or inactivated virus- and new mRNA vaccines that can be categorized into two types -non-replicating and self-amplifying. Self-amplifying has additional RNA sequences that allow the RNA to replicate in a subject. If RNA can be replicated in a subject, can the RNA be passed on to others as with the spike proteins?

The following identified ingredients of importance are found in the Pfizer or Moderna mRNA vaccines:

- **Polyethylene glycol (PEG)** - a nanoparticle compound derived from petroleum -has never been used before in a vaccine- and had been assumed inert for many years. The mRNA lipid nanoparticle is attached to these PEG molecules for the vaccine's stability and life span. PEGs are used in products like toothpaste, laxatives, and shampoos but have never been used as an ingredient to be injected. On December 6th, 2016, the journal of Analytical Chemistry published a study *Analysis of Pre-existing IgG and IgM Antibodies against Polyethylene Glycol (PEG) in the General Population*, showing that during the late 1990s, roughly 72% of the U.S. population showed signs of anti-PEG antibodies, with rates higher today than in the 1990s (Anal Chem. 2016 Dec 6;88(23):11804-11812.). This means there is a significant risk of potential adverse allergic reactions to PEG when injected. Neither Pfizer nor Moderna -both uses PEG in its vaccines- screened trial subjects for anti-PEG antibodies. Anti-PEG antibodies can also reduce the potential efficacy of the COVID19 vaccines. In August 2020, the journal of Laboratory Animals published a study *A cautionary note: Toxicity of polyethylene glycol 200 injected intraperitoneally into mice*, showing adverse events of pain and discomfort in the flanks of the mice after PEG injection (Lab Anim. 2020 Aug;54(4):391-396.).

- **Potassium chloride** - is a salt composed of potassium and chlorine and is used in vaccines to help balance the acidity in a body. It is used in fertilizer, food processing, and medicine for those with low blood potassium. It is also used in lethal injections by overloading a body with potassium, causing the heart to have an abnormal heartbeat and go into cardiac arrest resulting in death. One of the influenza vaccines contains potassium chloride -no other vaccines do. Potassium chloride should not be used in those with high potassium levels since it could send the individual into hyperkalemia, causing heart palpitations, muscle pain, weakness, numbness, or death. This is in the Pfizer vaccine but not the Moderna vaccine.

- **Monobasic potassium phosphate** - is an inorganic compound used in vaccines to help balance the acidity in a body. It is often used as a fertilizer, food additive, and buffering solution to help maintain pH levels in a solution. It is also used to treat those with low blood levels of phosphorus. Those with high potassium, low calcium, and high phosphorus levels should avoid taking or injecting this compound. Side effects can be confusion, light-headedness, numbness, nausea, muscle weakness, loss of movement, and slowed heart rate. This is in the Pfizer vaccine but not the Moderna vaccine.

mRNA vaccines have recoded mRNA strands that trick the cells into acting beyond what we naturally have in our DNA and genes. Basically, mRNA vaccines conduct a man-in-the-middle attack on the cells by altering the instructions our cells need to function correctly to produce what was instructed in the injection. Can we trust that these mRNA instructions are written to do what we are told they should be doing, having our cells produce the COVID19 spike proteins and nothing else?

The FDA currently defines gene therapy as a process that "seeks to modify or manipulate the expression of a gene or to alter the biological properties of living cells for therapeutic use [and] a technique that modifies a person's genes to treat or cure disease." Gene expression is transforming DNA instructions into a product like a protein. This process is achieved by transcription and translation. Transcription is when DNA is copied to create mRNA, and translation is when the mRNA has delivered the DNA message to the intended cells. Using the definition of gene therapy and gene expression, we can see that the new mRNA COVID19 vaccines are, in fact, highly experimental gene therapies, while not meeting the standard definition of vaccines that had been used for decades before the definition was updated after the public release of the COVID19 vaccines.

Since David Baltimore and his colleagues discovered reverse transcriptase (RT), the general assumption for decades has been that humans do not have these RT enzymes occurring naturally in our systems. Quick Internet searches show that many articles claim humans do not have RT, so COVID19 vaccines can't modify DNA showing why they are not gene therapy products. However, RT has now been found in bacteria, yeast, slime molds, animals, plants, human leukemic cells, cancerous cells, eukaryotic organisms - humans have eukaryotic cells- and viruses like retroviruses, e.g., HIV.

On August 3rd, 1989, the journal of MicroReview published the study *Reverse transcriptase in bacteria*, which confirmed that RT is found in more than only retroviruses (Mol Microbiol. 1989 Aug;3(8):1141-4.).

On February 11th, 2016, the journal of Frontiers in Chemistry published the study *The Reverse Transcriptase Encoded by LINE-1 Retrotransposons in the Genesis, Progression, and Therapy of Cancer*, which found RT activity within human cancer cells, human tumorigenesis, formation of tumors, and human embryogenesis - initial embryo formation- while also playing a significant role in epigenetic -gene expression- regulation (Front Chem. 2016; 4: 6.). Epigenetic regulators play a substantial role in controlling and regulating gene expression.

On April 19th, 2021, the journal PNAS published the study *Reverse-transcribed SARS-CoV-2 RNA can integrate into the genome of cultured human cells and can be expressed in patient-derived tissues*, which found COVID19 could modify DNA through reverse transcription and the long interspersed nuclear element-1 (LINE-1) found in humans (Proc Natl Acad Sci U S A. 2021 May 25;118(21):e2105968118.). The study further explains that the modification of DNA could explain why some individuals test positive for COVID19 long after they stop showing symptoms.

On February 25th, 2022, the journal of Current Issues in Molecular Biology published the study *Intracellular Reverse Transcription of Pfizer BioNTech COVID-19 mRNA Vaccine BNT162b2 In Vitro in Human Liver Cell Line*, which found that the Pfizer mRNA COVID19 vaccine was reversed transcribed into DNA after six hours of exposure to the vaccine through the gene expression of LINE-1 (Curr Issues Mol Biol. 2022 Feb 25;44(3):1115-1126.). LINE-1 is a retrotransposon, a transposable element with a copy-and-paste function found abundant in many eukaryotes' genomes.

These studies, and several others, have shown that there is a mechanism in place that will allow mRNA COVID19 vaccines to modify human DNA through reverse transcription via the RT enzyme and LINE-1 pathway and that these vaccines are gene therapies being experimented on millions of individuals worldwide who had no idea what they were injecting themselves with. Once DNA is modified, the new genetic profile is passed down to future children. What are the long-term effects of these potential changes on future children? How sure can we be that catastrophic changes won't manifest symptoms in our children's developmental process? How long, if ever, would it take to discover and link potential changes to these experimental vaccines?

During an interview -while presented with the 2020 Axel Springer Award- Elon Musk explained that with a properly encoded synthetic mRNA, like computer software, aging could be stopped, or someone could even be turned into a butterfly with enough effort. How sure can we be that different mRNA experiments weren't conducted on many during the initial stages of the COVID19 vaccines -traditional and mRNA- public release?

"The fact that scientists developed safe, effective vaccines in record time is an unbelievable achievement. And yet despite the fact that we've now, essentially clinically tested the vaccine on billions of people worldwide, around 1 in 5 Americans is still willing to put themselves at risk and put their families at risk rather than get vaccinated. People are dying because of misinformation." – President Obama, *Stanford University speech to address "disinformation,"* April 22nd, 2022

Before the COVID19 vaccines, there were no mRNA products on the market. After years of research and attempts, none of the potential mRNA products were approved for use, nor did any of the experimental trials succeed -never making it to human trials due to massive failures and deaths during animal testing. In 2013, Moderna and AstraZeneca signed a five-year deal to develop mRNA products, and as of 2020, only a single product could pass the initial Phase 1 trial but failed during further trials. Yet, their liability-free vaccine product is safe and effective for all after being designed, developed, and produced within a year?

In May 2020, the Trump administration launched Operation Warp Speed to develop a coronavirus vaccine specific to COVID19 by the end of 2020 and deliver 300 million vaccine doses by the end of 2020, which crosses unethical and immoral practices using taxpayer funds to produce brand-new liability-free vaccines within a year. By September 2020, President Trump was telling the public that he was activating the military to help with logistics and delivery of the COVID19 vaccines to help meet the fast pace timeline of his operation. This is a slippery slope when using active duty military for these missions -even discussing it as an option- due to the chances of a tyrannical ruler using the military for other purposes.

Phase 3 COVID19 vaccine trials won't have final reports provided to the FDA until 2025, showing the FDA hasn't officially reviewed the results of Phase 3 human trials even though hundreds of millions of U.S. citizens have already been convinced to take the experimental injections. Pfizer and Moderna's clinical trials excluded individuals with a history of allergies to ingredients found in the vaccines. Yet, the government pushes these vaccines upon everyone without adequately informing the masses to confirm if they have allergies to these ingredients.

We have witnessed the most extensive immoral and unethical human experimentation in the written history of humanity dealing with these COVID19 vaccines. The only mRNA products available today are liability-free injections with no long-term studies to confirm their safety. However, the government and mainstream media still push these products as our only path out of the pandemic, even though coronaviruses are endemic.

Currently, mRNA can only be delivered through injection; however, in January 2021, the journal of Medical Hypotheses published a letter to editors about *Passive inhaled mRNA vaccination for SARS-Cov-2* hypothesizing that future mRNA vaccines could be distributed via aerosol inhalation as a massive and passive immunization effort for at-risk populations (Med Hypotheses. 2021

Jan; 146: 110417.). With the potential aerosol inhalation of vaccines, we will also need to worry about self-spreading and self-disseminating vaccines designed to cause an injected subject to be a carrier who then spreads the "vaccines" to those around them for some time -similar to the shedding of a vaccine-derived live virus.

On July 27th, 2020, the journal Nature Ecology & Evolution published the study *Self-disseminating vaccines to suppress zoonoses*, which discusses the potential benefits of using self-disseminating vaccines to target infectious diseases (Nat Ecol Evol. 2020 Sep;4(9):1168-1173.). With the current round of mRNA vaccines having the ability to self-amplify or self-replicate, it is not a stretch to see mRNA vaccines having official human trials conducted around self-disseminating mRNA vaccines in the future.

If this becomes a reality, it will be a perilously slippery slope since it would be straightforward for the government or various organizations to fly over or inject some to vaccinate entire areas without informed consent. This can't be discounted due to the history of the government conducting non-consenting experiments and attacking large populations with callous disregard for innocent life and rights. Governments, corporations, and organizations may have already started testing this path forward under the guise of our safety and protection. How sure can we be that this isn't the case?

Since the COVID19 vaccines were introduced to the public, we were told that the vaccines would stop transmission of COVID19 and that the vaccines were the only way out of the pandemic. On October 11th, 2022, Pfizer's president of international developed markets, Janine Small, told the EU Parliament that preventing transmissions was never studied in the Pfizer trials for their COVID19 vaccine. This is in contrast to what Pfizer's CEO, Dr. Albert Broula, has told people since they began pushing their vaccine on the general public.

"If they [unvaccinated] don't vaccinate they will become the weak link that will allow this virus [COVID19] to replicate." – Dr. Albert Bourla, *NBC News interview*, September 8th, 2020

"We know that in animals, [there is] significant protection from transferring the virus… We haven't [proven that in] humans yet." – Dr. Albert Bourla, *EPP Group health event*, January 13th, 2021

Plenty of politicians and government officials echoed the narrative that if we got the COVID19 vaccines, we would not be able to transmit COVID19 to others, therefore protecting everyone and society. This, of course, was either direct lies or misinformation being spread. Clinical studies for the COVID19 vaccines didn't test nor focus on protection against infectability or transmissibility.

"We are learning now with recent studies that even if you do get a breakthrough infection when you're vaccinated, the chances of you transmitting it to someone else is exceeding low—so low likelihood of transmission, low likelihood of getting infected. When you do get infected, chances are you are going to be without symptoms. And because of that, that was the accumulating scientific data that promoted the CDC to make that recommendation. That when people are vaccinated, they can feel safe that they are not going to get infected. Whether they are outdoors or indoors, that's the bottom line of that to get people to appreciate. You get vaccinated, and you're really quite safe from getting infected. There will always be breakthrough infections, but given the denominator of people who are vaccinated, that's a very very rare event. So, the bottom line, Chris, it's good news, and in many respects, it really is a big endorsement for why people should be getting vaccinated." – Dr. Anthony Fauci, *MSNBC All In with Chris Hayes interview*, May 17th, 2021

"But again, one last thing. I — we don't talk enough to you about this, I don't think. One last thing that's really important is: We're not in a position where we think that any virus — including the Delta virus, which is much more transmissible and more deadly in terms of non — unvaccinated people — the vi- — the various shots that people are getting now cover that. They're — you're okay. You're not going to — you're not going to get COVID if you have these vaccinations." – President Joseph Biden, *CNN Town Hall with Don Lemon*, July 21st, 2021

If stopping and preventing transmission was the key to stopping COVID19 and ending the pandemic, why did government officials and pharmaceutical corporation executives tell us that the vaccines were the only path forward when preventing transmission had never been studied? How many decided to vaccinate because they thought it would stop transmission and end the pandemic? These are criminal actions and clear signs of propaganda used to generate engineered consent. We shouldn't hold our breath to see anyone answer for the crimes against humanity conducted for profit and potentially other nefarious reasons.

"It's crucial to discuss immunity from infection, because abundant research shows natural immunity conveys excellent protection against covid. One Centers for Disease Control and Prevention study found that vaccinated people who never had covid were at least three times as likely to be infected as unvaccinated people with prior infection. And a Lancet study found that those who were vaccinated but never had covid were four times as likely to have severe illness resulting in hospitalization or death compared to the unvaccinated who recovered from it." – Dr. Leana Wen, *Washington Post Opinion: A compromise on the military covid vaccine mandate*, December 18th, 2022

Dr. Leana Wen is a physician, columnist at The Washington Post, and medical analyst for CNN. She has been a loud proponent and advocated for COVID19 vaccines throughout the pandemic. Here are the two studies that Dr. Wen talks about in the quote above:

- On January 28th, 2022, the CDC published the Morbidity and Mortality Weekly Report (MMWR) study *COVID-19 Cases and Hospitalizations by COVID-19 Vaccination Status and Previous COVID-19 Diagnosis — California and New York, May–November 2021* (MMWR Morb Mortal Wkly Rep. 2022 Jan 28;71(4):125-131.).
- On November 11th, 2022, the journal Lancet Microbe published the study *Protection from previous natural infection compared with mRNA vaccination against SARS-CoV-2 infection and severe COVID-19 in Qatar: a retrospective cohort study* (Lancet Microbe. 2022 Dec;3(12):e944-e955.).

Dr. Robert Malone, one of the few main contributors to mRNA technology for decades with multiple patents focused on DNA and RNA, has been an outspoken opponent of the government's forced push to use these COVID19 mRNA vaccines on the general public. Dr. Malone maintains that his work is fundamentally different from the current mRNA vaccines used for COVID19 since his work focused on natural RNA. In contrast, the COVID19 mRNA vaccines use synthetic RNA. Once Dr. Malone started voicing his concern over the mRNA vaccines, the scientific community quickly turned against him, including having his social media accounts -e.g., Twitter- suspended for providing his professional view on these mRNA vaccines.

On January 6th, 2022, PolitiFact published the hit piece *Who is Robert Malone? Joe Rogan's guest was a vaccine scientist, became an anti-vaccine darling*, which quotes other doctors like Dr. Paul Offit -chair of vaccinology at the University of Pennsylvania's Perelman School of Medicine- who said, "He's [Dr. Malone] a legitimate scientist, or at least was until he started to make these false claims." This is propaganda and is used to censor opposing views which is anti-science. Both sides of a debate should have a voice, with those listening and reading the material presented being allowed to make up their mind about what is or isn't true.

Dr. Malone attempted to bring attention to the fact that the spike proteins produced by the COVID19 mRNA vaccine can freely travel to every organ and spot within the body instead of remaining primarily near the injection site, as claimed. A biodistribution study - a method of tracking where compounds and particles of interest travel in an experimental human or animal subject- conducted by BioNTech and Pfizer (study number: PF-07302048) and released by the Japanese government shows that the COVID19 vaccine spike proteins can get into the blood circulating for multiple days and accumulating in organs and tissues; e.g., liver, ovaries, adrenal glands, spleen, brain, and bone marrow.

On December 16th, 2020, the journal of Nature Neuroscience published a study *The S1 protein of SARS-CoV-2 crosses the blood–brain barrier in mice*, showing injected S1 spike proteins crossed the mice's blood-brain barrier (Nat Neurosci. 2021 Mar;24(3):368-378.). On October 1st, 2022, the journal of Vaccines published the study *A Case Report: Multifocal Necrotizing Encephalitis and Myocarditis after BNT162b2 mRNA Vaccination against COVID-19*, which determined that the vaccine-induced spike proteins were found to have traveled to the brain and heart of a deceased individual who died three weeks after receiving their third COVID19 vaccination (Vaccines (Basel). 2022 Oct 1;10(10):1651.). Dr. Malone has also repeatedly stated that those vaccinated with mRNA COVID19 could shed the spike proteins to others around them.

The spike proteins of COVID19 -the same spike proteins the mRNA vaccines cause our cells to produce- can enter the human blood-brain barrier -confirmed in the Journal of Neurobiology of Disease Temple University study (Neurobiol Dis. 2020

Dec;146:105131.) previously discussed- causing neurological symptoms and brain damage while producing cytotoxic effects. Cytotoxic is defined as "poisonous to cells." Dr. Malone has explained in numerous interviews how the mRNA vaccines are causing antibody-dependent enhancement, which can enhance the COVID19 virus entry and cell replication, intensifying the immune response in future infections and leading to potentially deadly situations.

Famed French virologist Dr. Luc Montagnier -who won the 2008 Nobel Prize in Physiology or Medicine for his discovery of HIV- echoed Dr. Malone, saying that the COVID19 vaccines would lead to antibody-dependent enhancement. One such forthcoming immune response to look out for is an increase in Respiratory Syncytial Virus (RSV) cases -usually mild cold and flu-like symptoms- which would be brought about through immunopathological reactions after vaccination and infections of other coronaviruses. RSV is one of the most common causes of bronchiolitis.

Significant increases in RSV cases were recorded in 2021 and 2022. In September 2022, Moderna announced it had enrolled more than 24,000 participants in its global Phase 3 mRNA RSV vaccine trial (mRNA-1345 – Clinical Trial Identifier: NCT05330975). The trial is testing the new mRNA RSV vaccine with a seasonal flu vaccine and their updated mRNA COVID19 vaccine in adults 50 years or older. There has never been an RSV vaccine approved for use in the U.S. This will be another liability-free product as the U.S. starts to see significant increases in RSV infections. Interestingly, we have seen significant increases in RSV cases since the COVID19 vaccines, and the mRNA RSV vaccine trial started. Is this an example of causing a problem and then providing a solution?

On April 20th, 2012, the journal PLoS One published the study *Immunization with SARS Coronavirus Vaccines Leads to Pulmonary Immunopathology on Challenge with the SARS Virus*, which found that animals who were injected with experimental SARS-CoV traditional vaccines lead to "induced enhanced disease and immunopathology" that caused a reaction in the lungs similar to RSV (PLoS One. 2012;7(4):e35421.). This risk still exists for all of the COVID19 vaccines and could be why we are seeing such high rates of RSV spiking in the U.S. after a year and a half of experimental vaccine injections.

In March 2021, The International Journal of Clinical Practice (IJCP) published the study *Informed consent disclosure to vaccine trial subjects of risk of COVID-19 vaccines worsening clinical disease*, which found that the COVID19 clinical trial protocols and consent forms obscured the non-theoretical risk of making future infections -like COVID19- worse through antibody-dependent enhancement (Int J Clin Pract. 2021 Mar;75(3):e13795.). In September 2021, the journal of Advances in Immunology published the study *Antibody dependent enhancement: Unavoidable problems in vaccine development*, showing how vaccines -including the new COVID19 vaccines- can potentially cause antibody-dependent enhancement making future coronavirus infections a greater risk to a subject's health (Adv Immunol. 2021;151:99-133.).

On May 2nd, 2022, Judicial Watch -an activist group that files FOIA requests and lawsuits against misconduct by government officials- posted that it had received over a thousand pages of biodistribution studies and records from the HHS that found Pfizer and J&J both relied on studies showing that critical components in their vaccines were found outside of the injection site, which we were told that wouldn't happen. This information was made available through a FOIA lawsuit -*Judicial Watch v. U.S. Department of Health and Human Services* (No. 1:21-cv-02418). Pfizer's lipid nanoparticles (LNPs) were found in the adrenal glands, ovaries, spleen, and liver in test animals eight to 48 hours after injection. Judicial Watch also found that J&J didn't submit any biodistribution studies on the spike protein in their application to the FDA.

"Unless we really have a compelling case, no one under age 30 should receive any one of these vaccines." – Dr. Peter McCullough, *Fox News program The Ingraham Angle interview*, July 7th, 2021

Dr. Peter McCullough -a cardiologist and former vice chief of Internal Medicine at Baylor University- has echoed Dr. Malone's concerns around the COVID19 vaccines. Recently, Dr. McCulllough pointed out a study by Helene Banoun -an independent researcher from the French Institute of Health and Medical Research- that focused on mRNA being able to transfer from the vaccinated to the unvaccinated. In 2022, the journal of TMR Infectious Diseases Research published Banoun's study *Current state of knowledge on the excretion of mRNA and spike produced by anti-COVID-19 mRNA vaccines; possibility of contamination of the entourage of those vaccinated by these products*, which explained how mRNA could be excreted from the recently vaccinated to the unvaccinated (Infect Dis Res. 2022;3(4):22.). The study explains that LNPs within the mRNA vaccines, that house the mRNA instructions, are similar to their natural equivalent -extracellular vesicles (EVs)- and that there have been reports and examples of unvaccinated suffering adverse events associated with the COVID19 mRNA vaccines after being around recently vaccinated individuals. It further explains that EVs can be inhaled, passed through sexual intercourse, absorbed through skin contact, and found in breast milk providing a mechanism for mRNA vaccines to self-disseminate -self-spread- to those otherwise unvaccinated. The study -goes against the official narrative- is currently listed as "Being questioned," which means it could be retracted in the future. We know shedding is a real thing. It would seem that there could be mechanisms in place that would allow spike proteins and mRNA-coded instructions to be shed to those near a recipient of an mRNA COVID19 vaccine.

From a religious standpoint -many are against vaccines for various reasons- including but not limited to the use of fetal cell lines of aborted fetuses from the mid-1900s in the research and development, testing, production, or manufacturing phases of vaccines. Both Pfizer and Moderna used fetal cell cultures -HEK293- as a proof of concept to test the efficacy of their mRNA COVID19 vaccines by determining how human cells would receive the mRNA messages to produce the SARS-CoV-2 spike proteins. J&J used aborted fetal cell cultures - PER.C6- to design, develop, test, produce, and manufacture their COVID19 vaccine. Even though these fetal cells were used in the design and development, testing, production, or manufacturing of the COVID19 vaccines, each corporation says that these fetal cells are not in their final COVID19 vaccine products.

On August 5th, 2020, the journal Nature published the study *SARS-CoV-2 mRNA vaccine design enabled by prototype pathogen preparedness*, which confirmed Moderna used HEK293 during testing (Nature. 2020 Oct;586(7830):567-571.). On September 3rd, 2020, the journal of Nature Medicine published the study *Ad26 vaccine protects against SARS-CoV-2 severe clinical disease in hamsters*, which confirmed that the J&J COVID19 vaccine used fetal cell cultures from PER.C6 (Nat Med. 2020 Nov;26(11):1694-1700.). On September 8th, 2020, the preprint server bioRxiv published the study *A prefusion SARS-CoV-2 spike RNA vaccine is highly immunogenic and prevents lung infection in non-human primates*, which confirmed Pfizer used HEK293 during testing (Version 1. bioRxiv. Preprint. 2020 Sep 8.).

Do you remember in January and February 2021 -when the new vaccines were introduced to the general public- many first-hand account reports and rumors started indicating that the mRNA vaccines were changing some women's menstrual cycles after receiving the vaccinations or after being near those who were recently vaccinated? Do you remember the push saying these reports and rumors were made-up fabrications and could not be possible since the vaccines were safe and effective, even though the vaccine trials did not collect data on menstrual health?

In April 2022, the journal of Obstetrics & Gynecology published the study *Association Between Menstrual Cycle Length and Coronavirus Disease 2019 (COVID-19) Vaccination*, which found that the COVID19 vaccines were associated with a change in cycle length (Obstet Gynecol. 2022 Apr 1;139(4):481-489.). This is only one example of the general public being lied to for the strict purpose of increasing vaccinations and forcing compliance.

What incentive do these for-profit billion-dollar pharmaceutical corporations have to research the dangers that come with their liability-free products? It will be years before we learn what these experimental vaccines are doing to those taking them. The more injections someone gets, the more significant the risk of damage they could be causing. If you have already been vaccinated, did you realize that you are part of the largest medical experiment in human history? Are you sure there will be no long-term side effects?

The FDA and CDC started pushing a 2nd or 3rd booster shot for many before the 2022-2023 Cold and Flu season and have begun to approve updated formula vaccines to "fight" against Omnicon subvariants even though we are several subvariants into Omnicon. By the end of 2022, the government started pushing a 3rd and 4th booster on top of the original dose series because of another winter of death and destruction for the unvaccinated. Heading into 2023, the unvaccinated are 2 and 0 against a winter of death and destruction.

On January 11th, 2023, CNN reported in the article *FDA vaccine advisers 'disappointed' and 'angry' that early data about new Covid-19 booster shot wasn't presented for review last year* that some of the FDA vaccine advisers were "disappointed" and "angry" at government scientists and Moderna for not presenting infection data when they voted on licensure approval for Moderna's COVID19 booster vaccine. The infection data showed that the updated boosters were not any more effective against circulating strains than the original series.

I have maintained since early 2020 that the new vaccines would become annually taken vaccines, even though the government swore and promised it would only be the initial one or two-dose series, depending on the product brand. With the constant lies being pushed by the government, why are we still listening to them? At no point in human history has any government or tyrannical ruler had the best interests of the innocent citizens under them at heart.

"The strongest analogy is to medicines. Is there something to worry about with medicines that some of them might have side effects? Do we need safety testing? We're taking things that are genetically modified organisms, and we're injecting them into little kids' arms; we just shoot them right into the vein. So, yeah, I think maybe we should have a safety system where we do trials and test things out." – Bill Gates, *Brussels event around GMO crops*, January 22nd, 2015

On November 2nd, 2021, the BMJ published an in-depth investigation brought on by whistleblowers *Covid-19: Researcher blows the whistle on data integrity issues in Pfizer's vaccine trial*, showing an extreme lack of data integrity around the Pfizer COVID19 vaccine trials, which is a cause for serious questions that need to be asked (BMJ. 2021 Nov 2;375:n2635.). Especially from a corporation that has shown a desire to lie and manipulate data to drive higher profits across the board.

Remember, Pfizer was assessed a criminal fine of $2.3 billion in 2009 by the Justice Department for the largest healthcare fraud in U.S. history, which has now been recouped 20-fold thanks to its COVID19 vaccine. Out of the 153 COVID19 vaccination test sites, only nine were inspected by the FDA. The FDA took Pfizer's COVID19 vaccine application for licensure at face value and did not send it for any independent or secondary review. This was after the previous FDA Commissioner resigned from his post and started working for Pfizer. Where is the guarantee that the data provided by Pfizer, which the FDA didn't want to be released for 75 years, is legitimate without errors and falsified data?

In 2020, Brook Jackson, the BMJ whistleblower, worked for two weeks as a regional director at Ventavia -a privately-owned clinical research company in Texas- that conducted Pfizer's COVID19 vaccination testing. Jackson repeatedly informed her leadership of poor laboratory management, patient safety concerns, and data integrity issues. After making waves about the lack of quality controls, Ventavia fired Jackson. Jackson filed a lawsuit -*United States of America ex rel. Brooks Jackson v. Ventavia Research Group, LLC* (1:21-cv-00008)- against Ventavia and Pfizer alleging that Pfizer and research groups contracted by Pfizer "deliberately withheld crucial information from the United States that calls the safety and efficacy of their vaccine into question" and that these corporations "concealed violations of both their clinical trial protocol and federal regulations, including falsification of clinical trial documents."

The attorney for Jackson said during an interview on May 29th, 2022, that Pfizer had filed a motion to dismiss the lawsuit -regardless of the truth to the allegations- due to the U.S. government endorsing their product -being a co-conspirator- and supplying a $1.95 billion-dollar check to Pfizer for 100 million doses of its COVID19 vaccine. Jackson has claimed to pledge all damages awarded to her to COVID19 vaccine victims.

On March 10th, 2021, the BMJ published *The EMA covid-19 data leak, and what it tells us about mRNA instability*, which is an investigation of leaked documents provided to the BMJ dealing with Pfizer's COVID19 vaccine (BMJ. 2021 Mar 10;372:n627.). The leaked documents came from a cyber hack of the European Medicines Agency (EMA) servers, where 40 megabytes of classified information was taken and released to the dark web. The documents, which the EMA confirmed as being predominantly legitimate, showed that the EMA was worried about the commercial manufacturing process not producing the COVID19 vaccines to the specifications expected. Quality assurance found that the percentage of RNA integrity should have been around 78%. Yet, the commercial product was only at 55%, and the impact of this loss in integrity on safety and efficacy was unknown. These were commercial products going out to market. BMJ reached out to the EMA, Pfizer, and the FDA to determine what level of degraded RNA strains was acceptable but did not receive an answer from anyone.

Since the FDA lost its bid to keep the Pfizer data secret, the FDA started releasing documentation that has now included nine pages worth of potential adverse events caused by the Pfizer COVID19 vaccine. Of course, Pfizer claims that the adverse events "may not have any causal relationship" to their vaccine. May not. Causal relationships are also loosely used as a way to hide the truth. Sophistry is a real thing.

Also, with the release of this information, the FDA redacted a secret proprietary ingredient that constituted roughly 22% of an undiluted vial of Pfizer's COVID19 vaccine. The FDA refused to release this redacted secret ingredient until a formal request was made. ICAN submitted the official FOIA request, which determined that the secret ingredient was water. The FDA hid this information because it was deemed a "trade secret" or "confidential commercial or financial information." This level of secrecy and redaction of necessary data is not only with Pfizer but with Moderna and J&J. Can we trust that Pfizer is not lying and manipulating data for profit? How can we trust the FDA if they were willing to hide water as a trade secret?

At the start of the pandemic government and mainstream media pushed Moderna as the frontrunner being first to market in the U.S. for the first COVID19 vaccine. By the end, Pfizer ended up being the first to market under the EUA and official licensure. The government and mainstream media's push for COVID19 vaccines caused Moderna's and Pfizers' stock valuation to jump significantly, quickly minting several new billionaires in the U.S. Moderna's inflated value was for a corporation with no products on the market before its COVID19 vaccine. Moderna's initial funding came from the international pharmaceutical corporation Merck, the Gates Foundation, and the U.S. Department of Health. The FDA approved Moderna to enter Phase 2 testing after what can be argued as failing Phase 1 testing, which continued to fast-track the corporation's liability-free product to the market. Many politicians in Congress own stock in Moderna and Pfizer, allowing some to make millions off driving the forced use of COVID19 vaccines.

J&J was awarded $456 million from the Trump administration to develop a traditional COVID19 vaccine that contained an inactivated virus -not a live virus- providing another option other than new gene therapy technology that has been the main focus of the government and mainstream media. The promise for J&J's vaccine was that it would only require a single dose, which later turned into needing booster shots as well.

In 2013, J&J was fined more than $2.2 billion for the promotion of using a few prescription drugs in a way that was not approved by the FDA while providing payments as kickbacks to physicians and pharmacy providers for pushing the overuse of a dangerous product. In 2019, a judge ordered J&J to pay $572 million in fines for fueling the opioid epidemic that has ravaged communities around the U.S. and has cost many lives. Being handed half a billion dollars to produce a liability-free product, which would net billions, is a no-brainer for a corporation that doesn't care about the people that use its products. Are you sure you're not at risk for adverse events when taking these products?

"If you take it and then a year goes by and everybody is fine. And then you say, okay that's good, now let's give it to 500 people, and then a year goes by and everything is fine. So well now let's give it to 1000s of people, and then you find out that it takes 12 years for all hell to break loose, and then what have you done." - Dr. Anthony Fauci, *HIV vaccine interview*, February 1999

VAERS Database

"There is abundant science out there that connects mercury exposure in vaccines to not only autism, but to ASD, to SIDS, to ADD, ADHD, language tics - which is like Tourette Syndrome - OCD, asthma, food allergies, and diabetes." – Robert Kennedy, Jr., *unconfirmed source and date*

The Vaccine Adverse Event Reporting System (VAERS) was established in 1990 to track the damages and deaths caused by liability-free vaccines, which the CDC and FDA manage. The VAERS database is the only official government source for tracking vaccine adverse events, so it can't be discounted because it is a voluntary reporting system. Many issues of VAERS have been ignored and left in place by government officials to help discredit the raw data found within it, making it easier to claim that the reports within VAERS are false positive cases or fabrications by those seeking monetary gain. Those who report false claims face penalties and other legal ramifications.

VAERS is estimated to account for fewer than 1% of the actual adverse events. Most reporting is done by healthcare professionals in caring for their patients or families willing to wade their way through a convoluted and confusing system. Still, since most healthcare professionals view vaccines as entirely safe and effective, many never report things they see as they attribute the symptoms to another cause. This less than 1% estimate was determined in the Lazarus investigation *Electronic Support for Public Health–Vaccine Adverse*

Event Reporting System (ESP:VAERS) (Grant ID: R18 HS 017045) with findings submitted to the Agency for Healthcare Research and Quality (AHRQ) U.S. Department of Health and Human Services in 2010.

OpenVAERS project (https://openvaers.com/) is a site that makes searching and viewing the VAERS database easier to navigate. As of November 25th, 2022, there have been 2,368,650 adverse events reported in VAERS, with 1,471,557 adverse events attributed to the COVID19 vaccines (62.1%) in less than two years the COVID19 vaccines have been in the market. There have been 42,189 reported deaths in VAERS, with 32,508 deaths attributed to the COVID19 vaccines (77.1%). There have been 268,888 reported hospitalizations in VAERS, with 184,796 attributed to the COVID19 vaccines (68.7%).

There have been more adverse events in less than two years for reported hospitalizations, deaths, and total counts attributed to COVID19 vaccines than all other vaccines combined -spanning over 30 years. The official reported numbers are only the cases that have been processed and approved to be displayed to the public. There is a significant backlog of cases within VAERS -meaning the actual damage isn't publicly known yet.

Even with the officially reported numbers, these numbers are seriously underreported and should be major red flags for everyone considering continuing to inject these COVID19 vaccines. A recent example of additional medical professionals coming forward and starting to speak out on the potential dangers around the COVID19 vaccines is the December 19th, 2022, report that Dr. Kerryn Phelps - former first female president of the Australian Medical Association- came out detailing the severe neurological reactions that she and her wife experienced due to the COVID19 vaccines and calling out government regulators on why they were censoring discussions around this topic. The risks are real and should be known and taken seriously. There are significant financial incentives for keeping information away from the masses.

If we took the reported numbers as only 10% of actual cases -more than ten times higher than the investigation found was being reported-meaning the COVID19 vaccines could have caused over 300 thousand deaths as a conservative estimate. The European Union has a similar adverse reaction event tracking database called EudraVigilance (https://www.adrreports.eu/). As of October 12th, 2022, EudraVigilance reported 2,155,843 adverse events for the five COVID19 vaccines available in the EU, with Pfizer's COVID19 vaccine having the most significant number of adverse events, which is similar to what is seen in the VAERS database. As shown in a previous chapter, the FDA quickly pulled non-liability-free products off the market after only a handful of reported adverse events and deaths. So why doesn't the FDA pull these potentially dangerous liability-free vaccines?

The restrictions and rollout of the COVID19 vaccines hit senior citizens the hardest. One potential example of propaganda use and what has been happening to senior citizens was when the CDC convinced baseball legend Hank Aaron, on January 5th, 2021, to get his COVID19 vaccination live on camera to help convince the black communities to get vaccinated. Seventeen days later, Hank Aaron had a sudden death, which was later classified as having died from natural causes. Was it due to natural causes?

Everyone thinks the vaccines are safe and effective, so those performing autopsies won't be looking for COVID19 vaccines as a cause or the trigger. Evidence of the contrary won't exist if it is not being looked for. As of October 21st, 2022, there are 10,220 registered reports in VAERS of those 65 and older who have died due to the COVID19 vaccines. How many senior citizens have potentially died from a COVID19 vaccine but due to their age and other potential comorbidities, the cause of death was attributed to something else?

As the governments push for additional boosters, these numbers will continue to climb. The U.S. government and pharmaceutical corporations started making a case for Omicron variant-specific COVID19 vaccines for fall 2022 and beyond. The change in COVID19 vaccine formulas mixing with previous COVID19 vaccines has not been tested and studied en masse as the government assumes that since the first round was "safe and effective," these new versions are "safe and effective." These COVID19 vaccines have become annual injections since COVID19 became endemic, which proves that everything the government told us was lies from the start. Do you trust that there is no risk in continuing these gene therapy injections? When a product is liability-free, what incentive is there to pull it from the market? The FDA has repeatedly confirmed that it is not responsible for pulling items off the market.

The CDC admits that the mRNA vaccines can increase the risk and have seen an increase in reported cases of myocarditis - inflammation of the heart muscle- and pericarditis -inflammation of the lining outside the heart. The CDC suggests reporting all cases of myocarditis and pericarditis after vaccination to the VAERS database, even though they also indicate that the VAERS database can't be trusted. On June 25th, 2021, the FDA added myocarditis and pericarditis warnings to the Pfizer and Moderna COVID19 vaccines but continued to indicate that the risk was very low without quantifying the actual risk.

"The risk of myocarditis and pericarditis appears to be very low given the number of vaccine doses that have been administered. The benefits of COVID-19 vaccination continue to outweigh the risks, given the risk of COVID-19 disease and related, potentially severe, complications." – Janet Woodcock, *Acting FDA Commissioner, Twitter*, June 25th, 2021

On October 18th, 2021, the Journal of Korean Medical Science published the study *Myocarditis-induced Sudden Death after BNT162b2 mRNA COVID-19 Vaccination in Korea: Case Report Focusing on Histopathological Findings*, which focused on and confirmed, a 22-year-old man who died of isolated atrial myocarditis five days after his first dose of the Pfizer COVID19 vaccine (J Korean Med Sci. 2021 Oct 18;36(40):e286.). This case study was the first case where the Korea Disease Control and Prevention Agency (KDCA) officially recognized the causality between COVID19 vaccination and myocarditis, showing how the COVID19 vaccines come with a real risk of death.

On October 7th, 2022, the Florida State Surgeon General, Dr. Joseph A. Ladapo, issued new guidance on the COVID19 mRNA vaccines recommending that males between 18 to 39 not get vaccinated with those products. This was due to the state finding evidence that there was an 84% increase in cardiac-related deaths within 28 days of being vaccinated with COVID19 mRNA vaccines. How many people believe these vaccines are safe and effective and scoff at the idea that they could cause any issues because they are told what to think? There is no such thing as a mild case of myocarditis or pericarditis either. The heart muscle does not repair itself, so if it is damaged, it is damaged for life. Initial damage might not be discovered until a cardiac event occurs, which could happen days, weeks, months, or years after the damage occurs.

Sudden Adult Death Syndrome (SADS) -or Sudden Arrhythmic Death Syndrome- spiked worldwide in 2021 and 2022, so much so that Australia started creating its first SADS registry to track these deaths. The U.S. and other countries have also started seeing a spike in unexplained deaths, classifying them as "excess deaths" that happen suddenly. Watch this term leading into the future as it will be used to cloud the real issue. These deaths are cardiac arrests or other unexplained reasons with no found cause as to why they happened. SADS is similar to SIDS, which has only continued to grow in the

U.S. and other developed countries. Around the world, there has been a massive increase in sudden deaths happening to athletes at all levels and sports -many dying on the field while playing or practicing- or performers conducting a concert on stage.

This global spike in sudden death events is attributed to myocarditis and pericarditis and is being ignored and underreported by mainstream media. Some deaths are being reported as being caused by changes in weather or even the term "happy heart syndrome," which is when someone dies suddenly because of how happy they were at the time. They can happen, but they are not normal events. In November 2021, Israeli Real-Time News (www.rtnews.co.il) reported on an investigation showing a 5-fold increase in sudden cardiac events and unexplained deaths in FIFA players in 2021 compared to previous years.

Towards the end of 2021, nearly 300 professional athletes worldwide collapsed or suffered cardiac arrests on the field or court shortly after taking a COVID19 vaccine, most later dying. In 2021, North American professional sports leagues -e.g., the National Football League (NFL)- started requiring players to undergo cardiac screening to continue playing their profession.

On March 4th, 2021, the journal of JAMA Cardiology published the study *Prevalence of Inflammatory Heart Disease Among Professional Athletes With Prior COVID-19 Infection Who Received Systematic Return-to-Play Cardiac Screening*, which discusses this new screening process (JAMA Cardiol. 2021 Jul 1;6(7):745-752.); however, this study attributes the screening due to previous COVID19 infections even though these professional sports leagues required all professional athletes to be vaccinated and boosted against COVID19. Five athletes out of 789 were confirmed in the study to have myocarditis or pericarditis, causing significant impacts on their careers.

Many videos and local news reports throughout 2021 and 2022 have shown athletes from the high school level to the professional level having sudden deaths on the courts and fields during games and practices -e.g., football, basketball, hockey, golf, tennis, track and field, etc.- showing a concerning trend of individuals having sudden death. There have been more athletes -under 35- in the U.S. who have suffered from cardiac events in 2021 and 2022 than from 1966 to 2020. This is not normal, regardless of how much the government and mainstream media try to push that it is normal. Can these statistics be ignored as not having a causal relationship or correlation to the COVID19 vaccine rollout? We can't afford to continue trusting the government and the narrative that COVID19 vaccines are safe and effective for everyone. There are real risks involved that must be accounted for.

A potential recent example of a professional athlete having a cardiac event during a game is Damar Hamlin -NFL safety for the Buffalo Bills- who had a sudden cardiac event during a Monday night football game on January 2nd, 2023. Hamlin made a routine clean tackle against a wide receiver running a mid-field route -moving less than 20 miles per hour. Hamlin took a hit to his protected and padded chest -a typical collision that is seen dozens of times in all NFL games- wrapped up the wide receiver and rolled the wide receiver over, going with the direction of force and making the tackle. Hamlin then jumps up quickly, motions like he is orienting himself, pauses, locks up, then drops backward, suffering from a cardiac event. Hamlin required CPR and oxygen and had his heart defibrillated on the field before being taken to the hospital. Hamlin suffered a secondary cardiac event while at the hospital. Hamlin was vaccinated and boosted per NFL policy and requirement to play.

"Look, I've never seen anything like it." – Troy Vincent, *NFL executive vice president of football operations, open press call,* January 2nd, 2023

"Well, I can only speak of what it was like to watch tonight because no one's experienced anything like this. [...] It really is unprecedented." – Troy Aikman, *ESPN SportsCenter interview with Scott Van Pelt*, January 2nd, 2023

Mainstream media immediately started to bring cardiologists on to be interviewed to explain that the most likely cause was a very rare injury called commotio cordis -a potential lethal disruption of the heart rhythm by a hit to the chest directly over the heart. Some reports indicate that commotio cordis is an extremely rare event that occurs in 1 in 264 million. Commotio cordis does happen, but it is typically in children who have not fully deployed their chest structure and heart and are hit directly over the heart with a small object -e.g., a baseball or fist- usually going at a speed of over 40 miles per hour. It is even rarer for someone over 20 to have commotio cordis. Over many decades of NFL games, no other player has ever had commotio cordis happen to them; however, those vaccinated have a much higher risk of cardiac events like this -especially during high-adrenaline activities. Could Hamlin have had a 1 in 264 million or higher chance of injury, or is he a picture of vaccine-induced myocarditis events to come caused by the effects of the experimental COVID19 vaccines?

"We are now in a super exciting program where we inject mRNA in people's heart after a heart attack to grow back new blood vessels and re-vascularize the heart." – Stéphane Bancel, CEO of Moderna, *Sky News interview*, January 9th, 2023

In 2022, the sudden deaths of entertainers, celebrities, journalists, government officials, and other prominent people began to occur more than I have ever seen before. One potential example is Raqhid Jevon Render "Lil Keed" -a 24-year-old rapper- who died on May 13th, 2022, after being admitted to a hospital over severe stomach and back pain. It was reported that Lil Keed had been vaccinated after being pressured by family, so rumors started spreading that his death could be due to the COVID19 vaccine he received, which caused many Fact Checkers to label that narrative as misinformation. Seven months after his death, the coroner ruled that Lil Keed died from natural causes due to eosinophilia. Mayo Clinic defines eosinophilia as "a higher than normal level of eosinophils," in which eosinophils are disease-fighting white blood cells.

On November 29th, 2022, the Cleveland Clinic published the article *New Onset Eosinophilic Fasciitis after COVID-19 Infection*, which stated that eosinophilic fasciitis -can be caused by eosinophilia- "has been documented after influenza vaccination and, more recently, has been described after a patient had received the COVID-19 mRNA vaccine." On August 25th, 2021, the Journal of Neurology published a Letter to the Editors *COVID-19 mRNA vaccine induced rhabdomyolysis and fasciitis*, which documented a case where a Moderna COVID19 vaccine caused fasciitis in a patient who complained about muscle pain in her extremities (J Neurol. 2022 Apr;269(4):1774-1775.). Could Lil Keed's death have been caused by the COVID19 vaccine, or was his sudden death a natural cause?

Another potential example is Adam Exton, who died suddenly at 35 years old on December 9th, 2022, with the cause of death not being released publicly at the time of writing this. Exton was Director of Parliamentary Affairs at Health Canada and led the team that directed Canada's response to the COVID19 pandemic and was pro-COVID19 vaccine. Dying suddenly is not a cause of death but a symptom of something. Could Exton be a victim of the COVID19 vaccines, or was it due to something like suicide? Suicides are typically determined quickly, with information being released to the public. Not releasing the cause of death only drives suspicion and theories around his death, especially with his connection to Canada's COVID19 pandemic response.

A final potential example is Grant Wahl -sports journalist and analyst- who died suddenly on December 10th, 2022, of an aortic aneurysm -a rupture or split in the artery wall of the heart- while covering the 2022 FIFA World Cup in Qatar. Wahl was married to Céline R. Gounder -physician and medical journalist specializing in infectious diseases- who graduated from the University of Washington (UW) School of Medicine and has worked as a post-doctoral fellow at Johns Hopkins Bloomberg School of Public Health, Director for Delivery in the Consortium to Respond Effectively to the AIDS/TB Epidemic -funded through the Gates Foundation- and was named on November 9th, 2020, by President Biden as a member of the COVID19 Advisory Board.

Wahl had spent weeks with little sleep and high stress over the covering of the World Cup; then he developed a cold -confirmed not to be COVID19- that lasted longer than ten days and grew into something more severe, requiring him to seek medical help. Doctors provided Wahl antibiotics, and heavy-duty cough syrup for what they suspected was bronchitis. Shortly after receiving medical help, Wahl died suddenly while reporting on a match. Wahl had been a major proponent of the COVID19 vaccines, even stating on Twitter that "if you're unvaccinated at this point, you're asking to be hospitalized or worse." Wahl had been recently arrested in Qatar for wearing a rainbow-colored shirt and had received numerous death threats, which is why his brother, Eric Wahl, claimed that he had been assassinated -plausible- but later retracted this claim. After Wahl's death, two other journalists covering the World Cup also died suddenly.

It is plausible that all three were targeted and assassinated by government actors. At the time of this writing, the cause of death of the other two hadn't been determined. If the three journalists were targeted for assassination, it shows that governments can cause cardiac events in those they are targeting. However, I find Wahl's spouse's connection to some institutions and players around COVID19 and Wahl's outspoken approval of the COVID19 vaccines highly suspicious.

Throughout 2021 and 2022, mainstream media began pushing the narrative that it is normal for children to have cardiac events due to various causes, including climate change, temperature changes, and COVID19, but not the COVID19 vaccines. Suspicious that this narrative is pushed as children were approved for the COVID19 vaccines even though the CDC admits that the COVID19 vaccines have caused heart inflammation in children. Will it be used to hide damages and deaths from the COVID19 vaccines?

On March 4th, 2022, the European Journal of Clinical Investigation published the study *BNT162b2 Vaccine-Associated Myo/Pericarditis in Adolescents: A Stratified Risk-Benefit Analysis*, which found that the risk-benefit analysis "suggests that among 12-17-year-olds, two-dose vaccination was uniformly favourable only in nonimmune girls with a comorbidity," however, "in boys with prior infection and no comorbidities, even one dose carried more risk than benefit according to international estimates" (Eur J Clin Invest. 2022 May; 52(5): e13759.). This study found 253 myocarditis and pericarditis cases, with 230 being male patients, and found that during the Delta and Omicron high hospitalization rates, boys 12 – 15 had 2.8 times higher risk of hospitalization after the second vaccination dose compared to the 120-day COVID19 hospitalization risk and that for boys 16 – 17 without comorbidities had a 6.5 times higher risk to myocarditis or pericarditis than the highest hospitalization risk by COVID19 infection.

"It absolutely is safe to get vaccinated [while breastfeeding]. I would say, if you are thinking about getting vaccinated, there is no bad time to get vaccinated. Get vaccinated while you're thinking about having a baby, before you're thinking about having a baby, while you're pregnant with your baby or after you've delivered your baby. There is no bad time to get vaccinated." - Dr. Rochelle Walensky, *Heidi Murkoff interview*, September 23rd, 2021

The initial COVID19 vaccine trials did not include pregnant women, so anyone saying that COVID19 vaccines were safe and effective, including long-term effects, for pregnant women when the COVID19 vaccines were released to the general public was lying or completely misinformed. There was no way of knowing if these vaccines were safe for pregnant women or their growing fetuses. Yet, many healthcare professionals followed the government's guidance and pushed pregnant women to get vaccinated. Due to this gap in evidence, the government started the V-safe COVID19 Vaccine Pregnancy Registry for pregnant women that received a COVID19 vaccine and wished to participate. This new registry does not report findings to VAERS. This shows that these women are being experimented on while pregnant, with many not realizing this; even though over a hundred thousand pregnant women reported receiving a COVID19 vaccination as of May 2nd, 2022, only 23,779 pregnant women registered in this registry.

Some studies promote using COVID19 vaccines as safe and effective during pregnancy. On September 8th, 2021, the journal JAMA published a study *Spontaneous Abortion Following COVID-19 Vaccination During Pregnancy*, which supported using the COVID19 vaccines during pregnancy (JAMA. 2021 Oct 26;326(16):1629-1631.). However, when the conflicts of interest are viewed, the study's authors received funding from Pfizer and served on Pfizer committees. Can the analysis of studies like these be trusted when Pfizer has a long and documented history of falsifying evidence and lying to the public and government officials?

On September 26th, 2022, the journal JAMA Pediatrics published the study *Detection of Messenger RNA COVID-19 Vaccines in Human Breast Milk*, which showed that mothers could pass on the genetically modified mRNA lipid nanoparticles through breastmilk resulting in exposure to infants to be vaccinated when no studies were showing the safety of giving infants younger than six months of age the COVID19 vaccine (JAMA Pediatr. 2022 Sep 26;e223581.).

On October 4th, 2022, Dr. Drew interviewed Dr. James Thorp, an OBGYN maternal and fetal medicine medical professional with Saint Louis, MO, SSM Health St. Mary's Hospital, who said that he had seen an "off the charts" increase in miscarriages and fetal abnormalities of pregnant women who were vaccinated against COVID19. Yet, the government is still forcing and pushing for anyone and everyone to be vaccinated with a complete disregard for safety.

How many years have pregnant women used Tylenol and ibuprofen, thinking they were "safe and effective" to use? Yet, it has recently been shown that Tylenol has been linked to an increased risk of autism during pregnancy, and more often, ibuprofen is discouraged during pregnancy due to potential adverse events. These medications are orally taken and have a much lower absorption rate than injections. Some types of fish, meats, fruits, and vegetables are suggested to be avoided while pregnant because they could cause miscarriages or other complications. Why should the government and these for-profit pharmaceutical corporations be blindly trusted when things we assume are usually safe when taken orally are not during pregnancy?

As of December 16th, 2022, using the OpenVAERS project, a disturbingly high number of reproductive health reports can be seen. For women, there have been 4,628 miscarriages, 35,460 menstrual disorders, 12,365 vaginal/uterine hemorrhages, and 149 stillbirths reported to VAERS being associated with the COVID19 vaccines. The highest peak of reported miscarriages in VAERS occurred in August and September 2021, when employment mandates and significant pushes occurred to get everyone vaccinated. These numbers look to be a rough 4,000% increase in miscarriages and stillbirths from previous years. Can we afford to discount all of these reports as being fake or misguided? The actual number is significantly underreported too.

OpenVAERS on miscarriages from December 2020 to December 31st, 2022

OpenVAERS on miscarriages/stillbirths by year through January 13th, 2023

Women weren't the only ones to see changes to their reproductive process. Some men also faced issues and difficulties after vaccination. On September 10th, 2022, the journal of Andrology published the study *Covid-19 vaccination BNT162b2 temporarily impairs semen concentration and total motile count among semen donors*, which found that Pfizer's COVID19 vaccine reduced semen donor's sperm concentration by 15.4% and total motile count by 22.1% (Andrology. 2022 Sep;10(6):1016-1022.). By October 21st, 2022, the VAERS database had registered 184 cases of testicular swelling, 17 cases of semen/sperm volume/concentration decrease, and 850 cases of erectile dysfunction. Remember, these are only the cases filed with VAERS -does not reflect the actual counts.

Neurological disorders -like Bell's Palsy and GBS- case counts have also significantly increased since the rollout of the COVID19 vaccines. On May 28th, 2022, The Telegraph published the article *AstraZeneca vaccine may increase risk of serious neurological condition*, by Sarah Knapton -Science Editor- reporting that the AstraZeneca and the J&J vaccines may increase the risk of GBS. As of November 25th, 2022, there have been 16,500 cases of Bell's Palsy and 4,580 cases of GBS reported to VAERS linked to COVID19 vaccines. The below image helps visualize the significant increase in reported cases to VAERS for GBS compared to previous years since the VAERS database started tracking adverse reactions. There is a substantial increase in the risk of developing severe neurological and autoimmune disorders compared to earlier vaccines.

(chart on the next page)

OpenVAERS on GBS through January 13th, 2023

Other autoimmune disorders -like hepatitis- have also been reported to VAERS. Several studies have shown that the COVID19 vaccines can cause hepatitis -with the patients testing negative for the hepatitis virus. In December 2021, the Journal of Autoimmunity published the study *Autoimmune hepatitis after COVID-19 vaccine – more than a coincidence*, which reported on a 65-year-old woman who was diagnosed with autoimmune hepatitis after being given the first dose of the Moderna COVID19 mRNA vaccine (J Autoimmun. 2021 Dec;125:102741.). The patient developed jaundice and choluria five weeks after vaccination. On September 1st, 2022, the Journal of Hepatology published the study *SARS-CoV-2 vaccination can elicit a CD8 T-cell dominant hepatitis*, which found that the Pfizer's BNT162b2 mRNA vaccine could be causing autoimmune liver disease and inflammation; a T-cell dominant immune-mediated hepatitis (J Hepatol. 2022 Sep;77(3):653-659.). These studies show that the COVID19 vaccines are not safe and effective for everyone and come with real risks that are discredited and ignored by those forcing compliance.

Remember, the potential actual counts of these specific adverse events are severely underreported, with many more examples showing the same scenario. Even if a fraction of these reported numbers were true, why would the FDA not pull these products off the market when they have done so with other medications for far fewer reported adverse events? Because vaccines are liability-free products, and there is no incentive to do so. The actual risks of these COVID19 vaccines may never be fully known. Still, it is highly likely that what we have been told from the start -anything labeled a vaccine is "safe and effective" for everyone- is anything but, especially when it comes to brand new types of vaccines -gene therapies- that have never been introduced to the market before. This is only the beginning, as we have yet to see the long-term effects of this largest unethical human experiment ever to be conducted in recorded history.

Blood clots have been another issue that has seen cases significantly increase. Our bodies naturally clot blood when blood vessels are damaged to keep us from bleeding. However, blood clots can become highly dangerous when they aren't needed but form - leading to heart attacks and strokes. Blood clots start to form long strands of fibrin -a fibrous protein involved in clotting- leading to an increase in risk the more significant the fibrin gets. Typically, this fibrin will dissolve and be absorbed by the body, but when it isn't, they require surgery to remove.

In September 2022, it was reported by a local news station in Wauseon, Ohio, that a junior high schooler's football career was officially over after doctors removed six feet' worth of blood clots from his legs. These blood clots were discovered after he started to complain about leg and back pain. Officials have commented, saying the cause of this significant find in blood clots is unknown.

In August 2021, the Journal of Autoimmunity published the study *Blood clots and bleeding events following BNT162b2 and ChAdOx1 nCoV-19 vaccine: An analysis of European data*, which compared the frequency of severe adverse events (SAEs) reported in the EudraVigilance European database between the AstraZeneca and Pfizer COVID19 vaccines focusing on blood clots and thrombocytopenia (J Autoimmun. 2021 Aug;122:102685.). The study found that those who received the AstraZeneca COVID19 vaccine had a higher risk for blood clots than if they took the Pfizer vaccine. On April 13th, 2021, the CDC admitted that the J&J

COVID19 vaccine could cause fatal "rare" blood clots, leading to a brief pause in market production for the J&J COVID19 vaccine.

In August 2022, a newly established journal, the International Journal of Vaccine Theory, Practice, and Research published the study in their second volume *Dark -Field Microscopic Analysis on the Blood of 1,006 Symptomatic Persons After Anti-COVID mRNA Injections from Pfizer/BioNtech or Moderna*, which found that the majority of subjects they sampled who received the mRNA vaccines showed abnormal blood samples months post-injection (IJVTPR, 2(2), 385–444.). These blood samples showed fibrin metallic-like particles, resembling graphene oxide and other metallic compounds, amassing in crystalline and lamellar formations. Since we have been told these mRNA COVID19 vaccine products do not contain graphene, why did these subjects show abnormal blood work? Were the injected products contaminated? Is the study wrong in its findings? Or is something else going on? Remember, we are only told what these mRNA instructions should be doing. How sure are you that additional secretive experimentation has not been occurring?

On July 14th, 2022, Dr. Marty Makary, a surgeon and public policy researcher at Johns Hopkins University, who writes for the Wall Street Journal and Washington Post, announced that the FDA and CDC were suffering significant staff shortages due to low morale caused by the agencies' leadership pushing "bad science" with regards to school closures and masking and vaccination requirements as well as guidance around COVID19. To further deepen the "bad science" decisions, as previously discussed, on October 20th, 2022, the CDC voted 15-0 to add the COVID19 vaccines to the Children's Immunization Schedule for six months and up.

What is the point of pushing these potentially dangerous vaccines on children when they aren't designed to fight against the currently circulating variants? If these vaccines indeed did what we were initially promised they would do -stop COVID19- then they shouldn't be needed for children to attend school leading into the future -

especially when children were at the absolute lowest risk of COVID19 compared to everyone else. The government will continue to move the goalposts requiring additional injections for the foreseeable future. Could these COVID19 vaccines cause a future pandemic targeted at children based on the vaccines being added to the Children's Immunization Schedule?

"The secret language of statistics, so appealing in a fact-minded culture, is employed to sensationalize, inflate, confuse, and oversimplify. Statistical methods and statistical terms are necessary in reporting the mass data of social and economic trends, business conditions, "opinion" polls, the census. But without writers who use the words with honesty and understanding and readers who know what they mean, the result can only be semantic nonsense." – Darrell Huff, *How to Lie with Statistics*, 1954

Alternative Treatments

"Whoever having undertaken to speak or write on Medicine, have first laid down for themselves some hypothesis to their argument, such as hot, or cold, or moist, or dry, or whatever else they choose, (thus reducing their subject within a narrow compass, and supposing only one or two original causes of diseases or of death among mankind,) are all clearly mistaken in much that they say; and this is the more reprehensible as relating to an art which all men avail themselves of on the most important occasions... For there are practitioners, some bad and some far otherwise, which, if there had been no such thing as Medicine, and if nothing had been investigated or found out in it... all would have been equally unskilled and ignorant of it, and everything concerning the sick would have been directed by chance. But now it is not so; for, as in all the other arts, those who practise them differ much from one another in dexterity and knowledge, so is it in like manner with Medicine. Wherefore I have not thought that it stood in need of an empty hypothesis, like those subjects which are occult and dubious... as, for example, with regard to things above us [meteorology, astronomy or astrology] and things below the earth [geology, Hades, antipodes, or outside of the Firmament]; if any one should treat of these and undertake to declare how they are constituted, the reader or hearer could not find out, whether what is delivered be true or false; for there is nothing which can be referred to in order to discover the truth." – Hippocrates, *Ancient Medicine*, translated by Francis Adams, *The Genuine Works of Hippocrates Vol. 1*, 1849

We need to stop using a one-size fits all approach to healthcare. Each person is unique, with different tolerances and allergies to various chemicals and compounds, and each person needs to be treated with this understanding. What might work for some might not work for others and could be catastrophic to their health. With all the allergies people have, why is it ignored that people could be allergic to what is found in vaccines? Why are doctors and medical professionals with different opinions being vilified and having their licenses pulled for speaking out against the use of vaccines? Why are only those in "authority" positions who hold your biases the only ones you view as providing accurate and truthful information?

Confirmation bias is a logical fallacy that is used a lot. A healthy debate should include all sides of a discussion. Science is a process of discovering the truth, and if one side is silenced and censored, then it isn't science but pseudoscience and tyranny. Fact Checkers -used to silence and censor anyone with an opposing view to the government rhetoric- are the initial stages of Thought Police described in George Orwell's book *1984*.

Billions of taxpayer funds have been spent on brand-new unproven gene therapy vaccines when a fraction of that money could have been spent on focusing on non-liability-free products that the FDA had already approved as being safe for human consumption. Why would we not concentrate on approved products that lessen the severity and provide natural immunity? "Follow the money" isn't some crazy crackpot idea that only the deranged spout. There is no limit to what some would do for money and power, and there is no money and power to be made and acquired when the masses understand how to take care of themselves -as the human race has done for our entire history. Relying on big pharma's liability-free products as our only path to health is a fallacy. Products that drive large amounts of adverse events also increase profits for other medications, like heart medication, pushed by these same for-profit pharmaceutical corporations that provide liability-free vaccines.

The EUA that the FDA approved for the COVID19 pandemic states that the FDA "may authorize unapproved medical products or unapproved uses of approved medical products to be used in an emergency to diagnose, treat, or prevent serious or life-threatening diseases ... when certain criteria are met, including there are no adequate, approved, and available alternatives". Based on the government website USA Spending (https://usaspending.gov/), as of September 30th, 2022, $4.5 trillion in taxpayer funds have been spent focusing on the response to COVID19, with none of the funds concentrating on alternatives to vaccines. Most of the funding went to special projects, politicians' net worth -many have tens of to hundreds of millions in net worth- and the pockets of the politically connected. At least 75 politicians, including many Congress members, own stock in the pharmaceutical corporations that produced the COVID19 vaccines. Few, if any, care about conflicts of interest these days. How much relief did the government send you over the past two years? Did it help? Do you feel it was $4.5 trillion worth of help?

Many alternatives were being researched early in 2020 to see how to alleviate the severity of COVID19, with doctors worldwide speaking out about the benefits some other options were producing. The Front Line COVID19 Critical Care (FLCCC) Alliance, a non-profit organization founded in March 2020 by critical care specialists, medical professionals, clinical advisors, and partner organizations from many different medical disciplines, was formed to focus on preventing and treating COVID19. The FLCCC created COVID19 treatment protocols to guide healthcare providers worldwide in dealing with prevention, early treatment, and Long COVID recovery. Each protocol developed by FLCCC includes medicines, vitamins, and minerals like Hydroxychloroquine (HCQ), Ivermectin, N-acetyl cysteine (NAC), vitamin C, vitamin D, Zinc, and Melatonin.

Yet, some of these alternatives were vilified and banned from use so the government could focus everyone on only using the COVID19 vaccines as the path forward. These vaccines should never have been made mandatory, approved under the EUA, nor been forced upon those who did not wish to inject themselves when healthy people had alternatives to these vaccines to keep from catching a disease that is more than likely a manufactured variant of a common cold, which all coronaviruses are common cold viruses.

Hydroxychloroquine

Hydroxychloroquine is an FDA-approved drug that has been used for over 60 years and was developed to treat malaria, but was later found to have immunomodulatory properties -modulation of the immune system- and could treat things like lupus, rheumatoid arthritis, and other inflammatory issues. Billions of doses of hydroxychloroquine have been given over the years, at a current cost of under a dollar per dose when paying in cash and not insurance, and has been significantly studied to treat various diseases with long-term effects studies conducted.

The WHO listed hydroxychloroquine as an Essential Medicine for humanity (*World Health Organization model list of essential medicines: 21st list 2019*). Yet, when COVID19 started to spread - and hydroxychloroquine was suggested as a potentially safe and effective option for protection- many were vilified and censored for spreading "misinformation." President Trump was given hydroxychloroquine as treatment when he contracted COVID19. Yet, it was utterly discouraged from the use by the masses in favor of COVID19 vaccines.

On May 20th, 1993, the Journal of Rheumatology published the study *Selective regulation of cytokine secretion by hydroxychloroquine: inhibition of interleukin 1 alpha (IL-1-alpha) and IL-6 in human monocytes and T cells*, which showed that hydroxychloroquine inhibited the production of IL-1 and IL-6 contributing to anti-inflammatory effects in autoimmune diseases (J Rheumatol. 1993 May;20(5):803-8.).

On August 22nd, 2005, the Virology Journal published the study *Chloroquine is a potent inhibitor of SARS coronavirus infection and spread*, which showed that chloroquine inhibited the SARS-CoV virus in cell culture (Virol J. 2005 Aug 22;2:69).

On April 15th, 2020, the BMJ Postgraduate Medical Journal published the study *Hydroxychloroquine and COVID-19*, which showed how hydroxychloroquine had an effect against COVID19 in vitro by inhibiting IL-1, IL-6, and TNFα and inhibiting COVID19 entry at the ACE2 receptor (Postgraduate Medical Journal 2020;96:550-555.).

In July 2020, the International Journal of Antimicrobial Agents published the study *Hydroxychloroquine and azithromycin as a treatment of COVID-19: results of an open-label non-randomized clinical trial*, which found that hydroxychloroquine paired with azithromycin significantly reduced the COVID19 viral load (Int J Antimicrob Agents. 2020 Jul;56(1):105949.).

On August 24th, 2020, the journal of Current Pharmacology Reports published the study *Hydroxychloroquine in COVID-19: Potential Mechanism of Action Against SARS-CoV-2*, which found that hydroxychloroquine affected the ACE2 binding site and prevented cytokine storms (Curr Pharmacol Rep. 2020;6(5):203-211.).

In November 2020, the journal of New Microbes and New Infections published the study *Hydroxychloroquine is effective, and consistently so when provided early, for COVID-19: a systematic review*, which found that hydroxychloroquine had a consistent clinical efficacy against COVID19 when delivered early during infection (New Microbes New Infect. 2020 Nov;38:100776.).

Each of these studies can be found in the NIH database; before COVID19 vaccines were approved for general public use under the EUA, so the government knew cheap alternate treatments existed for

COVID19 yet still only continued to push and mandate the COVID19 vaccines netting corporations' tens of billions in taxpayer funds and driving massive unethical experimentation on most of the world.

Ivermectin

Ivermectin is an FDA-approved antiparasitic drug -with antiviral properties- that was discovered in 1975 and used in veterinary sciences. In 1987, ivermectin was approved for human applications and use and has grown to treat scabies, head lice, filaria worms, roundworms, whipworms, and some anti-inflammatory diseases and viruses -e.g., pseudorabies virus and Zika virus.

The WHO listed Ivermectin as an Essential Medicine for humanity (*World Health Organization model list of essential medicines: 21st list 2019*). Ivermectin costs a few dollars per dose when paying with cash in the U.S. Do you remember when the mainstream narrative was pushed that ivermectin was only for horses -not for human use- and that only crazy conspiracy theorists advocated its use to fight against COVID19? The FDA still advises against its use to combat COVID19. With billions of doses taken by humans over 30 years, long-term studies have shown its safety profile regarding human consumption.

In November 2008, the journal of Inflammation Research published the study *Ivermectin inhibits LPS-induced production of inflammatory cytokines and improves LPS-induced survival in mice*, which showed how ivermectin significantly inhibited the production of TNFα, IL-1ß and IL-6 in vivo and in vitro (Inflamm Res. 2008 Nov;57(11):524-9.).

In June 2020, the journal of Antiviral Research published the study *The FDA-approved drug ivermectin inhibits the replication of SARS-CoV-2 in vitro*, which found that ivermectin caused a significant reduction of COVID19 viral material within 48 hours (Antiviral Res. 2020 Jun;178:104787.).

On December 2nd, 2020, the International Journal of Infectious Diseases published the study *A five-day course of ivermectin for the treatment of COVID-19 may reduce the duration of illness*, which found that ivermectin was an inhibitor of COVID19 and was effective when provided during early-onset for COVID19 (Int J Infect Dis. 2021 Feb;103:214-216.).

In June 2021, the American Journal of Therapeutics published a study *Ivermectin for Prevention and Treatment of COVID-19 Infection: A Systematic Review, Meta-analysis, and Trial Sequential Analysis to Inform Clinical Guidelines*, which reviewed 15 clinical studies and found that there was a "moderate-certainty" that ivermectin reduced risk of death for COVID19 (Am J Ther. 2021 Jun 21;28(4):e434-e460.).

NAC and Glutathione

N-acetylcysteine (NAC) was developed in 1960 and has been used medically in humans since 1968. NAC is FDA-approved to treat paracetamol -acetaminophen- poisoning and respiratory issues like pneumonia and bronchitis. It has been used in off-label issues like heart disease, cancer, and HIV, and is inexpensive.

The WHO listed NAC as an Essential Medicine for humanity (*World Health Organization model list of essential medicines: 21st list 2019*). NAC works with paracetamol poisonings by increasing glutathione (GSH) levels -an antioxidant in tissues that help prevent damage to cells by mitigating oxidative stress.

On May 28th, 2020, ACS Infectious Diseases published the study *Endogenous Deficiency of Glutathione as the Most Likely Cause of Serious Manifestations and Death in COVID-19 Patients*, which found that moderate and severe cases of COVID19 were associated with low levels of GSH (ACS Infect Dis. 2020 Jul 10;6(7):1558-1562.).

On September 25th, 2020, the journal of Antioxidants published the study *Glutathione Supplementation as an Adjunctive Therapy in COVID-19*, which showed that GSH deficiency was associated with severe COVID19 symptoms, and that administration of liposomal GSH supplementation would be beneficial to high-risk COVID19 patients (Antioxidants. 2020 Sep 25;9(10):914.).

In October 2020, the journal of Clinical Immunology published the study *Therapeutic blockade of inflammation in severe COVID-19 infection with intravenous N-acetylcysteine*, which found that after NAC administration, there was a significant drop in inflammatory markers due to an increase in GSH levels (Clin Immunol. 2020 Oct; 219:108544.).

On March 25th, 2021, the World Journal of Virology published the study *Bottom-up analysis of emergent properties of N-acetylcysteine as an adjuvant therapy for COVID-19*, which found several studies showing that NAC was successful at reducing viral load and replication against influenza A -H3N2 and H5N1- and that NAC can reduce pro-inflammatory cytokines which are produced during a COVID19 infection (World J Virol. 2021 Mar 25;10(2):34-52.).

Vitamins and Minerals

Vitamins and minerals are vital to our survival, immune system, and maintaining our quality of health. Vitamins and minerals are essential organic micronutrients that our cells use to carry out a wide range of functions. Some vitamins and minerals have antioxidant, antimicrobial, and immunomodulatory properties and roles for maintaining a balanced immune system and fighting off viral infections and diseases. Most of the general public in the U.S. are deficient in vitamins and minerals due to the quality of food given in grocery stores, exercise habits, and the general eating habits -e.g., fast food- that have become a staple in diets.

It is no surprise that increasing essential vitamins and minerals during infection can significantly reduce COVID19 symptoms and severity. Depending on the person, the terrain, and what symptoms they have will determine the various combinations of high-dose vitamins that could be needed. Injectable verse oral vitamins have different absorption rates and require quantity amounts for each person. From personal experience, I had witnessed a significant increase in my vitamin C intake -oral- while being sick that, when taken at a fraction of the amount, would have induced lite diarrhea when I was healthy -not ill. Lite diarrhea indicates that the body cannot process the entire amount of vitamin C taken. Monitoring vitamin C absorption levels can be an excellent way to monitor if someone is starting to become sick and how sick they are.

Zinc activates over 300 enzymes that affect digestion, metabolism, nerve function, DNA synthesis, and protein production. On May 2nd, 2017, the Journal of the Royal Society of Medicine published the study *Zinc lozenges and the common cold: a meta-analysis comparing zinc acetate and zinc gluconate, and the role of zinc dosage*, which showed how zinc lozenges could reduce the duration of the common cold -e.g., coronaviruses- from 33% to 45% (JRSM Open. 2017 May 2;8(5):2054270417694291.). In vitro, a zinc deficiency enhances IL-6 and IL-1β production leading to inflammation and cytokine storms.

On November 1st, 2020, the International Journal of Infectious Diseases published the study *COVID-19: Poor outcomes in patients with zinc deficiency*, which showed that roughly 57.4% of COVID19 patients were found to be zinc deficient and that an increase in zinc inhibits the ACE2 keeping the COVID19 spike protein from making an entry (Int J Infect Dis. 2020 Nov;100:343-349.).

On April 2nd, 2020, the journal Nutrients published the study *Evidence that Vitamin D Supplementation Could Reduce Risk of*

Influenza and COVID-19 Infections and Deaths, which found that supplementing with high doses of vitamin D3 reduced the risk of infections and death from acute respiratory infections like COVID19 (Nutrients. 2020 Apr 2;12(4):988.).

On August 27th, 2020, the journal Clinical Infectious Diseases published the study *Reduced Vitamin K Status as a Potentially Modifiable Risk Factor of Severe Coronavirus Disease 2019*, which found that severe hospitalized COVID19 patients had a significant increase in the inactive vitamin K-dependent MGP (dp-ucMGP) correlating to a vitamin K deficiency leading to elastic fiber damage and thrombosis (Clin Infect Dis. 2021 Dec 6;73(11):e4039-e4046.).

On November 16th, 2020, the journal of Molecules published the study *The Role of Vitamin C, Vitamin D, and Selenium in Immune System against COVID-19*, which showed that COVID19 patients with acute respiratory tract infections were deficient in vitamin D and selenium -that vitamin D stimulates the production of antimicrobial peptides and that selenium enhanced cytotoxic effector cells- and that vitamin C increased the survivability rate of COVID19 infections (Molecules. 2020 Nov; 25(22): 5346.).

On December 20th, 2020, the journal of Frontiers in Nutrition published the study *Zinc, Vitamin D and Vitamin C: Perspectives for COVID-19 With a Focus on Physical Tissue Barrier Integrity*, which found that supplementation with vitamin C, vitamin D, and zinc could mitigate respiratory infections (Front Nutr. 2020 Dec 7;7:606398.).

On January 7th, 2021, the journal of Risk Management and Healthcare Policy published the study *Effects of Vitamin D on COVID-19 Infection and Prognosis: A Systematic Review*, which reviewed nine studies and found that 7 (77.8%) of those studies showed a clear correlation between COVID19 infection and mortality rate to vitamin D levels (Risk Manag Healthc Policy. 2021 Jan 7;14:31-38.).

Even though vitamins and minerals are vitally important, it is also essential to know about the potential toxicities of taking supplements over short and long periods. We should only take supplements when we need to and the amount required to get us to a healthy immune system or maintain our healthy immune system. For example, we cannot reach vitamin D toxicity through diet or exposure to the Sun; only possible through supplementation, but we can reach vitamin D toxicity through large doses of vitamin D at a time or constantly over time when we are not vitamin D deficient. Vitamin D toxicity can cause calcium buildup in the blood, leading to weakness, nausea, and vomiting. Zinc toxicity through supplementation is also possible and can drive copper and iron deficiencies, leading to nausea, cramps, vomiting, diarrhea, and flu and cold-like symptoms. It is crucial for each of us to know our bodies and immune systems and adjust each of our needs when determining the amounts of vitamins and minerals we should supplement.

Melatonin

Melatonin, discovered in 1958, is a hormone produced in the brain at night that helps regulate our natural sleep-wake cycle. Melatonin helps regulate our immune system, has anti-inflammatory and antioxidant properties, and is viewed as a free radical scavenger.

On April 22nd, 2013, the journal of International Journal of Molecular Sciences published the study *Melatonin: Buffering the Immune System*, which showed that melatonin could reduce and lower TNFα, IL-1β, and IL-6 production (Int J Mol Sci. 2013 Apr 22;14(4):8638-83.). Our natural melatonin production increases when it becomes dark, peaks in the middle of the night, then decrease to lower levels by morning.

On December 1st, 2007, the journal of Scoliosis and Spinal Disorders published the study *Melatonin the "light of night" in human biology and adolescent idiopathic scoliosis*, which showed how melatonin production fluctuates throughout our daily lives and lifetimes (Scoliosis. 2007 Apr 4;2:6.). Described in figure 4 of the study, melatonin production peaks around seven years of age then begin to drop in peak production around 12 years of age decreasing over time and reaching negligible production levels around 58 years of age and older. The melatonin production levels correlate to why children are significantly less susceptible to COVID19 compared to those reaching the end of their lives.

On April 29th, 2020, the journal of International Reviews of Immunology published the study *Can melatonin reduce the severity of COVID-19 pandemic?*, which showed that melatonin inhibits programmed cell death resulting in lung fibrosis damage caused by coronaviruses, blocks inflammatory signals, and reduces anxiety and sleep deprivation (Int Rev Immunol. 2020;39(4):153-162.).

On June 1st, 2020, the journal of Life Sciences published the study *COVID-19: Melatonin as a potential adjuvant treatment*, which reviewed 22 randomized controlled trials and found that supplemental use of melatonin was associated with a significant reduction of TNFα and IL-6 cytokine levels, and that melatonin may potentially lower COVID19 cytokine levels (Life Sci. 2020 Jun 1;250:117583.).

On June 9th, 2021, the journal of Endocrine Practice published the study *Melatonin for the Early Treatment of COVID-19: A Narrative Review of Current Evidence and Possible Efficacy*, which discussed how melatonin indirectly inhibits COVID19's ability to bind to cells through the ACE2 receptor thereby reducing cytokine-induced inflammation and showing melatonin as an effective treatment for COVID19 even starting on the day of diagnosis (Endocr Pract. 2021 Aug; 27(8): 850–855.).

Cannabis

Cannabis, Cannabis Sativa, has been cultivated for up to ten thousand years and benefits our endocannabinoid system, which plays a significant role in our health, immune system, and cognitive processes. Cannabis has been used to produce a long list of products and has been used as a farming food source until recent history. Livestock was fed cannabis, providing CBDs to individuals through the local food consumed. The founding fathers also grew cannabis viewing it as a vitally important resource based on the products that could be created with it and the health benefits.

In 1937, the U.S. government established the Marihuana Tax Act of 1937, which taxed cannabis sales in the U.S. Few people registered to sell cannabis under the Act. Hence, it became a criminal law that imposed fines and sanctions upon anyone who was not registered. In 1969, Timothy Leary -famed professor and activist- won his U.S. Supreme Court case *Leary v. United States, 395 U.S. 6 (1969)*, proving the Marihuana Tax Act of 1937 was unconstitutional by violating the Fifth Amendment.

U.S. Constitution – Fifth Amendment

"No person shall be held to answer for a capital, or otherwise infamous crime, unless on a presentment or indictment of a grand jury, except in cases arising in the land or naval forces, or in the militia, when in actual service in time of war or public danger; nor shall any person be subject for the same offense to be twice put in jeopardy of life or limb; nor shall be compelled in any criminal case to be a witness against himself, nor be deprived of life, liberty, or property, without due process of law; nor shall private property be taken for public use, without just compensation."

In this instance alone, for 32 years, the government violated the Constitution. Due to the courts finding the 1937 Act unconstitutional,

Congress repealed and replaced it with the Comprehensive Drug Abuse Prevention and Control Act of 1970, which implemented the massively failed Drug War and considered cannabis a Schedule 1 drug making it highly illegal -ruining the lives of millions over the last 50 years and leading to massive social inequity. More people were arrested for cannabis in 2019 than all violent crimes put together, according to FBI statistical data. Over the past decade, legislation changes have led to the decriminalization of cannabis -in some states- making them more available to the general public. Now more and more information and studies have shown how vital cannabis -THC/CBD/Terpenes- is to our health -helping to modulate gene expression and inflammation while protecting against autoinflammatory diseases and cancers.

On January 19th, 2021, the Aging Journal published the study *Fighting the storm: could novel anti-TNFα and anti-IL-6 C. sativa cultivars tame cytokine storm in COVID-19?*, which found that strains of cannabis -the various THC and CBD compounds and the different terpenes in each strain- played a significant role in reducing the effects of cytokines -pro-inflammatory cytokines- of TNFα and some key interleukins like IL-6 (Aging (Albany NY). 2021 Jan 19;13(2):1571-1590.). The study found that some of the strains of cannabis "significantly down-regulated cytokine-cytokine receptor interaction pathway, rheumatoid arthritis pathway, chemokine signaling, Toll-like receptor signaling, JAK-STAT signaling and other pathways involved in inflammation, immunity and autoimmunity, as well as tissue remodeling and fibrosis."

On March 10th, 2021, the preprint server for biology bioRxiv published the study *Cannabidiol Inhibits SARS-CoV-2 Replication and Promotes the Host Innate Immune Response*, which found that CBD inhibited COVID19 from binding to the ACE2 protein and making entry into cells (bioRxiv. 2021 Mar 10;2021.03.10.432967.).

On January 10th, 2022, the Journal of Natural Products published the study *Cannabinoids Block Cellular Entry of SARS-CoV-2 and the*

Emerging Variants, which determined that CBGA and CBDA from extracts of hemp -Cannabis sativa L.- inhibited the COVID19 spike protein from making entry into a cell through the ACE2 protein (J Nat Prod. 2022 Jan 28;85(1):176-184.).

We each have a personal responsibility and fundamental right to learn how to monitor and maintain our health and immune system. When issues arise that are beyond our comprehension and ability to handle, we must seek out professional assistance. We have a right to seek medical assistance, but we do not have a right to receive medical assistance, which is a service requiring the labor and effort of someone else -rights are inherent. However, when seeking assistance, we must be cautious when taking advice and weigh it against the potential of the professionals' intentions and skills.

Medical malpractice accounts for 250 thousand deaths annually in the U.S.; over the years, many doctors and other medical professionals have been arrested for illegally prescribing things like significant quantities of opioids and fentanyl-based sublingual sprays while receiving kickbacks from the pharmaceutical corporations making the products. On top of this, insurance corporations can and do provide financial incentives to pediatricians' offices who achieve a set vaccination percentage for those in their care. It is a slippery slope when the amount a doctor can make depends on how much product they can push onto those in their care.

Can we trust medical professionals who receive kickbacks for pushing unnecessary and potentially dangerous products? Will they do what is the highest benefit to their self-interests when the decision directly affects their pocket? Can we trust medical professionals who push vaccines because if they tried to push a different alternative, they could have their professional licenses suspended, thereby affecting their livelihood?

The system we see today being constructed is a structure of compliance with heavy censorship for those who do not fall in line and speak with the groupthink. Other things work to help combat and fight against COVID19 besides the COVID19 vaccines, and it should be up to each of us to determine what treatment best suits our bodies, lifestyles, and terrain, including the acceptance of seeking out no treatment or help. No form of treatment and medication should be forced unwillingly upon anyone.

"From inability to let well alone; from too much zeal for the new and contempt for what is old; from putting knowledge before wisdom, science before art and cleverness before common sense; from treating patients as cases; and from making the cure of the disease more grievous than the endurance of the same; Good Lord, deliver us." – Sir Robert Hutchison, *British Medical Journal 1: 671*, 1953

Masks

"*Frederick Douglass taught that literacy is the path from slavery to freedom. There are many kinds of slavery and many kinds of freedom, but reading is still the path.*" – Carl Sagan, *The Demon-Haunted World: Science as a Candle in the Dark*, 1995

During the COVID19 pandemic, the government pushed the universal usage of masks -specifically cloth masks- through threats and intimidation to combat COVID19. The government's stated assumption is that anyone could be asymptomatic -still capable of spreading COVID19- so masks were needed to reduce the spittle people produce while in public, thereby reducing the potential infection rate. This guidance and dictation were after months of health officials -like Dr. Fauci- telling everyone not to wear face masks at the start of the COVID19 pandemic. Of course, we have now seen that asymptomatic people are never the drivers of pandemics -was known prior- yet asymptomatic individuals were focused on the most as the reason natural rights needed to be violated.

Cloth and homemade masks were forced on the general public with ferocity and violence while recommending not to use medical-grade N95 respirators or superior protection to help keep supplies of properly rated respirators for healthcare workers' usage. N95 respirators were developed to protect construction workers from dust particles and are only rated for specific things. COVID19 virus particulates are significantly smaller than dust particulates. We were told that "my mask protects you, your mask protects me" (State of

Illinois Department of Public Health flyer - *COVID-19 Protecting Each Other* - May 29th, 2020), with tens to hundreds of thousands of lives on the line that statistically could be saved through universal mask usage.

Models released in April and June 2020 by the UW Institute for Health Metrics and Evaluation (IHME), an independent research institute primarily funded by the Gates Foundation -hundreds of millions of dollars- showed between roughly 19 thousand to 73 thousand COVID19 deaths could be avoided through near-universal -95% or higher- mask usage and social distancing. The Trump administration, Dr. Fauci, and the CDC used these statistical models to form guidelines and policies, leading to mask and distancing rules enforced at the federal, state, and local levels. The models used by the government as actionable intelligence were purely statistical modeling, with many assumptions used to create them.

A problem with some of the studies the CDC and Dr. Fauci use as evidence showing the "effectiveness" of cloth masks is that they fail to address real-world scenarios. On February 19th, 2021, the Morbidity and Mortality Weekly Report (MMWR) published the study *Maximizing Fit for Cloth and Medical Procedure Masks to Improve Performance and Reduce SARS-CoV-2 Transmission and Exposure, 2021*, which found that using cloth masks could reduce aerosol particulates of various sizes, between 0.1 to 7 μm, reducing transmission rates with efficiency depending on adequately fitting the mask (MMWR Morb Mortal Wkly Rep 2021;70:254–257.).

The study indicates that we need to wear a mask fitter over a surgical mask -different from a cloth mask- to "potentially" increase protection to >= 90% for aerosols ranging in size from 7 μm or less. This study highlights that cloth masks are not PPE. The study looked at microns from 0.1 to 7 μm in size -COVID19 is between .06 to .14 μm. By looking at microns up to 7 μm, the study statistically skews the results in favor of mask usage since COVID19 isn't even close to being that large in size, nor does the study account for the particulates smaller than 0.1 μm. If the study changed the range to 1 μm or less, the statistical models displaying the effectiveness would significantly drop -indicating that masks do not work as promised.

Additionally, using a headform and mannequin in a laboratory setting to simulate a person coughing doesn't consider things like how people move around, turn their heads, adjust their masks, contaminate masks by touching them, breathe in those contaminates, how often the masks are replaced, how the masks are fitted over different subjects, how subjects can be infected through the eyes, and the different airflows and pressure in each contaminated environment.

These laboratory-based experiments do not reflect real-world situations and fail to provide sound evidence of the effectiveness of masks that are not rated to offer protection against COVID19. Yet, government and mainstream media focus on these studies as a "gold standard" in how studies should be conducted, but only because the studies confirm the official narrative. Any information or study that goes against the official narrative is called pseudoscience. This pseudoscience term is a fallacious ad hominem used to target and censor opposing views and information.

" 'Pseudoscience' is an empty category, a term of abuse, and there is nothing that necessarily links those dubbed pseudoscientists besides their separate alienation from science at the hands of the establishment." – Michael D. Gordin, The Pseudoscience Wars: Immanuel Velikovsky and the Birth of the Modern Fringe, 2012

Math isn't science; science is a process. Math is a tool to be used when conducting scientific experiments, but there still needs to be objective empirical evidence to go with the math. Statistical correlation does not always correlate to real-world scenarios - correlation versus causation. How much truth is behind the idea that cloth and homemade mask usage plays a critical role in combating

COVID19? Being forced to protect others violates our natural rights since that is not how natural rights and liberties work -rights are inherent in each of us. Since we are responsible for our health, shouldn't we wear something that protects us?

Our lungs form part of the excretory system and function by pulling clean oxygen into our bodies and dispelling CO_2 that builds up in our system. When we breathe without a mask, we generally breathe roughly 460 parts per million (ppm) of CO_2. The American Conference of Governmental Industrial Hygienists (ACGIH) recommends and sets an occupational exposure limit for CO_2 at 5,000 ppm. When 1,000 ppm of CO_2 concentration is reached, symptoms that form can be decreased mental performance and Sick Building Syndrome Complaints (SBS), which is a condition where someone develops symptoms of illnesses and can be infected with a chronic respiratory disease. Acidosis can form at 7,000 ppm of CO_2 concentration, which increases the acidity in our bodies that can cause headaches, exhaustion, confusion, weakness, tremors, and decreased cognitive function -that, when left untreated, can result in a coma or death.

On September 15th, 2022, the journal of Environmental Health Insights published the study *Inhaled CO2 Concentration While Wearing Face Masks: A Pilot Study Using Capnograph*, which found that when subjects between 10 to 90 years old wore a surgical mask -loose-fitting single-use disposable device- or FFP2 respirator for 5 minutes while seated for 10 minutes of rest, the CO_2 concentrations levels significantly increased between 4379 ± 978 ppm to $13\,665 \pm 3655$ ppm depending on age and health status (Environmental Health Insights. 2022;16.). Children had significantly higher levels of CO_2 concentration that were breathed in compared to adults and the elderly. The study found that higher respiratory rates resulted in higher CO_2 concentrations breathed in. Long COVID -post-COVID19 syndrome- come with symptoms of headaches, shortness of breath, exhaustion, weakness, and cognitive dysfunction, which is very similar to the effects of inhaling higher concentrations of CO2 for prolonged periods.

I am not saying everyone who has Long COVID is due to wearing masks all the time, but some who have had it were constantly wearing masks because they were told it would protect them -which drove their symptoms, not COVID19.

"Breathing is really a very complex activity. It does not only consist of taking in air, absorbing oxygen from it and letting it out again as carbonic acid gas! The breathing has a tremendous effect on the character, determining the mood, courage, strength of purpose, health and inspiration from day to day." – Vera Stanley Alder, *Humanity Comes of Age, A study of Individual and World Fulfillment*, 1950

We should not be breathing in what we exhale; that is not how we evolved to function. Doing so can lead to an increased risk of respiratory infections -like Pneumonia and RSV. If we use a mask when we exhale or cough, the large respiratory droplets get caught, contaminating the mask we breathe in -with small respiratory aerosol droplets passing through effortlessly.

In March 2018, the Journal of Aerosol Science published the study *Bacterial pathogens were detected from human exhaled breath using a novel protocol*, which found that 36.2% of the recruited subjects who had respiratory tract infections, and flu symptoms, had their exhaled breath tested positive for Methicillin-resistant Staphylococcus aureus (MRSA), Escherichia coli, Haemophilus influenzae, Pseudomonas aeruginosa, Stenotrophomonas maltophilia, and Staphylococcus aureus (J Aerosol Sci. 2018 Mar;117:224-234.). These bacterial pathogen particulates ranged in size between 0.5 and 1 μm -all significantly larger than COVID19- in which humans can emit millions of aerosol particles each minute. We can breathe in up to one million microorganisms each day -depending on the environments we spend our time. This is why it is crucial to protect ourselves using properly rated and properly used equipment for the activity and issue we are trying to address.

Small respiratory aerosol droplets spread by symptomatic individuals -the real driver of pandemics- pass easily through cloth and surgical masks, especially when improperly fitted, causing the contamination of the environments around the symptomatic individual. Remember, COVID19 has a size of .06 to .14 μm. To measure a mask or respirator's efficiency in filtering out particles, bacteria, and viruses, three tests can be conducted: Particle Filtration Efficiency (PFE), Bacteria Filtration Efficiency (BFE), and Viral Filtration Efficiency (VFE).

Surgical mask BFE standards for the U.S. is rated for particle sizes of 3.0 μm -roughly 20 times larger than COVID19. Surgical masks - regulated under 21 CFR 878.4040- are designed to filter large respiratory droplets, splashes, or splatter that could contain viruses or bacteria -COVID19 spreads through small respiratory droplets. This is discussing FDA-cleared surgical masks -intended to be worn while in an operating room during surgical procedures- which are not the ordinary surgical masks handed out in stores. The efficiency of masks and respirators depends on properly fitting over a subject and the rated material being used. Most do not wear masks correctly to achieve any proper fit -they can't be fit-tested. Cloth masks are significantly less effective than FDA-cleared surgical masks - possibly do more harm than good.

As we touch surfaces and adjust our masks, we contaminate the masks because every place we go should be considered a contaminated environment. This is why we are told not to touch or adjust the mask once worn. Once a mask has been contaminated, we breathe in everything being caught in the mask, increasing infection rates. It gets even worse when masks are not replaced every 45 minutes to an hour of use. We should always assume all environments are contaminated unless we are in a clean room designated as sterile, which takes significant effort to keep sterile. This is not happening in our homes, vehicles, or stores we shop in. Protecting ourselves protects society, so we must wear proper PPE to protect ourselves, or we could potentially do more harm than good -the opposite of the stated goal of wearing masks. Why are surgical masks used in contaminated environments when they are not rated for this general use? In contaminated environments, any potential benefit from surgical masks is significantly reduced and requires changing the masks in shorter intervals.

When looking at large datasets, studies have shown no statistical evidence that surgical masks reduce infection rates during surgical operations. Some studies have shown that when taken in smaller datasets, there is a slight decrease in infection rates. Still, the statistical advantage goes away as more data is collected, indicating that the reduced infection rates might only be a correlation instead of causation.

On April 29th, 2016, the Cochrane Database of Systematic Reviews published the study *Disposable surgical face masks for preventing surgical wound infection in clean surgery*, which found that there was no statistically significant difference in infection rates between groups using disposable surgical masks and those not wearing masks during surgery dealing with open wounds (Cochrane Database Syst Rev. 2016 Apr 26;4(4):CD002929.).

On April 22nd, 2015, the BMJ Open published the study *A cluster randomised trial of cloth masks compared with medical masks in healthcare workers*, which found that cloth masks were significantly less effective at combating Influenza and other respiratory viruses than medical surgical masks and standard operating procedures, which included using surgical masks and non-mask use (BMJ Open. 2015 Apr 22;5(4):e006577.). The study found that cloth masks possibly increased infection rates due to cloth mask reuse, poor cloth mask cleaning -viruses could survive on the surface of the facemask- and increased moisture retention leading to respiratory infection. It also found no significant difference between medical mask usage and the control standard practice, which led the authors to recommend that healthcare workers not use cloth masks.

Cloth masks offer significantly lower "protection" than surgical masks in all laboratory studies and simulations. On May 5th, 2020, the BMJ journal of Global Health published the study *Facial protection for healthcare workers during pandemics: a scoping review*, which found that alternative forms of facial protection offered insufficient protection compared to medical-grade PPE, like N95 or higher-rated respirators (BMJ Glob Health. 2020 May;5(5):e002553.). On November 20th, 2020, the Cochrane Database of Systematic Reviews published the study *Physical interventions to interrupt or reduce the spread of respiratory viruses*, which found that wearing no mask, compared to wearing a mask, made little to no difference in the outcome of laboratory-confirmed influenza, and that viral infection was not reduced with mask usage (Cochrane Database Syst Rev. 2020 Nov 20;11(11):CD006207.).

When wearing masks, how often do you replace them? How often do you touch your mask? How often do you clean your mask? Are you sure your mask is working as promised? Where are all the store biohazard bins to dispose of used single-use masks that have been contaminated? We are talking about a highly contagious, deadly disease, correct?

Millions of single-use cloth and surgical masks clog waterways, beaches, and oceans -leading to environmental disasters. This waste will only grow as governments continue to require mask usage or when the next pandemic starts and the mask restrictions start again. The Global Disposable Face Masks market has increased in value by hundreds of millions. The market is projected to increase significantly in demand and profitability over the next few years. The majority of masks provided by stores were manufactured in China. Can they be trusted to provide protection? Why are proper controls dealing with infectious agents -established for decades- not followed in stores and the general public? If control measures are not followed correctly, infection rates increase.

Next time you are in a store handing out surgical masks for COVID19, look at the product box and instructions. You'll most likely see that the product instructions specifically state that the surgical masks do not offer protection for or against COVID19. Now, look at how those masks are being handed out. Is the employee touching it before handing it to you? Are the masks sitting out open in the contaminated environment? Why would you keep wearing masks when they do nothing to help you or others from catching COVID19? If masks don't help, what is the real purpose of the government forcing people and businesses to wear them under the threat of violence and intimidation? If a business didn't listen to and enforce government dictation, its license was threatened with revocation. The business would be forcibly shut down, with the owner arrested for defying tyranny. Being forced to wear a mask is not about our safety or the safety of others around us. It is about compliance and breaking the masses' will, making them easier to manipulate and control.

"There's no reason to be walking around with a mask. When you're in the middle of an outbreak, wearing a mask might make people feel a little bit better and it might even block a droplet, but it's not providing the perfect protection that people think that it is. And, often, there are unintended consequences — people keep fiddling with the mask and they keep touching their face." – Dr. Anthony Fauci, *60 Minutes interview*, March 8th, 2020

Dr. Fauci began the pandemic by following industry standards and proper scientific studies, saying masking up was neither needed nor beneficial, but he quickly changed his viewpoint. A few months into the pandemic, Dr. Fauci started to push universal mask use after George Gao -Director of the Chinese Center for Disease Control and

Prevention- said everyone in the West needed masks and to stay masked. At this point, the WHO even changed its tune and started pushing mask use. The insanity even grew to require people to wear up to three masks at a time. Interestingly, when you see how the politicians who pushed mask use were socializing in private -they never wore masks. Yet, politicians still required children to wear masks around them during photo ops when they were maskless. This is a mass psychosis tactic -keeping people in fear- and it was wildly successful.

Industrial hygienists are Subject Matter Experts (SMEs) capable of assessing physical, chemical, environmental, and biological hazards within a workplace and environment that could lead to workplace injury, illness, or death. They are specialists in appropriate control mechanisms -administrative controls- and PPE. PPE is protective clothing, goggles, respirators, and other items worn and used by individuals to protect themselves in dangerous and contaminated environments. Each PPE item is rated for various levels of protection. Not all items can protect against everything. All environments are considered contaminated and treated as such unless it has been sterilized through appropriate control measures. Industrial Hygienists are those individuals who should be the go-to experts that help set policies and procedures for protection against things like COVID19.

Why are some industrial hygienists SMEs being ignored and vilified when they speak out against using masks for COVID19? Why should we trust career politicians and other government officials who are constantly lying and have incentives to lie?

Dr. Stephen Petty is one such SME in the industrial hygiene field who has been censored during the COVID19 pandemic. He holds nine U.S. patents and has written a book *Forensics Engineering: Damage Assessments for Residential and Commercial Structures 2ⁿᵈ Edition*. Dr. Petty has been deposed nearly 100 times and has given court testimony in roughly 20 trials. His testimony and expertise were critical in having a Kentucky Judge invalidate Kentucky Governor Bashear's State of Emergency Actions in June 2021 for private schools. Dr. Petty also testified before the Senate Committee in defense of a New Hampshire bill (HB1131) that prohibited school boards and accredited nonpublic schools from requiring students or members of the public to wear facial coverings -passed by legislators but then vetoed by New Hampshire Governor Chris Sununu.

Hierarchy of Controls is used to minimize exposure and infections, with PPE being the least effective option to reduce and control diseases and viruses such as COVID19. In March 2021, Dr. Petty discussed PPE, aerosols, and how to control exposures through proper industry standards. The video of this discussion has been continuously removed from YouTube for violating community guidelines because it went against the narrative that cloth or surgical masks worked -censorship at work. Dr. Petty has repeatedly explained that respirators are PPE, not masks. Masks have never been respirators or PPE because they offer no protection and are not medically rated.

PPE stands for Personal Protective Equipment, not Protect Everyone Else Equipment (PEEE). Masks are PEEE -pun intended- and should be treated as such regarding COVID19 in the general public. If the item we wear is not protecting us, then it is not PPE -by definition and acronym. If we protect ourselves, we protect society at large since we are protected. Even OSHA -has strict requirements for respira guidance on masks or mask usage. On June 17th, 2020, OSHA issued a Frequently Asked Questions (FAQ) page explaining that cloth and surgical masks are not PPE. Even if masks somehow worked as promised, they would be ineffective when worn by those with facial hair, yet the government and those pushing mask use ignore this information.

"We should be keeping the events that are safe and also the events that have fun for people too. We can't be canceling everything --

especially if we are going to be living with COVID for the foreseeable future. I would say if you choose to go, make sure that you are vaccinated and boosted. Make sure that you are wearing a mask even though it's outdoors. If there are lots of people packed around you, wear a three ply surgical mask. Don't wear a cloth mask. Cloth masks are little more than facial decorations. There is no place for them in light of omicron. And so wear a high quality mask, at least a three ply surgical mask, and if you are going to be visiting elderly relatives or immunocompromised people after, wait three days, get tested and then see those vulnerable people. " – Dr. Leana Wen, *CNN interview*, December 21st, 2021

We are not a risk to society and others if we are not sick and symptomatic. If we are a risk to others because we are sick, it is their responsibility to protect themselves. This doesn't mean we can purposely intend to infect others and follow through with that act against their wishes. We must take precautions to protect ourselves, not others. Not following proper PPE and industry standards can and will increase infection rates. This has been the industry standard for decades and has proven true through many studies. It is not upon others to protect us and look out for our health, except someone's job -e.g., the doctor in an ER that we are taken to or a parental figure over their children. Government is not and should never be considered a parental figure. We all need to learn the risks we might encounter throughout life and how to accept and manage those risks.

"A monotonous life, lived without any purpose or direction, is not worth much. To achieve anything big in life, you should be prepared to risk your all and take a leap of faith for whatever they believed in." – Deendayal Upadhyaya, *quoted from L.K. Advani, My Country My Life*, 2008

Timeline

"Since I entered politics, I have chiefly had men's views confided to me privately. Some of the biggest men in the United States, in the field of commerce and manufacture are afraid of somebody, are afraid of something. They know that there is a power somewhere so organized, so subtle, so watchful, so interlocked, so complete, so pervasive, that they better not speak above their breath when they speak in condemnation of it." – Woodrow Wilson, *The New Freedom*, 1913

In the early 1900s, John D. Rockefeller was hated by many of his workers and people of the public for how he ran his businesses and treated people -becoming a significant public relations issue. His business practices led to antitrust lawsuits, breaking his company Standard Oil into 34 separate entities that he still maintained control over. This turned out to be a great way to combat this negative view. Rockefeller rebranded himself into a philanthropist, took control of medical schools, and worked to take over the medical and medicine industry.

Rockefeller founded the University of Chicago, the Rockefeller University -formally the Rockefeller Institute for Medical Research- and the Rockefeller Foundation. Non-profit foundations do not pay taxes, which is lucrative for those with hundreds of millions to billions in wealth. Rockefeller pushed to create the Federal Reserve System while helping implement a national tax on income. During the 1920s through 1939, the Rockefeller Foundation significantly supported and established eugenic programs and institutions in Germany and Austria. Eugenics is about creating a master race of pure blood through selective breeding or destroying other bloodlines. Gates and Mark Zuckerburg have modeled their business methodologies and philanthropy efforts after Rockefeller.

Bill Gates -William Henry Gates III- is an entrepreneur, businessman, and philanthropist who used technological innovations and aggressive business tactics to help found Microsoft. This now trillion-dollar corporation has deep contracts worth billions in annual revenue with multiple governments worldwide. Gates has expanded his control into many different industries since going through Microsoft's antitrust lawsuit -U.S. Court of Appeals for the District of Columbia Circuit *U.S. v. Microsoft Corp.*, 253 F.3d 34 (D.C. Cir. 2001).

Like Rockefeller, Gates was hated by many for his ruthless business practices until he rebranded himself as a philanthropist investing in healthcare, food production, and farming industries. Gates openly said that getting into the healthcare industry was his best investment. Since its founding, the Gates Foundation has invested in hundreds of businesses, corporations, projects, and initiatives. Roughly $10 billion have been given to four main groups: GAVI, the Global Fund to Fight AIDS, Tuberculosis and Malaria, and the Global Polio Eradication Initiative.

"It's been $100 billion overall that the world has put in (to global health organizations aimed at increasing access to vaccines). Our foundation (Gates Foundation) has a bit more than $10 billion. We feel there's been over a 20-to-1 return. So, if just you look at the economic benefits, that's a pretty strong number compared to anything else." – Bill Gates, *CNBC interview on "Squawk Box" from the WEF in Davos, Switzerland*, January 23rd, 2019

Gates was born to William H. Gates Sr. and Mary Maxwell. Gates Sr., a lawyer in Washington State, served on the board of Planned Parenthood and the Gates Foundation and as director for Costco Wholesale. Planned Parenthood was started in 1916 by Margaret Sanger, a vocal eugenics enthusiast. The Nazis learned about unethical programs -like the Negro Project- that were advocated by Sanger and, in turn, used them against the Jews. I bring this up because it sets a theme that has followed Gates. Gates' mother, Maxwell, was the first woman to sit on the First Interstate Bank of Washington's board of directors. Her father, James Willard Maxwell, was president of the National City bank in Seattle and a branch director of the Federal Reserve Bank of San Francisco. Maxwell worked with the CEO of IBM on the bank's board and, through that connection, got IBM to hire Microsoft to build an operating system for IBM's first personal computer.

Gates never finished college and dropped out of Harvard University -a focal point for recruitment into the CIA- to focus on computer software which led to a successful career -even though he was a ruthless schemer and manipulator. Gates is not a doctor nor a medical professional, yet his name keeps showing up everywhere, dealing with the health of others. Senator Lindsey Graham even said that he would "double" the funding to the WHO if Gates was put in charge of it, even though nothing qualifies Gates for the position except that Gates is a household name with significant resources.

Bill and Melinda Gates started the William H. Gates Foundation in 1994, focusing on education, world health, and investment in low-income communities worldwide. After Gates studied Andrew Carnegie and John D. Rockefeller -robber barons known for ruthless and unethical business tactics- Gates said that he realized he had an obligation to give his wealth to charity. By 2000, Gates combined several family foundations -totaling a $28 billion-dollar contribution- and started the Bill and Melinda Gates Foundation. In June 2010, Gates and Warren Buffett founded The Giving Pledge, a non-profit organization to recruit billionaires to join the campaign and pledge to give away the majority of their wealth for philanthropic causes while alive or when they die. Prominent pledges include Elon Musk, Mark Zuckerberg, David Rockefeller, Ted Turner, and George Lucas. This effort currently has over 150 individuals and couples who have pledged to the cause.

"I think that some decisions that we made early on to localize the website and keep it separate for each college on the network kept it really useful, because people could only see people from their local college and friends outside. That made it so people were comfortable sharing information that they probably wouldn't otherwise, which made it useful in the long term for people to look up information about other people on the site." – Mark Zuckerberg, *Bambi Francisco interview*, 2005

Mark Zuckerberg is an entrepreneur, businessman, and philanthropist who co-founded Facebook on February 4th, 2004. Zuckerberg had been attending Harvard University but dropped out to finish developing the Facebook project. In mid-2003, DARPA started soliciting for the creation of a "LifeLog" program that would create "an ontology-based (sub)system that captures, stores, and makes accessible the flow of one person's experience in and interactions with the world in order to support a broad spectrum of associates/assistants and other system capabilities" which traced an individual's life by focusing on "data capture and storage, representation and abstraction, and data access and user interface" (DARPA BAA # 03-30). On February 3rd, 2004 -the day before Facebook was founded- the solicitation was officially canceled due to privacy concerns. Coincidence or could the concept or some prototype developmental work have been provided to Zuckerberg -a potential CIA or intelligence asset- to provide the government an avenue to data mine users without drawing attention to the violation of privacy?

Facebook (Meta) is currently worth hundreds of billions of dollars. Zuckerberg is another individual who is hated by many for his ruthless business tactics. Over the last decade, Zuckerberg has focused on expanding his philanthropic efforts to help combat this negative view of him. Zuckerberg has had to testify before congress on several occasions for data breaches and his role in dealing with Fact Checkers and censorship on his platforms. In January 2017, Zuckerberg filed eight lawsuits against hundreds of native landowners in Hawaii to acquire small parcels of land the natives owned, around the 700 acres of land Zuckerberg had purchased in 2014. This bid would have forced families off their property and provided them with a "fair share" market value. The government does this with Eminent Domain and rarely benefits those families who do not wish to move. This push to acquire native land failed.

Zuckerberg has repeatedly said that Gates was a hero to him while growing up and that he views Gates as a mentor and inspiration. Zuckerberg followed in Gates' footsteps and got involved with vaccine research and the health of others. In December 2015, Mark and Chang Zuckerberg formed the Chan Zuckerberg Initiative (CZI), an LLC that focuses on technological innovations around infectious diseases. In 2016, CZI gave $600 million to create the tax-exempt non-profit Chan Zuckerberg Biohub (CZ Biohub). This independent medical research organization boosts collaboration between Sandford University, US Berkeley, and UC San Francisco. Over the years since the formation, both CZI and CZ Biohub have partnered with the Gates Foundation to research and investigate detecting novel and emerging pathogens and launching an analytical platform for the surveillance of infectious diseases. In September 2018, Zuckerberg said he was committed to selling roughly $13 billion in Facebook stock to help continue funding CZI.

"The world today has 6.8 billion people. That's headed up to about 9 billion. Now, if we do a really great job on new vaccines, health care, reproductive health services, we could lower that by perhaps 10 or 15 percent. But there we see an increase of about 1.3." – Bill Gates, *TED2010 speech on innovating to zero carbon emissions globally by 2050*, February 18th, 2010

Timeline

The below list of information is a timeline of what I believe are important events that have led us to our current situation and will play a role in the future of tyranny we will witness and experience. The majority of this information was discussed throughout the book, but some additions were not discussed prior:

- On February 3rd, 1913, the Sixteenth Amendment of the U.S. Constitution was ratified, granting the government power to implement a Federal Income Tax on all U.S. citizens. This was a significant turning point for the U.S. that has helped lead the U.S. to worldwide imperialism and the tyrannical push we are witnessing today.

U.S. Constitution – Sixteenth Amendment
"The Congress shall have power to lay and collect taxes on incomes, from whatever source derived, without apportionment among the several states, and without regard to any census or enumeration."

- On December 23rd, 1913, the Federal Reserve System was enacted by the Federal Reserve Act after the manufactured financial crisis and panic of 1907, which caused the push for centralized control of the U.S. monetary system and supply. A group of private banks runs the Federal Reserve System; it is not a federal agency. Federal income taxes go to paying interest charged by the Federal Reserve System.

- On December 10th, 1974, the National Security Study Memorandum (NSSM) 200, also called the Kissinger Report, laid out guidelines and policies for the U.S. to adhere to reduce the world's population growth. This plan focused on dozens of third-world countries using the withholding of food, forced sterilizations, military force to curb population growth, and implementation of economic warfare to force population control policies.
- On March 22nd, 1980, the Georgia Guidestones were erected and opened for public viewing. The Georgia Guidestones was a granite monument sometimes referred to as an American version of Stonehenge with many astronomic features. The monument was ordered to be built by an anonymous group that cost $100 thousand in 1980 -it outlined in eight different languages- how humanity could balance with nature, provide a structure of governance, establish a one-world government, and population and reproduction control. The first inscription read, "Maintain humanity under 500,000,000 in perpetual balance with nature."
- On December 12th, 1980, the U.S. government passed the Bayh-Dole Act, allowing individuals to retain ownership of inventions and patents created using federal government-funded research. This allows some to receive royalties if their patents and inventions are used. E.g., Vaccine patents used by pharmaceutical corporations.
- On November 14th, 1986, the U.S. government passed the NCVIA, shielding for-profit pharmaceutical corporations by making all vaccines liability-free.
- In 2000, GAVI was created to bring together the WHO, UNICEF, the World Bank, and the Gates Foundation to focus on bringing vaccines to underdeveloped communities and poor societies worldwide.

- In 2002, the Gates Foundation bought a stake in Pfizer to expand access to the corporation's all-in-one injectable contraceptive - Sayana Press- to women in developing countries.
- In 2003, the Human Genome Project (HGP) announced that it had completed mapping the entire human genome, identifying and mapping the genes that cover all physical and functional aspects of humans. The funding for the HGP came from the U.S. government and the NIH. The data discovered through this project has led to the discovery of the VMAT2 gene -God Gene- where beliefs and desires come from. The conspiratorial assumption is that if they can reduce the levels of VMAT2 through vaccines, they can reduce "radicalism," making people more docile and easier to control.
- In 2003, FactCheck.org formed -a nonprofit website focusing on U.S. politics, misinformation, and hoaxes. The Annenberg Foundation primarily funds FactCheck.org and later started receiving funding from Facebook and Google.
- In 2004, SARS "accidentally leaked" twice, in two separate incidents, from a top laboratory in Beijing, China.
- In 2004, the CDC filed a patent application for an isolated human coronavirus (SARS-CoV), US7220852B1. This patent is not for the COVID19 virus.
- In 2005, the Gates Foundation granted $436.6 million to three Canadian scientific teams. One of the teams was with Dr. Frank Plummer, a well-known HIV researcher, whose research lab in 2017 and 2018 had shady dealings with the BSL-4 facility in Wuhan, China, around coronaviruses. Samples of coronavirus were smuggled out of their lab and flown to Wuhan, China. In October 2019, the Canadian government started investigating the scientists and the lab's dealings. Dr. Plummer died from a heart attack in February 2020 before seeing the end of the investigation. Convenient timing, no?
- In 2005, the U.S. government passed the Real ID Act, which aligns the U.S. with the U.N.'s Agenda 2030 and ID2020.

- Starting in 2005, the DoD's Cooperative Threat Reduction Program – Biological Threat Reduction Program (BTRP) has partnered with the Government of Ukraine to create public health facilities and biological laboratories to study pathogens that can become endemic.

- In 2006, the Gates Foundation and the Rockefeller Foundation started the Alliance for a Green Revolution in Africa (AGRA), which focused on increasing the incomes and improving food security for 30 million farming households in 11 African countries by 2021, which aligned with the U.S. SGN goals.

- In 2007, the UW IHME was formed by the Gates Foundation with a $105 million grant. UW IHME provides global health statistics and was used to justify universal mask usage by the U.S. government during the COVID19 pandemic.

- In 2007, PolitiFact.com -a non-profit fact-checking journalism project- was established by the Tampa Bay Times and was acquired in February 2018 by the Poynter Institute. PolitiFact claims that it focuses on being independent and transparent - journalism you can trust. Currently, PolitiFact receives more than 5% of its funding from Facebook (Meta) and TikTok.

- In 2008, the Institute for Disease Modeling (IDM) was created as part of the Gates Foundation's Global Health Division. IDM's modeling provides a framework to study the spread of disease and alternative eradication strategies. Statistics and modeling from UW IHME and IDM have turned out to be incorrect over time, especially around the COVID19 pandemic.

- In May 2008, the Gates Foundation gave $1.3 million to the UW-Madison School of Veterinary Medicine for influenza research, which virologist Yoshihiro Kawaoka led. Kawaoka focused on identifying avian influenza virus mutations that could lead to a pandemic.

- On December 31st, 2008, Kawaoka published the study *Genes That Made 1918 Flu Lethal Isolated* which mixed and matched a currently circulating avian influenza virus with the "Spanish flu," allowing the researchers to identify a set of three genes that allowed the significant virulence of the 1918 virus (ScienceDaily, 31 December 2008). These genes propagate in mammals' lungs, giving the virus high potency. This was GoF research paid for by the Gates Foundation. This research poses a significant risk to the human population by making bird flu highly infectious in humans.

- On November 19th, 2009, the Gates Foundation provided a $9.5 million five-year grant to UW-Madison, specifically to Kawaoka's work, to identify virus mutations that could serve as an early warning to future potential pandemic influenza viruses. This research would be achieved by looking for mutations in the viral proteins that would allow avian influenza viruses to bind to human receptors or facilitate replication in human cells. Kawaoka said that "social distancing" and "vaccine development" could be used as intervention methods.

- On February 24th, 2010, Kawaoka published the study *Virus hybridization could create pandemic bird flu*, which he and researchers combined H5N1 with seasonal flu (H1N1) and found that a gene called PB2 -allowing for human infectibility- swapped into H5N1, causing the avian influenza virus to become highly pathogenic in mice and ferrets (ScienceDaily, 24 February 2010). This is more GoF research conducted by the Gates Foundation.

- In 2010, the WHO partnered with UNICEF, NIAID, and the Gates Foundation to create a Global Vaccine Action Plan that would affect vaccine communities internationally. This plan would focus on discovering, developing, and delivering vaccines to the poorest countries.

- In 2010, Derrick Rossi, an assistant professor at Harvard University Medical School, solicited $5 million from fellow faculty member Timothy Springer to found Moderna -formerly ModeRNA Therapeutics- to focus on mRNA technologies.

- In August 2010, the Gates Foundation invested $27.6 million (500,000 shares) into the corrupt Monsanto corporation, which is heavily involved in controlling the seed and farming market.

Monsanto has been creating headlines for scandals and lawsuits for years.

- On January 24th, 2011, the journal PLoS One published the study *Highly Pathogenic Avian Influenza (H5N1): Pathways of Exposure at the Animal-Human Interface, a Systematic Review*, which looked for the various ways H5N1 could be transmissible to humans (PLoS One. 2011; 6(1): e14582.). The Gates Foundation funded this study.

- On February 22nd, 2011, the U.S. Supreme Court sided with vaccine manufacturers in the case *Bruesewitz v. Wyeth, LLC*, 562 U.S. 223 (2011), confirming the liability protections provided by the NCVIA of 1986.

- On November 17th, 2011, The New England Journal of Medicine published the study *First Results of Phase 3 Trial of RTS,S/AS01 Malaria Vaccine in African Children*, which was a Gates Foundation-funded study -that had 151 deaths and severe adverse reactions in 18% of the children reported (N Engl J Med. 2011 Nov 17;365(20):1863-75.).

- In 2013, AstraZeneca invested $240 million in Moderna to produce mRNA products.

- In 2014, Kawaoka was able to manipulate the 2009 pandemic flu strain genetically, causing it to "escape" the human immune system's antibodies making the human population completely defenseless if it was to get out. At that time, he did not publish his study's work, but there was still a pushback and public outcry that he was allowed to conduct this GoF research. This research drove the opposition to stop GoF research through a moratorium until 2019.

- In 2014, the Gates Foundation and the Clinton Foundation partnered to measure global progress for women and girls. The Clinton Foundation has had several scandals come to light over the years -e.g., selling access to the U.S. State Department through donations to the Clinton Foundation. Gates and Bill Clinton -associates and friends with convicted pedophile and billionaire Jeffrey Epstein- flew on the Lolita Express -Epstein's pedophile plane even after Epstein was released from prison for the first time. Clinton flew to Epstein's private island over a dozen times. President Trump also had ties to Epstein. President Trump was a frequent dinner guest at Epstein's home in New York and once attended a dinner party honoring Clinton.

- In 2014, Dr. Fauci sent $3.7 million through the NIH grants and EcoHealth Alliance to the BSL-4 facility in Wuhan, China, to study GoF research around coronaviruses from caves in Yunnan, China.

- In October 2014, MIT Media Lab Director, Joi Ito, wrote in an email that Epstein directed Gates to provide a $2 million donation to Epstein's MIT project.

- In 2015, Gates pushed for government-approved education, including advocating the failed Common Core standards that Public and Charter schools were forced to incorporate into their curriculum.

- In 2015, Lead Stories LLC (LeadStories.com), funded by Facebook, was launched, focusing on innovative fact-checking and debunking stories shared on the Internet.

- In 2015, the Gates Foundation invested $52 million into CureVac, which had a platform for an mRNA-based vaccine. CureVac produced a COVID19 mRNA vaccine used throughout Europe.

- In 2015, the Pirbright Institute filed a patent application for "a live, attenuated coronavirus comprising a variant replicase gene encoding polyproteins comprising a mutation in one or more of non-structural protein(s)" (US10130701B2). The Pirbright Institute patent focuses on farm animals and various viruses that deal with non-humans. Two grants were the only connection between Pirbright Institute and Gates -that I could find. The first grant, totaling $189,232, from the Gates Foundation, was provided to Pirbright Institute in November 2013 to "improve our understanding of, and effective use of, current control tools and measures (including vaccines) against peste des petits ruminants and foot and mouth disease, two serious diseases affecting livestock that are widespread in developing countries." The second grant, totaling $385,144, from the Gates Foundation was provided to Pirbright Institute in June 2016 to "test a novel universal influenza vaccine." None of the patented viruses is the COVID19 virus, nor do they seem to form the base structure of COVID19. COVID19 was not a patented virus. Pirbright Institute does claim that the Gates Foundation is a significant stakeholder.

- In 2015, the U.N. started Agenda 2030 and the Sustainable Development Goal after all members of the U.N. adopted the agenda. The United Nations has been fraught with scandals and corruption since its formation.

- In 2015, the CDC and FDA approved the use of Jynneos by Bavarian Nordic, a smallpox monkeypox vaccine based on a live, attenuated vaccinia virus.

- In November 2015, the Gates Foundation provided a $382,997 grant to the Poynter Institute (owner of PolitiFact) "to improve the accuracy in worldwide media of claims related to global health and development."

- On December 11th, 2015, Elon Musk founded OpenAI -a for-profit artificial intelligence (AI) research laboratory- which produces and runs ChatGPT. Since its inception, Microsoft has invested one billion dollars into it and is currently -at the time of writing this- in talks about investing another ten billion.

- In 2015 and 2016, Dr. Fauci registered several patents focusing on HIV gp120 -Patent numbers: 20160075786, 9441041, 20160333097, and 9896509- in which gp120 was confirmed as having some matches within the COVID19 spike protein sequence.

- In January 2016, the Gates Foundation partnered with Moderna within a global health project framework to advance mRNA technologies.

- In 2016, AstraZeneca invested $140 million in Moderna, raising its stake in the corporation to 9%.

- In 2016, Accenture, GAVI, Microsoft, and the Rockefeller Foundation partnered up to form the ID2020 nongovernmental organization with a focus on creating a digital ID for the worldwide population using "technologies like blockchain and other decentralized ledger systems create a pathway towards viable solutions in the quest for identity for all. By 2020, we're aiming to have a proof of concept with real world pilot projects deployed in several locations. By 2030, our goal is to enable access to digital identity for every person on the planet." ID2020 is in service to the U.N.'s Agenda 2030.

- In 2016, FactCheck.org became a fact-checking partner with Facebook.

- In 2017, the Gates Foundation, as a lead investor, invested roughly $15 million in Vir Biotechnology Inc. to help develop a safe and effective Tuberculosis (TB) vaccine.

- In 2017, Gates invested in both Impossible Foods and Beyond Meat which has begun to be adopted worldwide. These engineered products are starting to be found in grocery stores and restaurants. Gates has been very vocal over the years, stating that rich countries must move to 100% synthetic beef.

- In 2017, the NIH announced that it was lifting the ban on GoF research.

- In 2017, Dr. Edwin Deagle, Jr., a former Army Intelligence Officer, national security expert, and assistant to the Secretary of Defense and the Deputy Secretary of Defense, who was educated at the U.S. Military Academy West Point and Harvard University, ran a private intelligence organization through the website deagle.com which provides news and intelligence reports of international military activities and technologies. Dr. Deagle Jr. was also a member of the Council of Foreign Relations (CFR) and Direct of International Relations with the Rockefeller Foundation. A Deagle report was filed in 2017, which has since been scrubbed from the Internet -some archived copies of the report still exist- showing that by 2025 there would be a massive population decline of up to 70%+ in mostly Western culture countries. This report showed that the U.S. would be reduced to a population of roughly 100 million people by 2025. Dr. Deagle Jr. passed away on February 16th, 2021.

- In May 2017, the Gates Foundation committed $100 million to Moderna, the same corporation that had FDA approval for a COVID19 mRNA vaccine.

- In June 2017, the Gates Foundation pledged $450 million to eradicate polio worldwide. This campaign pushed the use of the no longer U.S.-approved cheaper oral polio vaccine (OPV), which has been proven to cause the shedding of polio. The Gates Foundation polio efforts in India led to vaccine-derived polio running more rampant in the wild, with numbers over-taking wild polio cases. Things became so bad that the Indian government moved to cut ties with the Gates Foundation, his vaccine program, and his immunization efforts. Even the WHO has admitted that roughly 70% of the global polio cases are from the polio vaccine.

- In 2018, Gates teamed up with Google co-founder Larry Page and pledged $12 million to develop a universal flu vaccine to start clinical trials by 2021. During this announcement, Gates cited that 33 million people could die within six months if an outbreak on the scale of the Spanish flu hit today. Gates cited research into disease modeling for his prediction -the same modeling government used as justification to shut down the economy during COVID19. Modeling that Gates was behind in developing. Serious questions about the origins of the Spanish flu are still unanswered -some evidence suggests it was caused by a failed vaccine experiment conducted by the Rockefeller Institute for Medical Research at Fort Riley, Kansas, that resulted in a new type of bacterial pneumonia being released, which was blamed on influenza.

- In April 2018, Gates started to back a $1 billion plan to help cover the Earth in satellites through a startup company called EarthNow. This is being added to the tens of thousands of satellites Elon Musk is sending into orbit. A new era of surveillance has begun.

- In May 2018, Gates, during an interview with MSNBC, said he convinced President Trump to stop looking into vaccines as a problem and to move away from using Robert F. Kennedy (RFK) Jr. as an adviser, which President Trump listened to and removed RFK Jr. from an advisory position at the White House.
- In the fall of 2018, Gates' private office -Gates Ventures- provided $20 million in funding for the Seattle Flu Study -a collaborative effort in the Seattle and King County region led by The Brotman Baty Institute, UW Medicine, The Fred Hutchinson Cancer Center, and Seattle Children's Hospital.
- On November 16th, 2018, the Cybersecurity and Infrastructure Security Agency (CISA) was established under the DHS, focusing on cybersecurity protections and disinformation after President Trump signed the Cybersecurity and Infrastructure Security Agency Act of 2018. This bill and CISA were used to censor information during the 2020 election, information on Hunter Biden's laptop, and information about COVID19 by partnering with major social media corporations.
- In March 2019, Kawaoka at UW-Madison was approved to continue his GoF research into dangerous avian influenza viruses. Many researchers and fellow scientists at this time spoke out against Kawaoka's research, saying it could cause a devastating flu pandemic if his enhanced viruses escaped from a laboratory or were replicated by terrorists.
- On May 30th, 2019, an FBI intelligence bulletin from the FBI's Phoenix field office describes conspiracy theorists as domestic extremists (terrorists).
- On August 10th, 2019, Epstein "committed suicide" in his cell, with the cameras malfunctioning, so no video evidence of his death exists. Serious questions about his supposed suicide have yet to be answered. As of now, the government has not gone after any of Epstein's clients for their crimes against children.
- In August 2019, Gates advocated for spraying millions of tons of dust into the air to help block out the Sun. His stated purpose of this would be to stop global warming and climate change. The

Gates Foundation is funding the project with research conducted by Harvard University scientists.

- In September 2019, California removed all exemptions, including most medical exemptions, dangerously forcing children into getting vaccines.

- In September 2019, the Gates Foundation bought a $55 million stake in BioNTech, focusing on developing vaccines and immunotherapies for HIV and TB. Convenient Gates bought it right before COVID19 was officially announced, and BioNTech partnered with Pfizer to create the leading COVID19 mRNA vaccine used in the U.S.

- In September 2019, the Chinese government abruptly and quickly entered the BSL-4 facility in Wuhan, China, and removed the leadership, documentation, and records around coronavirus research.

- In September 2019, the FBI, DHS (CISA), and the Office of the Director of National Intelligence met with Facebook, Google, Twitter, Wikipedia, and Microsoft to discuss security, misinformation, and disinformation. By 2020, these corporations and agencies began meeting monthly and sometimes weekly to censor dissenting opposing views.

- On October 18th, 2019, Event 201: A Global Pandemic Exercise was conducted by the Gates Foundation, WHO, Johns Hopkins Bloomberg School of Public Health – Center for Health Security, and the WEF, which focused on a global pandemic simulation that was caused by a coronavirus originating in Brazil.

- On October 28th, 2019, the Gates Foundation committed $100 million -in partnership with the NIH and Dr. Fauci- to develop gene-based therapies for two diseases: HIV and sickle cell.

- On November 12th, 2019, a dispatch out of the BSL-4 facility in Wuhan, China, referenced a biosecurity breach.

- On November 12th, 2019, Labyrinth Global Health Inc. was granted a DoD sub-awarded contract (19-6192) totaling $369,511 for "SME manuscript documentation and COVID19 research."

- On November 15th, 2019, the CDC posted a Public Health Advisor (Quarantine Program) with the job summary "serves as a project representative for a program responsible for preventing the importation and spread of communicable diseases."
- In December 2019, COVID19 was officially announced as having been discovered and classified as a disease of concern.
- In December 2019, Gates announced he was partnering up with MIT to develop a new invisible quantum dot, "Tattoo ID," that gets injected into the skin with a vaccine, keeping track of the individual's medical history. The Science Translational Medicine published the study *Biocompatible near-infrared quantum dots delivered to the skin by microneedle patches record vaccination* that details this new quantum dot tattoo ID (Sci Transl Med. 2019 Dec 18;11(523):eaay7162.).
- On December 19th, 2019, the FDA approved Ervebo -the first vaccine to prevent Ebola.
- In January 2020, Dr. Charles Lieber, a chair of Harvard's Chemistry and Chemical Biology Department, was federally indicted with two others after lying about his dealings with the BSL-4 facility in Wuhan, China. Dr. Lieber was granted $15 million by the NIH and DoD, which required that he disclose foreign funds. Dr. Lieber lied to federal investigators about his affiliation with the BSL-4 facility and his contract to help attract talent to China.
- In January 2020, the WHO started its Immunization Agenda 2030 (IA2030), which coincides with the U.N.'s Agenda 2030. IA2030 will play a critical role in achieving the UN's Agenda 2030. IA2030 uses the Global Vaccine Action Plan (GVAP), backed by the Gates Foundation, to unite everyone in a shared vision and strategy.
- In January 2020, the Seattle Flu Study team pivoted to focus on detecting COVID19 throughout the Seattle area.
- On January 8th, 2020, President Trump signed into law the Secure 5G and Beyond Act (H.R.2881) that required his administration to work with the Federal Communications Commission (FCC),

the Department of Homeland Security, and DoD to develop a plan to secure 5G networks and infrastructure within and outside of the U.S. -first steps towards nationalizing 5G and beyond technology. This plays into the direction of a complete surveillance state being implemented worldwide.

- On January 12th, 2020, the first patent application for a COVID19 vaccine was filed by the military virologist Zhou Yusen, which focused on using the virus' spike protein as receptor binding - Patent number: CN111333704B. Yusen had been a key member in the MERS vaccine research in China. In May 2020, Yusen died under mysterious circumstances.
- On January 21st, 2020, the allegedly first U.S. COVID19 case was detected in a man living close to Seattle, Washington.
- On January 31st, 2020, President Trump declared a public health emergency under the Public Health Service Act for COVID19.
- In January and February 2020, 33 U.S. States reported significant increases in flu-like symptoms and pneumonia, with most of the U.S. listed as having the highest level of infection.
- In February 2020, the Department of Education started investigations into Harvard University and Yale University dealings and their foreign funding. This investigation yielded $6.5 billion in foreign financing from countries like China and Saudi Arabia.
- In March 2020, the Gates Foundation started funding and experimenting with at-home testing kits for COVID19 in the Seattle area. The testing kits worked with individuals swabbing their noses and then sending the samples back to get a response within two days. There is little to no information on how effective these kits are.
- In March 2020, CZI committed $125 million to help set up the "COVID-19 Therapeutics Accelerator," which focuses on treatments for COVID19 -Gates Foundation organized the effort.
- On March 13th, 2020, President Trump declared a national emergency around COVID19.

- On March 21st, 2020, Mike Pompeo, 70th US Secretary of State and former Director of the CIA, said in a COVID19 brief that "we're in a live exercise here." In a military sense, a live-fire exercise is when realistic scenarios are worked through using real ammunition in a controlled manner. The point of this would be to see how citizens react, what gaps exist for maintaining government control, communication breakdowns, where the line for tyranny is for freedom fighters and the general public to fight back, how to deal with the dissenters, how to discredit opposing views from official government rhetoric, how fast field hospitals could be set up, and how a wild virus can burn through a populace during a pandemic.

- On March 23rd, 2020, President Trump signed the Broadband DATA Act (S.1822) into law which expands and changes how and what information the FCC collects around broadband access and develops a granular National Broadband Map to help identify gaps in coverage. The Broadband DATA Act and the Secure 5G and Beyond Act move the U.S. closer to a nationalized broadband surveillance apparatus that will be used to maintain control.

- In April 2020, GlaxoSmithKline plc (GSK) partnered with Vir Biotechnology, Inc. -Gates Foundation is the lead investor- to create solutions for COVID19, including research into a coronavirus vaccine.

- In April 2020, Gates vowed to find a coronavirus vaccine even if it meant "wasting" billions of dollars.

- In April 2020, Oxford University promised to overhaul its vaccine business by donating the rights to their COVID19 vaccine to any drug maker -reversed the decision a few weeks after being urged by the Gates Foundation. Oxford eventually signed an exclusive vaccine deal with AstraZeneca. The Gates has provided hundreds of millions to Oxford University over the years.

- In April 2020, Microsoft produced an ad -pulled quickly over a considerable backlash- with "spirit-cooking" Satanic artist Marina Abramovic. This was near the time when Melinda Gates was photographed wearing what people considered a Satanic upside-down cross during an interview. This, of course, pushes the rumor that they are Satanists. The inverted cross is also the Cross of Saint Peter -known for being an occult symbol. I bring Abramovic up because of the connection Abramovic has to those involved with the conspiracy theory Pizzagate.

- By May 2020, the Gates Foundation committed more than $300 million to the global COVID19 response.

- In May 2020, New York Governor Andrew Cuomo announced that the government was partnering up with the Gates Foundation to "reimagine education" to better focus on the 4.2 million students absent from their classrooms in New York due to government restrictions.

- In May 2020, a Board of Directors member for Moderna, Dr. Moncef Slaoui, resigned from his position so he could take up an appointment to oversee President Trump's Operation Warp Speed operation and to help fast-track a coronavirus vaccine by the end of 2020.

- On December 11th, 2020, the FDA approved the Pfizer COVID19 vaccine under the EUA.

- On December 18th, 2020, the FDA approved the Moderna COVID19 vaccine under the EUA.

- In 2021, Gates was named the largest private farmland owner in the U.S. -more than 269,000 acres- where he grows Monsanto GMO potatoes used to create fries at Mcdonald's.

- In January 2021, President Biden issued executive orders mandating mask-wearing on federal properties and required federal workers and contractors to be vaccinated with the new COVID19 vaccines. At the same time, President Biden mandated that employers with over 100 employees require their employees to become vaccinated.

- On February 27th, 2021, the FDA approved the J&J COVID19 vaccine under the EUA.

- On March 17th, 2021, the Nuclear Threat Initiative (NTI), a non-profit organization founded by Ted Turner, brought together government officials from the U.S. and China, the WHO, the U.N., multiple pharmaceutical corporations, and the Gates Foundation at the Munich Security Conference to take part in a tabletop exercise to respond to a biological terror attack involving a lab-enhanced monkeypox virus that would eventually kill hundreds of millions worldwide throughout a 19-month pandemic. An official report detailing the exercise was released in November 2021 titled *Strengthening Global Systems to Prevent and Respond to High-Consequence Biological Threats.* This simulation exercise had a May 15th, 2022, release date, which ended the same week a real-world monkeypox outbreak was first detected.

- On June 25th, 2021, the FDA added myocarditis and pericarditis warnings to the Pfizer and Moderna COVID19 vaccines but continued to indicate that the risk was very low without quantifying the actual risk.
- On August 23rd, 2021, the FDA approved the first COVID19 vaccine developed by Pfizer for licensure (COMIRNATY) not under the EUA -BNT162b2.
- On November 16th, 2021, a laboratory technician discovered several smallpox vials in a freezer at the Merck Upper Gwenydd facility in North Wales, Pennsylvania. Smallpox is considered so dangerous that only two laboratories worldwide -the CDC's leading laboratory in Atlanta and a facility in Russia- are allowed to handle the smallpox virus. Merck is investigating how the vials managed to be stored and forgotten about at their facility.
- On November 23rd, 2021, the FDA approved the Audenz H5N1) vaccine for use in anyone six months of age and older and started stockpiling Audenz in case of a bird flu pandemic. At the time of this approval, the U.S. had never had a case of human-contracted H5N1. Currently, H5N1 is harmless to humans and does not transmit from human to human.
- In December 2021, it was reported that influenza cases had all but vanished for the year -compared to previous years- even though COVID19 cases were still spiking. Endemics are never-

ending, so they are things we need to deal with as part of our everyday life.

- In December 2021, the CDC's Real Time RT-PCR laboratory alert went into effect, meaning laboratories needed to find a new way of testing for COVID19.

- In December 2021, the White House (Biden administration) announced it was planning to send out over 500 million "free" at-home testing kits to U.S. citizens beginning in January 2022, which was funded through congressional legislation. These testing kits were manufactured by China's Andon Health Co.'s unit, iHealth Labs Inc. -founded in 2010- which contracted with the U.S. Army Contracting Command for roughly $1.3 billion. They were approved for use under Emergency Use Authorization. Before this product, iHealth had not produced any other testing product.

- On December 17th, 2021, President Biden warned that those not vaccinated against COVID19 would face severe illness and death from the Omicron variant if they didn't get vaccinated. The government started pushing the first or second booster shot depending on when an individual got vaccinated.

- In January 2022, the Biden administration announced it would order 1 billion at-home testing kits for U.S. citizens.

- In January 2022, The Rockefeller Foundation launched the Project Access COVID Tests (Project ACT) in partnership with iHealth Labs Inc., Care Evolution, Amazon, and six State Health Departments to provide "free" at-home COVID19 tests.

- On January 13th, 2022, the U.S. Supreme Court struck down President Biden's employer vaccine mandate.

- On January 31st, 2022, the FDA approved Moderna's COVID19 vaccine for licensure -Spikevax- not under the EUA.

- On March 10th, 2022, the Russian Defense Ministry announced that it had captured settlements and areas during the Ukrainian war, which included some U.S.-funded biological laboratories. Within these biological laboratories, there was evidence indicating that research into bat coronaviruses and studies of contagious bird flu (H5N1) was being conducted under the U.S. Project UP-4. The studies included highly pathogenic H5N1 flu that could have a 50% mortality rate for humans. The report indicated that a total of 145 different transcontinental migration birds -their potential to spread infections- were studied.

- On March 30th, 2022, Dr. Robert Redfield, a former CDC Director, said during a CenterPoint interview that the COVID19 pandemic was a wake-up call and that the great pandemic is still coming. Dr. Redfield said that the great pandemic would be a bird flu pandemic -with a significant mortality rate in the 10% to 50% range.

- On April 19th, 2022, a federal judge voided the U.S. national mandate requiring universal mask-wearing compliance on public transport.

- On April 27th, 2022, President Biden formed the DGB under the DHS to combat the information the government deemed disinformation. The DGB was dissolved after four months of being open.

- In April and May 2022, news reports detailing a highly pathogenic bird flu was making its way through chicken and poultry flocks in the U.S., causing the government to issue slaughter mandates to millions of animals. By the end of April 2022, the first-ever U.S. H5N1 case in a human was reported.

- In May 2022, the WHO confirmed that a monkeypox outbreak spread to 12 countries.

- In May 2022, President Biden ordered 13 million doses of Jynneos - a live-virus monkeypox vaccine- which means it could shed monkeypox on those around newly vaccinated individuals.

- On June 7th, 2022, Moderna announced that the Phase 3 study on its mRNA universal influenza vaccine (MRNA-1010) had started.

- On June 29th, 2022, Pfizer announced it would start testing a universal vaccine for all coronaviruses in humans during the second half of 2022. This new liability-free experimental injection will be pushed at record speed. It will have the same failures in testing protocols and corruption that Pfizer's current mRNA COVID19 vaccine was surrounded by.

- On July 6th, 2022, an explosive device was set off, damaging part of the Georgia Guidestones, which caused the city to tear down the rest of the monument. Video evidence shows a vehicle driving away, but at this time, no suspects have been announced, and no arrests have been made.

- In August 2022, Dr. Fauci announced he would be stepping down from his position as Director of NIAID to start the next chapter of his career. This could be a move to avoid the mounting calls for formal investigations and potential criminal charges around his role and influence on the creation of COVID19.

- In September 2022, Moderna announced it had enrolled more than 24,000 participants in its global Phase 3 mRNA RSV vaccine trial (mRNA-1345 – Clinical Trial Identifier: NCT05330975). The trial is testing the new mRNA RSV vaccine with a seasonal flu vaccine and their updated mRNA COVID19 vaccine in adults 50 years or older. There has never been an RSV vaccine approved for use in the U.S. This will be another liability-free product as the U.S. starts to see significant increases in RSV infections.

- On September 14th, 2022, Pfizer announced it had started the Phase 3 study of their mRNA universal influenza vaccine.

- On September 19th, 2022, President Biden claimed on 60 Minutes that the COVID19 pandemic was over.

- On October 9th, 2022, Moderna CEO Stéphane Bancel was interviewed by SkyNews Business Australia, where he said that the corporation was working on a new mRNA injection that goes into the heart where it would grow back blood vessels and tissue.

- On October 20th, 2022, the CDC panel voted 15-0 to add the COVID19 vaccines to the recommended childhood vaccine schedule starting in 2023. Meaning public and private schools in various states will begin to require children of all ages to be vaccinated against COVID19 to attend school.

- On October 23rd, 2022, the Gates Foundation, WHO, and Johns Hopkins Center for Health Security ran a pandemic tabletop exercise at the Grand Challenges Annual Meeting in Brussels, Belgium called *Catastrophic Contagion*, which focused on a new deadly contagion -set in 2025- with a higher mortality rate than COVID19 and that it primarily affected children and young people. The new contagion was named Severe Epidemic Enterovirus Respiratory Syndrome 2025, and it accounted for 20 million people dying worldwide, with 15 million being children. The same group was spot on with Event 201 coronavirus and the NTI monkeypox tabletop exercises, so why would they not be correct with this exercise? Do they already know what is circulating or going to be circulating soon?

- On October 27th, 2022, a trial court in Peru, the Criminal Chamber of Appeals court located in Chincha and Pisco, ruled that Bill Gates, the Rockefeller Foundation, Sorors, and other financial elites created COVID19 and driving the COVID19 pandemic.

- On October 27th, 2022, an interim report -commissioned by Senator Richard Burr and released by the U.S. Senate Committee on Health, Education, Labor & Pensions (HELP)- concluded that the COVID19 pandemic was "more likely than not, the result of a research-related incident."

- November 2022, Pfizer and Moderna launch trials to determine and track health issues that arise years after getting COVID19 vaccines.

- On November 15th, 2022, the Federal Reserve Bank of New York, in partnership with Citigroup, HSBC Holdings, Mastercard, and Wells Fargo, started a 12-week pilot program focused on testing a central banking digital currency.

- On November 15th, 2022, the U.S. Senate voted to terminate the COVID19 national emergency. This was the third time the Senate voted to end the COVID19 pandemic emergency. However, the Democrat-controlled U.S. House has never voted on ending the emergency crisis. Even if the U.S. passed the measure, President

Biden announced he would veto it even though President Biden declared the pandemic over two months earlier.

- On November 16th, 2022, the FDA announced that the lab-grown meat from Upside Foods was safe for human consumption. Investors in Upside Foods include but are not limited to Gates, Richard Branson, Tyson Foods, Cargill, and Kimbal Musk - brother to Elon Musk.

- On November 17th, 2022, 22 states' attorney generals filed a petition under the Administrative Procedures Act, seeking the Biden administration and HHS CMS to repeal the IFR vaccine mandate for healthcare workers.

- On December 14th, 2022, a Consumer Reports investigation was released, which found high levels of lead and cadmium - dangerous heavy metals- in dark chocolate from Hershey's, Trader Joe's, and others that, when exposed to small amounts over long periods can lead to significant health problems - developmental problems, lower IQ, Alzheimer's, and dementia. If dark chocolate eaten -orally taken- for decades could lead to these severe health issues, what severe health issues could arise from injecting gene therapy "safe and effective" vaccines?

- On December 16th, 2022, the Twitter Files were released showing that the FBI -for years- flagged individual and business accounts for Twitter to suspend or ban from its platform over "misinformation" dealing with the 2020 and 2022 elections, the Hunter Biden laptop story -confirmed true- and the COVID19 pandemic in a clear violation of the First Amendment of the U.S. Constitution. The FBI gave Twitter approximately $3.4 million from October 2019 to early 2021 for its services in censoring identified accounts. The FBI was not the only federal agency working with Twitter.

- On January 9th, 2023, Stéphane Bancel, CEO of Moderna, announced they were accelerating their mRNA RSV Phase 3 and Flu Phase 3 human trials while having rapid advancements in "promising cardiology programs."

- On January 11th, 2023, CNN reported that some of the FDA vaccine advisers -who approved the Moderna mRNA booster vaccine for public use- were "disappointed" and "angry" at government scientists and Moderna for not presenting infection data. The infection data showed that the updated boosters were not any more effective against circulating strains than the original series. Would they still have voted for approving the vaccines had they been provided the data? Probably.

"You know, we'll have to prepare for the next one. That, you know, I'd say is, ah, will get attention this time." – Bill Gates, *A Special Edition of Path Forward interview*, June 23rd, 2020

The Future

"Never let the future disturb you. You will meet it, if you have to, with the same weapons of reason which today arm you against the present." – Marcus Aurelius, *Meditations, Book VII*, from 161 to 180 AD

Can the future be predicted? Great chess players can predict likely outcomes based on the locations of each piece and the systematic understanding of the game. As moves continue, likely outcomes can change to a smaller pool of possibilities. It is possible to predict with precision the movement of the planets and stars -with visual confirmations. On August 21st, 2017, I witnessed a Totality -when the Moon completely covers the Sun's surface- and looked upon what I immediately knew as the source of some myths and legends that significantly impacted humanity's history. It was one of those life-changing movements that I feel everyone should witness. No picture taken does a Totality justice. This event was predicted with mathematical precision and confirmed visually. In a plasma universe, patterns -fractal patterns- are written into the fabric of our reality, so if we can understand a pattern for what it is, how it came to be, what factors are influencing it, and why it repeats, then we can potentially predict how the future will be written -to an extent.

Philosophy is the "love of knowledge, pursuit of wisdom; systematic investigation" (Online Etymology Dictionary). Critical thinking is required to understand and discuss philosophy, gods and deities, and the rules written into the fabric of our reality. We must understand the grammar, discuss the logic, and produce rhetoric of any given situation. By doing this consistently, we become better equipped to predict possible futures.

"We are talking about the spatial and temporal phenomenon of language, not about some non -- spatial, non -- temporal phantasm. But we talk about it as we do about the pieces in chess when we are stating the rules of the game, not describing their physical properties. The question "What is a word really?" is analogous to "What is a piece in chess?" It was true to say that our considerations could not be scientific ones. It was not of any possible interest to us to find out empirically that, contrary to our preconceived ideas, it is possible to think such-and-such -- whatever that may mean. (The conception of thought as a gaseous medium.) And we may not advance any kind of theory. There must not be anything hypothetical in our considerations. We must do away with all explanation, and description alone must take its place. And this description gets its light, that is to say its purpose, from the philosophical problems. These are, of course, not empirical problems, they are solved, rather, by looking into the workings of our language, and that in such a way as to make us recognize those workings: in despite of an urge to misunderstand them. The problems are solved, not by giving new information, but by arranging what we have always known. Philosophy is a battle against the bewitchment of our intelligence by means of language." – Ludwig Wittgenstein, *Philosophical Investigations*, 1953

The future has yet to be written, but plans upon plans have been laid out before us as we are driven like cattle down a very dangerous path. A path seemingly designed to cause us pain and suffering as we traverse it. A path we have only started moving through as it becomes steeper and steeper, with death potentially awaiting around every turn. The worldwide events we are witnessing today are not random coincidences of chance but coordinated efforts by those with the resources and power to upend our way of life by reducing our freedom and rights to a negligible idea that is best ignored. Are we being led to slaughter? Is that the future we will meet -our fate?

Fate -a predetermined course of life- is the culmination of our choices and actions and the choices and actions of others. Like a spiderweb of life, each intersection of the web is a choice and action, while our fate is the line to the next intersection of the web. At times the choices and actions of others influence us more than our own choices and actions. The more we are aware of our reality and the choices and actions of others, and the more knowledge we can gather and understand, the more we can plan to meet the future with confidence and determination -have greater control over our fate.

Knowledge is power. Since knowledge is power, our first step to true freedom is having the knowledge -power- to control ourselves. This knowledge comes from the systematic understanding of our reality and the movement and actions of the pieces within it. By having greater control of ourselves, we can potentially determine our fate and guide it down any path we choose. This is, in essence, what freedom means -freedom of movement, free from shackles and chains, even in the metaphysical sense. Innocent free adults have no need to be controlled or forced into compliance. We are not children or criminals -no victim, no crime- in need of control, so we should be free to exercise our inherent natural rights without restraint.

"Power tends to corrupt, and absolute power corrupts absolutely. Great men are almost always bad men, even when they exercise influence and not authority: still more when you superadd the tendency or the certainty of corruption by authority. There is no worse heresy than that the office sanctifies the holder of it." – Lord Action, *Letter to Mandell Creighton*, April 5th, 1887

Why do we give others absolute power over ourselves if absolute power corrupts? Why do many settle for "voting for the lesser of two evils"? Voting for evil is still evil, and we should never vote for evil things. Voting and advocating for a corrupt and unethical tool of control is not an intelligent play, especially when it always leads to tyranny. What has voting harder gotten everyone? More tyranny.

Every election seems to be the most important election of our lifetime. Rinse and repeat. Many believe their political choice is the only path forward, pushed with a feverish cult-like attitude and determination. If all choices for elected officials have a secret allegiance to others -not the voters they promise to represent- how can we expect anything to change for the better through voting?

"I'm not sure you should assume I'm not corrupt, but thank you for that, though. The system does produce corruption, and I think implicit in the system is corruption when in fact, whether or not you can run for public office, and it costs a great deal of money to run for the United States Senate, even for a small state like Delaware, you have to go to those people who have money, and they always want something." – President Joseph Biden, *The Advocates interview*, February 6th, 1974

In 2012, the GOP showed their nomination process was corrupt and unethical by handing it to Mitt Romney when Ron Paul had the votes to secure the nomination. I know some who witnessed the corruption of the 2012 GOP nomination in Tampa, Florida. In 2016, the DNC showed its nomination process was corrupt and unethical when the DNC colluded with Hillary Clinton to hand the nomination to Clinton when it should have gone to Bernie Sanders -it was confirmed as accurate through the DNC Leak, which was quickly blamed as election interference of our "democracy" by the Russian government. Is this the democracy many screams about protecting?

The people's will was not represented during these elections nor the decades preceding them.

The mentality of "next election, we'll vote them out" is a pattern many don't seem to recognize, so they doom themselves to repeat it. Should we trust our livelihoods -safety and protection- to those who are in a position to increase their wealth and power by lying, manipulating, and forcing us into docile obedience? There is no depth to the violence and atrocities a human will commit for money or the correct sociological and psychological pressures. No individual is immune to corruption when given authority and power over the innocent. Individuals make up organizations, corporations, and governments, so each entity is not immune to corruption. If we cannot trust others to rule their own lives, how can we entrust others to rule over our lives?

Nothing in the thousands of years of history dealing with the government shows that we should blindly trust what those in power tell us or try to convince us to believe as truth. The government, its agents, and those pulling the strings of government are not here to protect and serve the innocent -confirmed by the U.S. Supreme Court. That has never been the true purpose of government -a tool and action of control. Government, historically and without fail, has always led to tyranny. This was true thousands of years ago when Plato explained the lifecycle of government, and it still holds today. The government is not a parental figure taking care of children, and we aren't children needing to be taken care of. The government controls the masses through a monopoly on violence, lies, and intimidation. If we are being controlled and manipulated, are we not slaves to this tyrannical system forced upon us?

We should be challenging and standing against government overreach and tyrannical actions at every step, or the future will be filled with tyranny for our children and their children. Without those willing to step up and speak out, this tyranny will only grow roots, digging itself deeper, and spread to a level we have never witnessed or experienced in the current publicly acknowledged recorded history of humanity. A dangerous and slippery slope of actions has begun, leading to a global economic disaster that will potentially cost billions of lives ushering in this new Age of Tyranny.

How certain can we be that those presented to us as choices and champions of our rights are not controlled opposition -e.g., President Trump, President Biden, or Elon Musk? Politicians or billionaires who are false choices would only lead us further down the path to greater tyranny. Do you believe a billionaire "Batman" is coming to our rescue? What better way to control an outcome of a political election or social issue than controlling all options in an election or solution? Tyranny comes in many forms and flavors.

"THESE are the times that try men's souls. The summer soldier and the sunshine patriot will, in this crisis, shrink from the service of their country; but he that stands it now, deserves the love and thanks of man and woman. Tyranny, like hell, is not easily conquered; yet we have this consolation with us, that the harder the conflict, the more glorious the triumph. What we obtain too cheap, we esteem too lightly: it is dearness only that gives every thing its value. Heaven knows how to put a proper price upon its goods; and it would be strange indeed if so celestial an article as FREEDOM should not be highly rated." – Thomas Paine, *The American Crisis*, *The Crisis No. I*, December 23rd, 1776

Is our current situation the new normal we want? We are responsible for our health and our actions. We are not responsible for others' health and actions. This is how fundamental natural rights work. We should focus on protecting ourselves -not accepting government rhetoric at face value and hoping the government will take care of us because we can't. Only standing up for our rights and the rights of the innocent people around us is how we enact real change and revolution, or my preference, evolution.

Revolution implies starting over -still statism- which always leads to tyranny. We can evolve past the need for government and the idea of needing to be controlled. We can have free and organized communities and economies based on natural rights and voluntarism using facilitating systems to help function. However, things need to change drastically to reach this potential future, but one can dream. The issues we are in cannot be voted away or solved through a corrupt justice system created to keep us controlled and obedient. We cannot vote our way from tyranny to freedom.

Found within all governments of the U.S. -from federal to local- we can find examples of public officials violating town charters, state constitutions, and the U.S. Constitution -which was created to place limits on what the federal and state governments could do, not list out our natural rights. These limits have been constantly tested and violated since inception. What good is a piece of paper if the government that should be limited by said paper has a monopoly on violence? Should we not consider a document that legalizes slavery a poor litmus test to what is morally and ethically correct? When control over the innocent is enacted, rights are violated. We can do better.

"The nine most terrifying words in the English language are: I'm from the Government, and I'm here to help." – President Ronald Reagan, *Press conference*, August 12th, 1986

Throughout this book, we have learned that the government and its agents have lied about the origins of COVID19, the lockdowns being for only two weeks, the number of vaccine doses we would need to return to normalcy, the effectiveness and safety of the vaccines, and the effectiveness of universal mask-wearing. The government has constantly lied without concern of accountability or facing criminal convictions using the idea that government officials are protected through qualified immunity or using power and resources to stop investigations. Trillions of dollars of wealth have been transferred from the general public and handed over to a select few. All the while, economies worldwide have begun to collapse. Everyone got their few COVID19 checks, though, right? How much did those help you? Do you think you got trillions of dollars worth of help?

On July 10th, 2020, it was reported that the U.S. Roman Catholic Church had received up to $3.5 billion in COVID19 Paycheck Protection Program (PPP) funding. This is only one example of wealth distribution that has taken place. If you looked at the COVID19 spending bills enacted since the start of the COVID19 pandemic, millions -billions in some cases- went to organizations and special projects that had nothing to do with COVID19 or the safety and protection of the average citizen. Over the years, the government has announced multiple times that it could not account for trillions of dollars in transactions -DoD failing multiple audits- yet the average U.S. citizen must account for and keep track of personal exchanges of $600 or more for tax purposes. A true do as I say, not as I do.

Massive food, water, and energy shortages have begun to spring up with more frequency -supply chains heavily affected by every natural and manufactured disruption- which has only been getting worse. Have you noticed the shelves at stores are a little thin or empty? More so than what you would have considered normal several years ago? Supply chain disruptions can lag years at times. Due to the COVID19 pandemic and governments worldwide enacting greater control of everything, supply markets are still seeking an adjustment to the new "normal" concerning laws and regulations. This supply chain disruption doesn't include the high inflation we are seeing due to the endless creation of new dollars, which directly affects supply and demand, devaluing the dollar and further straining supply chains.

How much more will supply chains collapse during the next pandemic? What additional controls and regulations will be added from now until then that will negatively affect the supply chains?

How many trillions in new dollars will be created to "help" during the next emergency, which will further drive an increase in inflation? If someone already has money and resources, surviving what is coming will be significantly more manageable than for the average citizen who is loaded with debt and is working paycheck to paycheck, barely getting by. Who do you think suffers during an economic collapse that is more like a controlled demolition?

This massive U.S. economic crisis -a worldwide crisis- that is fast approaching, partly thanks to the creation of trillions in new money during the COVID19 pandemic, will be used to justify the need for more government control and regulation while helping lead the way to significant changes in global economies and cultures. A direction that takes us closer to the publicly stated and secretive goals of the Great Reset.

Things will worsen the more government does in the name of our safety and protection because that is far from its true goal and purpose. The scripted knee-jerk reaction governments worldwide have participated in during the COVID19 pandemic has been costlier in terms of economic value and lives lost than the COVID19 virus could have done on its own when ignored. The solution to this nightmare of a situation should not be more government tyranny but a concerted effort by many to step back and start critically thinking about our current situation to determine the root cause of our problems -not the scripted problems being fed to us.

Blindly and repeatedly injecting ourselves with liability-free experimental gene therapy medical procedures while eating things like Mcdonald's or other processed fast foods and sugars is not a standard for health anyone should follow. Most do not understand proper health, and sadly many of us have become addicted to the processed foods and sugars that have flooded our supply chain. A robust immune system -our terrain- is our best protection against diseases and infections, not the singular focus on pharmaceutical drugs that can be highly addictive and damaging. Eating correctly -

not what is currently considered normal for society- with foods sourced locally or personally grown as much as possible is an excellent way to start. Learn to grow your food, which can be done in an urban setting. The more we grow or produce, the less strain and reliance we have on an already highly-strained supply chain.

Many government measures and restrictions -e.g., forcing gyms to close, requiring COVID19 vaccines to work out in a gym, or limiting access to sunlight and fresh air- can weaken our immune systems and cause us to live unhealthy lives, which seems like the potential true goal of some of these tyrannical measures. People have the right to accept the risk of catching an infectious disease while being in public and possibly dying. Everyone has the ability and right to assess their risk by weighing the information they find and research -comparing it to what their physician or medical adviser recommends- to make decisions based on true informed consent.

"The communist, meanwhile, does not allow himself the luxury of inertia. He is intensely active. Because of him, the menace of communism in this country will remain a menace until the American people make themselves aware of the techniques of communism. No one who truly understands what it really is can be taken in by it. Yet the individual is handicapped by coming face-to-face with a conspiracy so monstrous he cannot believe it exists. The American mind simply has not come to a realization of the evil which has been introduced into our midst. It rejects even the assumption that human creatures could espouse a philosophy which must ultimately destroy all that is good and decent." – J. Edgar Hoover, *Communist "New Look" A Study in Duplicity*, The Elks Magazine, August 1956

What if the COVID19 pandemic was only a live-fire exercise in preparation for something significantly worse -more terrifying, that could be coming soon- pushed by a secret group of influential and powerful people with a nefarious purpose and intent? What if the

COVID19 pandemic was the first step to where the majority worldwide will own nothing, be happy, and be controlled by corporations run by a select few? If that is the goal, how could that be implemented on a global scale? What steps would need to be taken? What lives would need to be sacrificed? What economies would need to collapse and be rebuilt? What level of biblical type armageddon scenarios would need to be caused to convince and manipulate people into being happy with owning nothing and accepting corporations controlling every aspect of our lives for our safety and protection?

- We have discussed some examples of the history, operations, and experiments on why we should not blindly trust any government official.
- We have reviewed various studies and grants focused on GoF research for coronaviruses and bird flu hybrid viruses that can infect humans easily at the hands of the Gates Foundation, Dr. Fauci, corporations, organizations, and government officials worldwide, which have partnered together over the years.
- We have seen that the government is more interested in violating the rights of the innocent than going after the politically and financially elite clients of a known pedophile who most likely did not commit suicide.
- We have discussed groups of individuals wishing to instill a new one-world government under the guise of a new form of capitalism run by corporations controlled by a select few -the Great Reset.
- We have seen evidence of secret groups wishing to see Earth depopulated -e.g., Georgia Guidestones- as a way to reach their perfect utopia because they feel overpopulation will be the death of humanity.
- We have reviewed a published intelligence report indicating a massive population decline in Western cultures by 2025 - potentially providing evidence of some truth to a depopulation plan and goal.

- We have gone over evidence that COVID19 was not as dangerous and deadly as governments and pharmaceutical corporations claimed it to be from the start.
- We have seen a significant increase in cases of injuries and deaths in the VAERS database at the hands of the experimental vaccines pushed quickly to market.
- We have discussed how the COVID19 pandemic is potentially only the beginning of a plan to reach the goals we are being driven towards and that, more than likely, there will be more dangerous pandemics that will be forced upon us by carefully designed and modified viruses -e.g., weaponized bird flu.

One aspect I purposely didn't focus on in this book is the religious undertones and connections with the individuals, organizations, corporations, and governments discussed within this book. The amount of religious connections, symbolism, numerology, and prophecies that can be found connected to COVID19, the direction we are heading, and the different individuals, organizations, corporations, and governments is staggering. Books can and have been written on this topic alone, but it was not this book's purpose.

It has been my experience that trying to discuss the points and evidence I have brought up in this book without adding in the religious and spiritual aspects of humanity and our current situation is challenging enough to convince others of the truth. Trying to address the religious and spiritual aspects of everything would make me look even more like a crazed individual on a street corner screaming, "The End is Near!" to anyone in shouting distance - regardless of the truth behind the words.

Within the top four religions, there are roughly 2.4 billion Christians, 1.97 billion Muslims, 1.2 billion Hindus, and 500 million Buddhists worldwide. That is roughly 6.07 billion out of 8 billion people who believe in heaven and hell, good and evil. Some individuals and groups within these religions worship both sides - good or evil- with feverish intent, so these religious connections cannot be discounted or ignored because they seem farfetched. There is no depth to the evil that some are willing to commit.

It is plausible that some nefarious actions and goals of those with the resources and power to enact global changes come from worshiping evil deities -e.g., Ba'al, Moloch, Satan, Baphomet, etc.- which potentially require things like child sacrifices. There is a long history of the ritualistic killing of children that spans thousands of years. These types of points and possibilities cannot be discredited as nonsense and must be considered in context as one part of influence to what we see happening today. When is a coincidence not a coincidence?

One potential "non-coincidence" religious example that I feel is important enough to discuss -due to the connections to things discussed in this book- is that of the 2022 ad scandal around a Balenciaga -high-end luxury clothing brand- Gift Shop and Spring and Summer 2023 collection advertisement photoshoots:

Balenciaga was founded in 1919 by famous fashion designer Cristóbal Balenciaga in San Sebastian, Spain. Balenciaga eventually took his brand to Paris, France, shortly before the Nazis occupied Paris. During the Nazi occupation of Paris, Balenciaga made clothes for the wives of Nazi generals. By 1968, Balenciaga decided to close his fashion business and retire abruptly. After Balenciaga died in 1972, the Bogart Group purchased the Balenciaga house brand to relaunch and revive the luxury brand.

After success, the Balenciaga brand was sold to the Gucci Group in 2001, owned by the international luxury retail giant Pinault-Printemps-Redoute (PPR) -founded by François Pinault in 1963. Pinault's eldest son, François-Henri Pinault, took over PPR in 2005. In 2013, PPR was rebranded to Kering S.A. François-Henri Pinault married famous actress Salma Hayek. Kering owns the brand Gucci and Balenciaga, among other high-end luxury brands. One of Kering's independent directors is famous actress Emma Watson, a

U.N. Women Goodwill ambassador who focuses on sustainable fashion for Kering.

In 2015, Kering became an official partner with the Cannes Film Festival, formerly known as the International Film Festival -which intelligence agencies have infiltrated the film industry worldwide. In 2017, Kering committed its global environmental impact to the U.N. SDGs -Agenda 2030. In January 2019, Gucci announced the Chime for Change campaign, which focused on gender discrimination - supported by Facebook, Kering Foundation, and the Gates Foundation. In August 2019, Kering presented at the G7 summit for a Fashion Pact. In 2020, Kering started working with the WEF around sustainability priorities.

One of Balenciaga's top designers -who also designs for Adidas- is Lotta Volkova, who has worked directly with Kanye West for Balenciaga. Volkova has also caused controversy following various image posts on Instagram that depict a child's bedroom covered in "blood" or of her and two baby dolls she is holding covered in red latex paint. Volkova has repeatedly posted about and made references to cannibalism -even using the hashtag "canniballotta" with some posts. There are many other examples of posts by Volkova of this type of theme and context -including individuals displayed in ritualistic killings on top of a pentagram in front of Baphomet -a deity and demon. In October 2022, Balenciaga officially cut ties with rapper Kanye West following what some consider anti-Semitic statements on social media posts. Balenciaga was quick to condemn West but seemed okay with suggestive imagery of violent acts towards children, cannibalism, and satanic occult rituals. This quick high-level information helps set the stage for the suspect Balenciaga photoshoots that quickly dominated news headlines.

On November 16th, 2022, Balenciaga published their Gift Shop campaign that showcased high-end -very expensive- "children's products" that could be purchased. The photoshoot is said to be a continuation of photographer Gabrielle Galimberti's *Toy Stories* line

-photos of children worldwide from different socioeconomic classes who stand in front of their favorite toys. Each photo Balenciaga published included very suggestive stuffed plush bears wearing Bondage, Discipline, Dominance, and Submission (BDSM) adult wear. One photo had wine glasses, and mugs staged in front of a child. Each photo had hoodies, hats, chains, and sunglasses strategically placed. Many of the products placed around the children are available for purchase.

There is one photo in particular in this campaign that I want to discuss. This photo is of a boy -around 8 or 9- in red shoes standing on a Balenciaga Hotel Resort mat in the center of a room. Behind the boy to the right is a child's drawing of what looks to be a monster with a red face and black horns. Placed around the boy are various items: a can with a white candle, a black hoodie, white and black tape, a teapot, and yellow "caution" tape with the word Balenciaga printed on it, which had been used in other photoshoots. However, in this photo, the tear on the tape and how it overlaps the word under spells out "Baalenciaga." Using Google Translate, the Latin phrase "Baal enci aga" translates to "Baal is the king." Ba'al-Hadad is a Canaanite deity -called Moloch in Hebrew biblical text- considered to be the king of gods that has a cult that conducts child sacrifices related to it. Religious biblical text reference children being passed through fire to Moloch as a sacrifice. Ba'al has been referred to as Satan and Beelzebub in other religious texts. There is an illustration of Satan in the *Codex Gigas* or *"The Devil's Bible"* from the 13th century that looks close to the monster drawing behind the boy in the Balenciaga photoshoot.

Within LaVeyan Satanism -founded in 1966 by Anton LaVey- Satan is viewed as positive representations of things like pride and lust, which are considered part of the Seven Deadly Sins: Pride, Greed, Lust, Envy, Gluttony, Wrath, and Sloth. LaVeyan Satanism involves using and practicing occult magic for rituals with an upside-down pentagram -a five-pointed star- as its primary religious symbol.

LaVey took teachings from Aleister Crowley -a famous British occultist who founded the religion of Thelema in the early 1900s- for the ritualistic ceremonies around magic within his LaVeyan Satanism religion. Thelema uses a unicursal hexagram -a six-pointed star- as its primary religious symbol. If you look at the Balenciaga photo with the boy with red shoes and draw lines between the five items strategically placed and the boy, you can form an upside-down pentagram or a unicursal hexagram.

Thelema comes from Greek roots meaning "to want, desire, or will." Thelema's central doctrine is "Do what thou wilt shall be the whole of the Law." Interestingly, using Google Translate, the Latin phrase "ba len ci aga" translates to "do what you want." Thelema views Baphomet -often associated with the Sabbatic Goat- as an important figure and deity. Éliphas Lévi -a French occultist who wrote books on Kabbalah, occultism, and magic- created the Sabbatic Goat in the mid-1800s. Baphomet also has a history of being associated with the Knights Templar and Freemasonry. Crowley often incorporated drug use, sexual practices, and orgies in his rituals and viewed himself as the "Great Beast 666" (Nova Religio (2004) 7 (3): 7–25.).

""The Devil" is, historically, the God of any people that one personally dislikes. This has led to so much confusion of thought that THE BEAST 666 has preferred to let names stand as they are, and to proclaim simply that AIWAZ, the solar-phallic-hermetic "Lucifer," is His own Holy Guardian Angel, and "The Devil" SATAN or HADIT, the Supreme Soul behind RA-HOOR-KHUIT the Sun, the Lord of our particular unit of the Starry Universe. This serpent, SATAN, is not the enemy of Man, but He who made Gods of our race, knowing Good and Evil; He bade "Know Thyself!" and taught Initiation. He is "the Devil" of the Book of Thoth, and His emblem is BAPHOMET, the Androgyne who is the hieroglyph of arcane

perfection." – Aleister Crowley, *Magick, Liber ABA, Book 4, Part III: Magick in Theory and Practice*, 1929

In 1925, Crowley became the head of the Ordo Templi Orientis (OTO) -an occult organization modeled after European Freemasonry- which realigned with the Thelema religion after Crowley became leader. In 1935, Wilfred Talbot Smith -a staunch advocate of Thelema- founded the Agape Lodge for OTO in Hollywood, California, which eventually attracted the likes of L. Ron Hubbard, who participated in occult sex rituals. Hubbard would take what he learned from Thelema -after filing bankruptcy- and start his religion of Scientology. Scientology has tens of thousands of official members worldwide with a significant presence in Hollywood -especially in the film industry, with members like John Travolta and Tom Cruise advocating for Scientology.

On November 21st, 2022, Balenciaga released their Spring and Summer 2023 campaign photoshoots which were office themed, with one photo depicting a messy office with documents spread all over. One of the documents in this photo was a U.S. Supreme Court decision -*United States v. Williams*, 553 U.S. 285 (2008)- where it was ruled that offering to sell child pornography -even with images that were not children, e.g., a computer-generated images- was not protected by the U.S. Constitution First Amendment. Another photo displayed the art book *Michaël Borremans: As Sweet as It Gets* – Borremans is a Belgian painter who often depicts children in suggestive and violent acts. Borremans' 2018 *Fire from the Sun* series depicts bloody toddlers playing with fire surrounded by human limbs. Eerily similar to a theme around child sacrificing by fire for Ba'al and Moloch.

Now, taken individually and looked at with a singular focus, each photo and item within the Balenciaga photoshoots can be explained away, ignored, or considered a coincidence -an innocent mistake. However, we must look at all information available holistically to see any patterns that might exist to discern the truth. So, what do we know that could indicate something more than a coincidence?

- We know there are secretive groups actively working for nefarious purposes that worship evil satanic deities.
- We know child sex trafficking is big business only possible with those in government allowing or complicit in it.
- We know that the politically and royally connected -those with the resources and power to enact change globally- had ties to Epstein and his child sex trafficking ring and have yet to be brought to justice.
- We know that child sacrifice has been part of human history for thousands of years.
- We know occult religions heavily involved with psychedelic drug use and ritualistic sex magic have found their way into the elite circles -including Hollywood actors and actresses.
- We know a handful of trillion-dollar asset firms control mainstream media and run scripted narratives, including controlled opposition.
- We know those who were honestly investigating the U.S. Pizzagate story -trying to find answers to troubling questions around child trafficking- were vilified and shut down from reporting.
- We know Pinault -the owner of Kering- has ties to known associates of Epstein.
- We know Kering is connected to those heavily involved with the potential creation of COVID19 and the systematic suppression and censorship of information around COVID19.
- We know Kering is working towards bringing the world closer to the goals of the Great Reset and Agenda 2030.

British royalty ate human flesh -some was part of medical cannibalism- only a few centuries ago. On May 21st, 2011, the Daily Mail published the article *British royalty dined on human flesh (but don't worry it was 300 years ago),* detailing how cannibalism was used by British royalty. Cannibalism, including medical cannibalism, has been traced back beyond Greek and Roman times. This gives credence to the theory that the elite are sacrificing children to harvest adrenochrome -medical cannibalism- a chemical produced during the oxidation of adrenaline.

Hunter S. Thompson wrote about taking adrenochrome in his famous 1971 book *Fear and Loathing in Las Vegas,* and that adrenochrome made "pure mescaline seem like ginger beer." Theories say that adrenochrome has extreme psychedelic and vitality-giving properties -primarily when harvested from children, which would be medical cannibalism. In 1962, the journal International Review of Neurobiology published the study *The Effect of Adrenochrome and Adrenolutin On the Behavior of Animals and the Psychology of Man,* which found that taking adrenochrome could have effects that lasted for days and is similar to those suffering from schizophrenia (Int Rev Neur. 1962;4: 307-371.). Should we assume the horrid cannibalistic practices stopped because we were told they were stopped?

Can we afford to assume things like the Balenciaga photoshoot are a pure coincidence and innocent at heart? Can we afford to ignore the religious connections and the ramifications of those connections? At what point do coincidences no longer become coincidences? Is it reasonable to assume the worst -not a coincidence- for this situation and many others like it?

Elon Musk is someone to keep an eye on. I have seen many in the liberty community recently speak positively of Musk for his takeover of Twitter and the release of the Twitter Files, proving once again that the government is wholly corrupt and unethical. However, so many seem to forget all of the suspect connections that he has ties to. It wouldn't be the first time those seeking a freer world were given a false choice. Do you think Musk is as altruistic as he is presented to us or is that only his demeanor -public persona- not his true nature?

On March 17th, 2008, Bloomberg published the article *Young Global Leaders--Anderson Cooper and Leonardo DiCaprio Are In The Most Exclusive Private Social Network In The World.*, which lists Musk as part of this exclusive group and organization -YGL is a Klaus Schwab organization. In October 2022, Musk unveiled his $7,500 "Devil's Champion" Halloween costume -a red armor suit with the Baphomet Sabbatic Goat on the front. Musk made an image of him in this suit as his profile photo on Twitter. He has made most of his fortune from companies he founded that receive billions in government grants and funding. Musk is heavily invested in China - working with government officials- which is where most of his production facilities are.

Musk founded the companies SpaceX, OpenAI, and Neuralink. SpaceX developed Starlink -satellite Internet constellations- intending to launch up to 42,000 satellites in low Earth orbit to help monitor Earth and provide Internet access -at a cost- to everyone worldwide. OpenAI -Microsoft is one of the largest investors- focuses on developing a "friendly AI" that would benefit humanity while being regulated by governments or an authoritative organization. Should we assume this AI would only be used for ethical and moral purposes? Of course, at the same time, Musk also claims that AI is the greatest threat to humanity -Climate Change being the second greatest threat (recently saying population collapse due to low birth rates is a more considerable risk than Climate Change). Musk is a proponent of government action and the WEF's focus on sustainability in fighting Climate Change. Neuralink focuses on developing brain-to-computer interfaces that are implantable within the brain, allowing thought to control digital actions. There is no guarantee that it would not work in reverse, which has terrifying ramifications.

"I don't think we should divide issues semi-randomly into "left" and "right" tribes, as it inhibits critical thinking. The idea that there are too many people generally stems from the axiomatic flaw that Earth's environment can't sustain its current population. It's not some illuminati plot to destroy humanity, but rather an extension of the well-meaning environmental sustainability movement that has gone too far. My reason for declining the Davos [WEF] invitation was not because I thought they were engaged in diabolical scheming, but because it sounded boring af [as fuck] lol [laugh out loud]" – Elon Musk, *CNN interview*, September 2015

Could the companies Musk founded be part of the WEF Great Reset -pushing Agenda 2030 "sustainability efforts"- and leading us down a new path towards transhumanism as a potential replacement to religions worldwide? Transhumanism is one of the goals of the WEF and Great Reset. Remember, controlled opposition would publicly denounce and "fight" against something while benefiting it and supporting it through action and direction. Could Musk be controlled opposition giving many a false choice into thinking someone with the resources and power to fight against this global cabal will come to save them, thereby keeping them from saving themselves? Similar to the Bystander Effect -people tend to ignore crimes and not offer help to victims when others are present due to thinking someone else will handle the problem. Could Musk's Neuralink implants be the "Mark of the Beast" prophesied to the mark showing humanity being enslaved to evil? These philosophical questions must be asked because the answers will dictate the future.

"AI is much more advanced than people realize. It would be fairly obvious if you saw a robot walking around talking and behaving like a person... What's not obvious is a huge server bank in a vault somewhere with an intelligence that's potentially vastly greatly than what a human mind can do. And it's eyes and ears will be everywhere,

every camera, every device that's network accessible... Humanity's position on this planet depends on its intelligence so if our intelligence is exceeded, it's unlikely that we will remain in charge of the planet." – Elon Musk, *CNN interview*, September 2015

The road to hell is paved with "good intentions," correct? Technology is a double-edged sword, and it will be turned on us to enact more control. It is not a stretch to see where this technology - within our current reality- is heading. Soon will be the days that thinking "illegal" thoughts -unspoken words to yourself- will be met with swift punishment and retribution through an uplink connecting our brains to an AI controlled by all-present intelligence -an intelligence possibly controlled by a select few. This technology Musk is pushing to bring to the market is the future of tyranny. Global conspiracies control what we see and hear -in the sense of theater- and will use this technology to their benefit. All of this would seem to be fact unless we believe in nothing but coincidences.

So, what is our fate? We have gone through a "great awakening," which quickly became a "woke" culture that is anything but awake. Remember, Rome burned from within and collapsed -like every other great civilization throughout human history. The U.S. is no different and will eventually meet the same fate with frightening speed. Not only do we have to worry about the man-made problems affecting us discussed throughout this book, but the potential ticking clock of the next Age Ender that seems to be fast approaching -possibly within our lifetimes, roughly 2035-2050. What if some push things to align us with their goals before the next Age Ender? Is it possible that the stage is being set to introduce a new global religion taking us into the next Age of humanity?

I will leave you with one theory I can see playing out soon -within the next five to ten years. I see the potential that the COVID19 pandemic could have been created to convince the masses to inject a true bioweapon -COVID19 vaccines- that was created to target Western culture with a timed "poison" that takes effect within two to five years from an injection. The potential being the more injections someone gets, the faster things like death are triggered. Remember, Gates, partnered with Pfizer in 2002 to create an all-in-one injectable contraceptive. I am not saying the vaccines are a 100% killer or will sterilize everyone, but the deaths and population decline will most likely be catastrophic. If this is true, we will see massive "excess" sudden deaths and low birth rates attributed to anything but the COVID19 vaccines leading into 2025, significantly reducing the population in Western countries -meeting the expectations of the 2017 Deagle intelligence report previously discussed. Of course, we should assume the die-off would include additional pandemics to enact further greater control of those who survive.

China is about maintaining its culture -the U.S. is not. China has tens of thousands of intelligence officers and recruited agents already established within the U.S. -they could be some of the nicest people we would ever meet but loyal to China. Politicians can be and are paid to be loyal to China -e.g., President Biden. Leading up to now, there was no way any country could invade the U.S. due to its military size and the significant amount of weapons in the hands of U.S. citizens. However, if this "mighty" military and civilian force are poisoned from within -vaccines, food supply, socio-economic changes, etc.- then that force would be significantly diminished, resulting in the inability to defend itself.

Suppose the next Age Ender is fast approaching, and the COVID19 vaccines are the true bioweapon -with additional pandemics- that will cause a significant population decline. In that case, it is reasonable to see China wanting to use the underground cities and highway systems built throughout the U.S. This would further secure China's culture leading into the next Age of humanity. An Age potentially dominated by transhumanism and tyranny. If true, global changes will be enacted after the population declines -

including countries like China invading the U.S. to secure these underground facilities. Am I wrong? I hope I am wrong, but time will tell.

If you read through this entire book and still think vaccines are your best option for protecting your health, then that is your decision, and no one should vilify you for making that decision. It is your health and your life on the line; you are responsible for it, so only you should be making these decisions with actual informed consent, not engineered consent. The same goes for those who choose not to vaccinate or get booster shots. No one should vilify them for deciding to protect themselves in the way they think is best. Forcing vaccinations and medical procedures will always end in disaster and spits in the face of actual freedom, rights, and bodily autonomy.

Nothing about our future looks bright, and things will only get worse. We allow it to happen by going along with tyranny and not speaking out against the atrocities committed here in the U.S. and worldwide. I feel sad for my children and the innocent people worldwide who will not understand the freedom I grew up with before the dawn of the Internet and the beginning of Tyranny on a global scale. That experience of true freedom is all but gone as we head into the future with "Big Brother" always watching and at our side, controlling and listening to our every move. As with everything, we can and will get through this next phase of Tyranny and eventually circle back to freedom and rights. How long this could take is anyone's guess. Hopefully, during this next great upheaval and cycle, we can evolve past the endless need for government.

Meet the future with confidence and determination

Welcome to the new Age of Tyranny

"To be hopeful in bad times is not just foolishly romantic. It is based on the fact that human history is a history not only of cruelty, but also of compassion, sacrifice, courage, kindness. What we choose to emphasize in this complex history will determine our lives. If we see only the worst, it destroys our capacity to do something. If we remember those times and places — and there are so many — where people have behaved magnificently, this gives us the energy to act, and at least the possibility of sending this spinning top of a world in a different direction. And if we do act, in however small a way, we don't have to wait for some grand utopian future. The future is an infinite succession of presents, and to live now as we think human beings should live, in defiance of all that is bad around us, is itself a marvelous victory." – Howard Zinn, *A Power Governments Cannot Suppress*, December 1st, 2006

References

1. Parker, C. *8 predictions for the world in 2030*. World Economic Forum. November 12th, 2016. (Statement in video) https://web.archive.org/web/20210802122435/https://www.weforum.org/agenda/2016/11/8-predictions-for-the-world-in-2030/ **(Page 8 & 75)**
2. Chief, W. *Countering Criticism of the Warren Report*. CIA. NARA Record Number: 104-10406-10110. January 4th, 1967. (JFK Assassination Documents) https://web.archive.org/web/20200810193235/https://www.maryferrell.org/showDoc.html?docId=9547 **(Page 21)**
3. District of Columbia Court of Appeals: *Warren v. District of Columbia*, 444 A.2d 1 (D.C. Ct. of App. 1981) **(Page 24)**
4. U.S. Supreme Court: *DeShaney v. Winnebago County Department of Social Services*, 489 U.S. 189 (1989) **(Page 24)**
5. U.S. Supreme Court: *Roe v. Wade*, 410 U.S. 113 (1973) **(Page 27)**
6. O'Neill, T. *CHAOS: Charles Manson, the CIA, and the Secret History of the Sixties*. Little, Brown and Company. June 25th, 2019 **(Page 32)**
7. Kissinger, H. *National Security Study Memorandum 200: Implications of Worldwide Population Growth for U.S. Security and Overseas Interests (NSSM200)*. United States National Security Council. December 10th, 1974. https://archive.org/details/NSSMHenryA.KissingerReport200435 **(Page 46 & 276)**
8. Hamer, D. *The God Gene: How Faith Is Hard-Wired Into Our Genes*. Random House Publishing Group. September 27th, 2005 **(Page 47)**
9. Rilstone, J., Alkhater, R., and Minassian, B. *Brain Dopamine–Serotonin Vesicular Transport Disease and Its Treatment*. N Engl J Med 2013; 368:543-550. doi:10.1056/NEJMoa1207281 **(Page 47)**
10. National Security Agency/Central Security Service (NSA/CSS), Signals Intelligence Directorate (SID), Office of General Counsel. *United States Signals Intelligence Directive (USSID) SP0018 (U) Legal Compliance and U.S. Persons Minimization Procedures*. January 25th, 2011. https://web.archive.org/web/20131120090356/https://www.dni.gov/files/documents/1118/CLEANEDFinal%20USSID%20SP0018.pdf **(Page 59)**
11. National Security Agency/Central Security Service (NSA/CSS), Signals Intelligence Directorate (SID), Office of Oversight and Compliance. *United States Signals Intelligence Directive (USSID) SP0019 (U) NSA/CSS Signals*

Intelligence Directorate – Oversight and Compliance Policy. November 13th, 2012.
https://web.archive.org/web/20141126033603/https://www.aclu.org/files/asset s/eo12333/NSA/United%20States%20Signals%20Intelligence%20Directive% 20USSID%20SP0019.pdf **(Page 59)**

12. Nightingale, S. and Farid, H. *AI-synthesized faces are indistinguishable from real faces and more trustworthy*. Proc Natl Acad Sci U S A. 2022 Feb 22; 119(8):e2120481119. doi:10.1073/pnas.2120481119. **(Page 67)**

13. Bendell, J. *Does capitalism need some Marxism to survive the Fourth Industrial Revolution?*. World Economic Forum. June 22nd, 2016.
https://web.archive.org/web/20160926233728/https://www.weforum.org/agen da/2016/06/could-capitalism-need-some-marxism-to-survive-the-4th-industrial-revolution/ **(Page 71)**

14. Klaus, S. and Malleret, T. *COVID-19: The Great Reset*. Forum Publishing. July 9th, 2020 **(Page 73)**

15. United Nations. *United Nations Sustainable Development – Agenda 21*. June 1992.
https://web.archive.org/web/20210318013442/https://sdgs.un.org/sites/default/ files/publications/Agenda21.pdf **(Page 82)**

16. World Health Organization. *Immunization Agenda 2030: A Global Strategy To Leave No One Behind*. April 1st, 2020.
https://web.archive.org/web/20201224144945/https://www.who.int/docs/defau lt-source/immunization/strategy/ia2030/ia2030-document-en.pdf **(Page 83)**

17. ID2020. *Alliance Manifesto*. September 2018.
https://web.archive.org/web/20200413080819/https://id2020.org/uploads/files/ ID2020-Alliance-Manifesto.pdf **(Page 83)**

18. World Economic Forum. *Investing in Forests: Business Case*. June 4th, 2021.
https://web.archive.org/web/20210612050347/http://www3.weforum.org/docs /WEF_Investing_in_Forests_2021.pdf **(Page 85)**

19. Labba, I., Steinhausen, H., Almius, L., et al. *Nutritional Composition and Estimated Iron and Zinc Bioavailability of Meat Substitutes Available on the Swedish Market*. Nutrients. 2022; 14(19):3903. doi:10.3390/nu14193903 **(Page 89)**

20. Makary, M. and Daniel, M., *Medical error—the third leading cause of death in the US* BMJ 2016; 353 :i2139 doi:10.1136/bmj.i2139 **(Page 92)**

21. U.S. Department of Justice. *2020 National Health Care Fraud and Opioid Takedown*. 2020.
https://web.archive.org/web/20201004081132/https://www.justice.gov/crimin al-fraud/hcf-2020-takedown/press-release **(Page 93)**

22. U.S. Supreme Court: *Daubert v. Merrell Dow Pharmaceuticals, Inc.*, 509 U.S. 579 (1993) **(Page 95)**

23. Lesné, S., Koh, M., Kotilinek, L. et al. *A specific amyloid-β protein assembly in the brain impairs memory*. Nature 440, 352–357 (2006). doi:10.1038/nature04533 **(Page 98)**

24. Stull, V., Finer, E., Bergmans, R. et al. *Impact of Edible Cricket Consumption on Gut Microbiota in Healthy Adults, a Double-blind, Randomized Crossover Trial*. Sci Rep 8, 10762 (2018). doi:10.1038/s41598-018-29032-2 **(Page 98)**

25. Alahmad, B., Khraishah, H., Royé, D. et al. *Associations Between Extreme Temperatures and Cardiovascular Cause-Specific Mortality: Results From 27 Countries*. Circulation. 2023 Jan 3;147(1):35-46. doi:10.1161/CIRCULATIONAHA.122.061832. **(Page 100)**

26. Davidson, B. *Weatherman's Guide to the Sun: Third Edition*. Space Weather News. September 1st, 2020 **(Page 103)**

27. Yu, F. and Luo, G. *Effect of solar variations on particle formation and cloud condensation nuclei*. Environ. Res. Lett. April 2014 9(4):045004 doi:10.1088/1748-9326/9/4/045004 **(Page 103)**

28. Maliniemi, V., Asikainen, T., Salminen, A., and Mursula, K. *Assessing North Atlantic winter climate response to geomagnetic activity and solar irradiance variability*. Q J R Meteorol Soc. 2019; 145: 3780– 3789. doi:10.1002/qj.3657 **(Page 103)**

29. Lee, Y., Kim, K., Kwak, Y., et al. *High-latitude mesospheric intense turbulence associated with high-speed solar wind streams*. Astrophys Space Sci 364, 210 (2019). doi:10.1007/s10509-019-3691-0 **(Page 103)**

30. Roll, S., Frode, F., and Eivin, R. *Solar activity at birth predicted infant survival and women's fertility in historical Norway*. Proc. R. Soc. B. 282:20142032. 20142032. 2015 doi:10.1098/rspb.2014.2032 **(Page 104)**

31. Laj, C., Guillou, H., and Kissel, C., *Dynamics of the earth magnetic field in the 10-75 kyr period comprising the Laschamp and Mono Lake excursions: New results from the French Chaîne des Puys in a global perspective*, Earth and Planetary Science Letters, vol. 387, pp. 184–197, 2014. doi:10.1016/j.epsl.2013.11.031. **(Page 105)**

32. Velikovsky, I. *Worlds in Collision*. Macmillan Publishers. April 3rd, 1950. **(Page 106)**

33. Thomas, C. *The ADAM and EVE STORY*. Time (parts of the publication was classified by the CIA). March 11th, 1966. https://web.archive.org/web/20210105180135/https://www.cia.gov/readingroom/docs/CIA-RDP79B00752A000300070001-8.pdf **(Page 107)**

34. Yang, Q., Zhang, Z., Gregg, E., et al. *Added Sugar Intake and Cardiovascular Diseases Mortality Among US Adults*. JAMA Intern Med. 2014;174(4):516–524. doi:10.1001/jamainternmed.2013.13563 **(Page 108)**

35. Kearns, C., Schmidt, L., and Glantz, S. *Sugar Industry and Coronary Heart Disease Research: A Historical Analysis of Internal Industry Documents*. JAMA Intern Med. 2016;176(11):1680–1685.doi:10.1001/jamainternmed.2016.5394 **(Page 108)**

36. McGandy, R., Hegsted, D., and Stare, F. *Dietary Fats, Carbohydrates and Atherosclerotic Vascular Disease*. N Engl J Med. 1967 Aug 3;277(5):245-7 concl. doi:10.1056/NEJM196707272770405 **(Page 108)**

37. O'Connor, A. *Coca-Cola Funds Scientists Who Shift Blame for Obesity Away From Bad Diets*. New York Times. August 9th, 2015. https://web.archive.org/web/20220809105832/https://archive.nytimes.com/well.blogs.nytimes.com/2015/08/09/coca-cola-funds-scientists-who-shift-blame-for-obesity-away-from-bad-diets/ **(Page 110)**

38. Bernays, E. *Propaganda*. Ig Publishing. 1928 **(Page 120)**

39. Bernays, E. *The Engineering of Consent*. The ANNALS of the American Academy of Political and Social Science, 250(1), 113–120. doi:10.1177/000271624725000116 **(Page 120)**

40. Kang, D., Adams, J., Coleman, D., et al. *Long-term benefit of Microbiota Transfer Therapy on autism symptoms and gut microbiota*. Sci Rep 9, 5821 (2019). doi:10.1038/s41598-019-42183-0 **(Page 124)**

41. Roossinck, M. *Virus: An Illustrated Guide to 101 Incredible Microbes*. Ivy Press, 2016 **(Page 126)**

42. Baltimore, D. *Sixty Years of Discovery*. Annu. Rev. Immunol. 2019 April; 37:1-17. doi: 10.1146/annurev-immunol-042718-041210 **(Page 127)**

43. Cathcart, R.. *Vitamin C, Titrating To Bowel Tolerance, Anascorbemia, and Acute Induced Scurvy*. Medical Hypotheses. 1981. 7:1359-1376 doi:10.1016/0306-9877(81)90126-2. **(Page 131)**

44. Gorton, H. and Jarvis, K. *The effectiveness of vitamin C in preventing and relieving the symptoms of virus-induced respiratory infections*. J Manipulative Physiol Ther. 1999 Oct;22(8):530-3.). doi:10.1016/S0161-4754(99)70005-9 **(Page 131)**

45. Hemilä, H. and Chalker, E. *Vitamin C for preventing and treating the common cold*. Cochrane Database Syst Rev. 2013 Jan; 2013(1): CD000980. doi:10.1002/14651858.CD000980.pub4. **(Page 132)**

46. Holick, M. *Vitamin D Deficiency*. N Engl J Med. 2007 Jul 19;357(3):266-81. doi:10.1056/NEJMra070553 **(Page 132)**

47. Lalongo, C., Labriola, R., Ferraguti, G., et al. *Vitamin K deficiency and covid-19*. Scand J Clin Lab Invest. 2020 Nov;80(7):525-527.). doi:10.1080/00365513.2020.1805122. **(Page 132)**

48. Israel, A., Shenhar, Y., Green, I., et al. *Large-Scale Study of Antibody Titer Decay following BNT162b2 mRNA Vaccine or SARS-CoV-2 Infection*. Vaccines. 2022; 10(1):64. doi:10.3390/vaccines10010064 **(Page 133 & 160)**

49. John, T. and Samuel, R. *Herd immunity and herd effect: new insights and definitions*. Eur J Epidemiol. 2000;16(7):601-6. doi:10.1023/A:1007626510002 **(Page 134)**

50. White, D. *Fears coronavirus arrived in Europe in OCTOBER 'when French athletes at World Military Games in Wuhan brought it home'*. The Sun. May 6th, 2020.

https://web.archive.org/web/20200507082707/https://www.thesun.co.uk/news/11565077/fears-coronavirus-europe-october-french-athletes-military-games-wuhan/ **(Page 137)**

51. Center for Health Security. *Event 201: A Global Pandemic Exercise.* October 18th, 2020. https://web.archive.org/web/20220707015503/https://www.centerforhealthsecurity.org/our-work/exercises/event201/about **(Page 137)**

52. Lu, R., Zhao, X., Li, J., et al. *Genomic characterisation and epidemiology of 2019 novel coronavirus: implications for virus origins and receptor binding.* Lancet. 2020 Feb 22;395(10224):565-574. doi:10.1016/S0140-6736(20)30251-8 **(Page 138)**

53. Pradhan, P., Pandey, A., Mishra, A. et al. *Uncanny similarity of unique inserts in the 2019-nCoV spike protein to HIV-1 gp120 and Gag.* Version 1. bioRxiv. Preprint. 2020 Jan 31. doi:10.1101/2020.01.30.927871 **(Page 139)**

54. Liu, S., Saif, L., Weiss, S., and Su, L. *HIV-1 did not contribute to the 2019-nCoV genome.* Emerg Microbes Infect. 2020; 9(1): 378–381. doi:10.1080/22221751.2020.1727299 **(Page 140)**

55. Ji, W., Wang, W., Zhao, X., et al. *Cross-species transmission of the newly identified coronavirus 2019-nCoV.* J Med Virol. 2020 Apr;92(4):433-440. doi:10.1002/jmv.25682 **(Page 140)**

56. Snider, J., You, J., Wang, X., et al. *Group IIA secreted phospholipase A2 is associated with the pathobiology leading to COVID-19 mortality.* J Clin Invest. 2021 Oct 1;131(19):e149236. doi:10.1172/JCI149236 **(Page 141)**

57. Brogna, C., Cristoni, S., Petrillo, M., et al. *Toxin-like peptides in plasma, urine and faecal samples from COVID-19 patients* [version 2; peer review: 2 approved]. F1000Research 2021, 10:550. doi:10.12688/f1000research.54306.2 **(Page 141)**

58. Chiu, D. and Duesberg, P. *The toxicity of azidothymidine (AZT) on human and animal cells in culture at concentrations used for antiviral therapy.* Genetica. 1995;95(1-3):103-9. doi:10.1007/BF01435004 **(Page 142)**

59. Andersen, K., Rambaut, A., Lipkin, W., et al. *The proximal origin of SARS-CoV-2.* Nat Med. 2020 Apr;26(4):450-452. doi:10.1038/s41591-020-0820-9 **(Page 144)**

60. Huff, A. *The Truth About Wuhan.* Skyhorse. December 6th, 2022 **(Page 144)**

61. Menachery, V., Yount, B., Debbink, K., et al. *A SARS-like cluster of circulating bat coronaviruses shows potential for human emergence.* Nat Med. 2015; 21(12): 1508–1513. doi:10.1038/nm.3985 **(Page 145)**

62. Department of Defense. *Fact Sheet: The Department of Defense's Cooperative Threat Reduction Program - Biological Threat Reduction Program Activities in Ukraine.* March 11th, 2022. https://web.archive.org/web/20220311175606/https://media.defense.gov/2022/Mar/11/2002954612/-1/-1/0/FACT-SHEET-THE-DEPARTMENT-OF-DEFENSE'S-COOPERATIVE-THREAT-REDUCTION-PROGRAM-

BIOLOGICAL-THREAT-REDUCTION-PROGRAM-ACTIVITIES-IN-UKRAINE.PDF **(Page 146)**

63. Buzhdygan, T., DeOre, B., Baldwin-Leclair, A., et al. *The SARS-CoV-2 spike protein alters barrier function in 2D static and 3D microfluidic in-vitro models of the human blood–brain barrier.* Neurobiol Dis. 2020 Dec;146:105131. doi:10.1016/j.nbd.2020.105131 **(Page 149 & 212)**

64. Hu, B., Huang, S., and Yin, L. *The cytokine storm and COVID-19.* J Med Virol. 2021;93:250–256. doi:10.1002/jmv.26232 **(Page 150)**

65. Wolff, G. *Influenza vaccination and respiratory virus interference among Department of Defense personnel during the 2017-2018 influenza season.* Vaccine. 2020 Jan 10;38(2):350-354. doi:10.1016/j.vaccine.2019.10.005 **(Page 152)**

66. Gurkan, O., O'Donnell, C., Brower, R., et al. *Differential effects of mechanical ventilatory strategy on lung injury and systemic organ inflammation in mice.* Am J Physiol Lung Cell Mol Physiol. 2003 Sep;285(3):L710-8. doi:10.1152/ajplung.00044.2003 **(Page 155)**

67. Park, S., Kim, Y., Yi, S., et al. *Coronavirus Disease Outbreak in Call Center, South Korea.* Emerg Infect Dis. 2020 Aug;26(8):1666-1670. doi:10.3201/eid2608.201274 **(Page 157)**

68. Gao, M., Yang, L., Chen, X., et al. *A study on infectivity of asymptomatic SARS-CoV-2 carriers.* Respir Med. 2020 Aug;169:106026. doi:10.1016/j.rmed.2020.106026 **(Page 157)**

69. Griffin, S. *Covid-19: Asymptomatic cases may not be infectious, Wuhan study indicates.* BMJ 2020;371:m4695. doi:10.1136/bmj.m4695 **(Page 157)**

70. Bender, J., Brandl, M., Höhle, M., et al. *Analysis of Asymptomatic and Presymptomatic Transmission in SARS-CoV-2 Outbreak, Germany, 2020.* Emerg Infect Dis. 2021 Apr;27(4):1159-1163. doi:10.3201/eid2704.204576 **(Page 157)**

71. Rothe, C., Schunk, M., and Sothmann, P. *Transmission of 2019-nCoV Infection from an Asymptomatic Contact in Germany.* N Engl J Med 2020; 382:970-971. doi:10.1056/NEJMc2001468 **(Page 158)**

72. Kronbichler, A., Kresse, D., Yoon, S., et al. *Asymptomatic patients as a source of COVID-19 infections: A systematic review and meta-analysis.* Int J Infect Dis. 2020 Sep;98:180-186. doi:10.1016/j.ijid.2020.06.05254 **(Page 158)**

73. Ma, Q., Liu, J., Liu, Q., et al. *Global Percentage of Asymptomatic SARS-CoV-2 Infections Among the Tested Population and Individuals with Confirmed COVID-19 Diagnosis A Systematic Review and Meta-analysis.* JAMA Netw Open. 2021;4(12):e2137257. doi:10.1001/jamanetworkopen.2021.37257 **(Page 159)**

74. Jayaweeraa, M., Pererab, H., Gunawardanaa, B., and Manatungea, J. *Transmission of COVID-19 virus by droplets and aerosols: A critical review on the unresolved dichotomy.* Environ Res. 2020 Sep; 188: 109819. doi:10.1016/j.envres.2020.109819 **(Page 161)**

75. Dawood, A. *Transmission of SARS CoV-2 virus through the ocular mucosa worth taking precautions.* Vacunas. 2021 Jan-Apr;22(1):56-57. doi:10.1016/j.vacun.2020.09.003 **(Page 162)**

76. Bleier, B., Ramanathan, Jr, M., and Lane, A. *COVID-19 Vaccines May Not Prevent Nasal SARS-CoV-2 Infection and Asymptomatic Transmission.* Otolaryngol Head Neck Surg. 2021 Feb;164(2):305-307. doi:10.1177/01945998209826 **(Page 162)**

77. Hachmann, N., Miller, J., Collier, A., et al. *Neutralization Escape by SARS-CoV-2 Omicron Subvariants BA.2.12.1, BA.4, and BA.5.* N Engl J Med. 2022 Jul 7;387(1):86-88. doi:10.1056/NEJMc2206576 **(Page 165)**

78. LKS Faculty of Medicine. *HKUMed finds Omicron SARS-CoV-2 can infect faster and better than Delta in human bronchus but with less severe infection in lung.* University of Hong Kong. December 15th, 2021. https://web.archive.org/web/20211215101251/https://www.med.hku.hk/en/news/press/20211215-omicron-sars-cov-2-infection **(Page 167)**

79. Crane, L., Decker, R., Flaaen, A., et al. *Business Exit During the COVID-19 Pandemic: Non-Traditional Measures in Historical Context.* J Macroecon. 2022 Jun;72:103419. doi:10.1016/j.jmacro.2022.103419 **(Page 177)**

80. AIER Staff. *Lockdowns Do Not Control the Coronavirus: The Evidence.* American Institute for Economic Research. December 19th, 2020. https://web.archive.org/web/20201220045718/https://www.aier.org/article/lockdowns-do-not-control-the-coronavirus-the-evidence/ **(Page 179)**

81. Panchal, U., Salazar de Pablo, G., Franco, M., et al. *The impact of COVID-19 lockdown on child and adolescent mental health: systematic review.* Eur Child Adolesc Psychiatry. 2021 Aug 18: 1–27. doi:10.1007/s00787-021-01856-w **(Page 180)**

82. Haile, C., Baker, M., Sanchez, S., et al. *An Immunconjugate Vaccine Alters Distribution and Reduces the Antinociceptive, Behavioral and Physiological Effects of Fentanyl in Male and Female Rats.* Pharmaceutics. 2022 Oct 26;14(11):2290. doi:10.3390/pharmaceutics14112290 **(Page 181)**

83. U.S. Supreme Court: *NFIB v. OSHA*, 590 U.S. ___ (2020) **(Page 184)**

84. U.S. Supreme Court: *Biden v. Missouri*, 590 U.S. ___ (2020) **(Page 185)**

85. U.S. Supreme Court: *Bruesewitz v. Wyeth, LLC*, 562 U.S. 223 (2011) **(Page 194 & 280)**

86. Good, P. *Evidence the U.S. autism epidemic initiated by acetaminophen (Tylenol) is aggravated by oral antibiotic amoxicillin/clavulanate (Augmentin) and now exponentially by herbicide glyphosate (Roundup).* Clin Nutr ESPEN. 2018 Feb;23:171-183. doi:10.1016/j.clnesp.2017.10.005 **(Page 198)**

87. U.S. Court of Federal Claims: *Boatmon v. Secretary of Health and Human Services*, 13-611 (Fed. Cl. 2017) **(Page 199)**

88. Block, S., Yogev, R., Hayden, F., et al. *Shedding and immunogenicity of live attenuated influenza vaccine virus in subjects 5–49 years of age.* Vaccine. 2008 Sep 8;26(38):4940-6. doi:10.1016/j.vaccine.2008.07.013 **(Page 201)**

89. Kekatos, M. *What to know about vaccine-derived polio after rare case found in New York*. ABC News. July 22nd, 2022. https://web.archive.org/web/20220722191425/https://abcnews.go.com/Health/vaccine-derived-polio-rare-case-found-york/story?id=87200349 **(Page 201)**

90. Yang, Q., Jacobs, T., McCallen, J., et al. *Analysis of Pre-existing IgG and IgM Antibodies against Polyethylene Glycol (PEG) in the General Population*. Anal Chem. 2016 Dec 6;88(23):11804-11812. doi:10.1021/acs.analchem.6b03437 **(Page 202)**

91. Thiele, W., Kyjacova, L., Köhler, A., and Sleeman, J. *A cautionary note: Toxicity of polyethylene glycol 200 injected intraperitoneally into mice*. Lab Anim. 2020 Aug;54(4):391-396. doi:10.1177/00236772198736 **(Page 203)**

92. Lim, D. and Maas, W. *Reverse transcriptase in bacteria*. Mol Microbiol. 1989 Aug;3(8):1141-4. doi:10.1111/j.1365-2958.1989.tb00264.x **(Page 204)**

93. Sciamanna, I., Luca, C., and Spadafora, C. *The Reverse Transcriptase Encoded by LINE-1 Retrotransposons in the Genesis, Progression, and Therapy of Cancer*. Front Chem. 2016; 4: 6. doi:10.3389/fchem.2016.00006 **(Page 205)**

94. Zhang, L., Richards, A., Barrasa, M., et al. *Reverse-transcribed SARS-CoV-2 RNA can integrate into the genome of cultured human cells and can be expressed in patient-derived tissues*. Proc Natl Acad Sci U S A. 2021 May 25;118(21):e2105968118. doi:10.1073/pnas.2105968118 **(Page 205)**

95. Aldén, M., Falla, F., Yang, D., et al. *Intracellular Reverse Transcription of Pfizer BioNTech COVID-19 mRNA Vaccine BNT162b2 In Vitro in Human Liver Cell Line*. Curr Issues Mol Biol. 2022 Feb 25;44(3):1115-1126. doi:10.3390/cimb44030073 **(Page 205)**

96. Yeoa, W. and Ngb, Q. *Passive inhaled mRNA vaccination for SARS-Cov-2*. Med Hypotheses. 2021 Jan; 146: 110417. doi:10.1016/j.mehy.2020.110417 **(Page 207)**

97. Nuismer, S. and Bull, J. *Self-disseminating vaccines to suppress zoonoses*. Nat Ecol Evol. 2020 Sep;4(9):1168-1173. doi:10.1038/s41559-020-1254-y **(Page 208)**

98. León, T., Dorabawila, V., Nelson, L., et al. *Cases and Hospitalizations by COVID-19 Vaccination Status and Previous COVID-19 Diagnosis — California and New York, May–November 2021*. MMWR Morb Mortal Wkly Rep. 2022 Jan 28;71(4):125-131. doi:10.15585/mmwr.mm7104e1 **(Page 211)**

99. Chemaitelly, H., Ayoub, H., AlMukdad, S., et al. *Protection from previous natural infection compared with mRNA vaccination against SARS-CoV-2 infection and severe COVID-19 in Qatar: a retrospective cohort study*. Lancet Microbe. 2022 Dec;3(12):e944-e955. doi:10.1016/S2666-5247(22)00287-7 **(Page 211)**

100. McCarthy, B. *Who is Robert Malone? Joe Rogan's guest was a vaccine scientist, became an anti-vaccine darling*. PolitiFact. January 6th, 2022. https://web.archive.org/web/20220106192213/https://www.politifact.com/artic

le/2022/jan/06/who-robert-malone-joe-rogans-guest-was-vaccine-sci/ **(Page 211)**

101. Rhea, E., Logsdon, A., Hansen, K., et al. *The S1 protein of SARS-CoV-2 crosses the blood–brain barrier in mice.* Nat Neurosci. 2021 Mar;24(3):368-378. doi: 10.1038/s41593-020-00771-8 **(Page 212)**

102. Mörz, M. *A Case Report: Multifocal Necrotizing Encephalitis and Myocarditis after BNT162b2 mRNA Vaccination against COVID-19.* Vaccines (Basel). 2022 Oct 1;10(10):1651. doi:10.3390/vaccines10101651 **(Page 212)**

103. Tseng, C., Sbrana, E., Iwata-Yoshikawa, N., et al. *Immunization with SARS Coronavirus Vaccines Leads to Pulmonary Immunopathology on Challenge with the SARS Virus.* PLoS One. 2012;7(4):e35421. doi:10.1371/journal.pone.0035421 **(Page 213)**

104. Cardozo, T. and Veazey, R. *Informed consent disclosure to vaccine trial subjects of risk of COVID-19 vaccines worsening clinical disease.* Int J Clin Pract. 2021 Mar;75(3):e13795. doi:10.1111/ijcp.13795 **(Page 214)**

105. Xu, L., Ma, Z., Li, Y., et al. *Antibody dependent enhancement: Unavoidable problems in vaccine development.* Adv Immunol. 2021;151:99-133. doi:10.1016/bs.ai.2021.08.003 **(Page 214)**

106. U.S. District Courts: *Judicial Watch v. U.S. Department of Health and Human Services* (No. 1:21-cv-02418) **(Page 214)**

107. Banoun, H. *Current state of knowledge on the excretion of mRNA and spike produced by anti-COVID-19 mRNA vaccines; possibility of contamination of the entourage of those vaccinated by these products.* Infect Dis Res. 2022;3(4):22. doi:10.53388/IDR20221125022 **(Page 215)**

108. Corbett, K., Edwards, D., Leist, S., et al. *SARS-CoV-2 mRNA vaccine design enabled by prototype pathogen preparedness.* Nature. 2020 Oct;586(7830):567-571. doi:10.1038/s41586-020-2622-0 **(Page 216)**

109. Tostanoski, L., Wegmann, F., Martinot, A., et al. *Ad26 vaccine protects against SARS-CoV-2 severe clinical disease in hamsters.* Nat Med. 2020 Nov;26(11):1694-1700. doi:10.1038/s41591-020-1070-6 **(Page 216)**

110. Vogel, A., Kanevsky, I., Che, Y., et al. *A prefusion SARS-CoV-2 spike RNA vaccine is highly immunogenic and prevents lung infection in non-human primates.* Version 1. bioRxiv. Preprint. 2020 Sep 8. doi:10.1101/2020.09.08.280818 **(Page 216)**

111. Edelman, A., Boniface, E., Benhar, E., et al. *Association Between Menstrual Cycle Length and Coronavirus Disease 2019 (COVID-19) Vaccination.* Obstet Gynecol. 2022 Apr 1;139(4):481-489. doi:10.1097/AOG.0000000000004695 **(Page 217)**

112. Cohen, E. *FDA vaccine advisers 'disappointed' and 'angry' that early data about new Covid-19 booster shot wasn't presented for review last year.* CNN. January 11th, 2023. https://web.archive.org/web/20230111114535/https://edition.cnn.com/2023/01/11/health/moderna-bivalent-transparency/index.html **(Page 217)**

113. Thacker, P. *Covid-19: Researcher blows the whistle on data integrity issues in Pfizer's vaccine trial*. BMJ. 2021 Nov 2;375:n2635. doi:10.1136/bmj.n2635 **(Page 218)**

114. Texas District Court: *United States of America ex rel. Brooks Jackson v. Ventavia Research Group, LLC* (1:21-cv-00008) **(Page 219)**

115. Tinari, S. *The EMA covid-19 data leak, and what it tells us about mRNA instability*. BMJ. 2021 Mar 10;372:n627. doi:0.1136/bmj.n627 **(Page 219)**

116. Lazarus, R. *Electronic Support for Public Health–Vaccine Adverse Event Reporting System (ESP:VAERS)*. Agency for Healthcare Research and Quality (AHRQ). September 30th, 2010. https://web.archive.org/web/20200211062606/https://digital.ahrq.gov/sites/def ault/files/docs/publication/r18hs017045-lazarus-final-report-2011.pdf **(Page 223)**

117. Choi, S., Lee, S., Seo, J., et al. *Myocarditis-induced Sudden Death after BNT162b2 mRNA COVID-19 Vaccination in Korea: Case Report Focusing on Histopathological Findings*. J Korean Med Sci. 2021 Oct 18;36(40):e286. doi:10.3346/jkms.2021.36.e286 **(Page 227)**

118. Martinez, M., Tucker, A., Bloom, J., et al. *Prevalence of Inflammatory Heart Disease Among Professional Athletes With Prior COVID-19 Infection Who Received Systematic Return-to-Play Cardiac Screen*. JAMA Cardiol. 2021 Jul 1;6(7):745-752. doi:10.1001/jamacardio.2021.0565 **(Page 228)**

119. Chawla, A. *New Onset Eosinophilic Fasciitis after COVID-19 Infection*. Cleveland Clinic. November 29th, 2022. https://web.archive.org/web/20221130011220/https://consultqd.clevelandclini c.org/new-onset-eosinophilic-fasciitis-after-covid-19-infection/ **(Page 231)**

120. Faissner, S., Richter, D., Ceylan, U., et al. *COVID-19 mRNA vaccine induced rhabdomyolysis and fasciitis*. J Neurol. 2022 Apr;269(4):1774-1775. doi:10.1007/s00415-021-10768-3 **(Page 231)**

121. Krug, A., Stevenson, J., and Høeg, T. *BNT162b2 Vaccine-Associated Myo/Pericarditis in Adolescents: A Stratified Risk-Benefit Analysis*. Eur J Clin Invest. 2022 May; 52(5): e13759. doi:10.1111/eci.13759 **(Page 233)**

122. Kharbanda, E., Haapala, J., DeSilva, M., et al. *Spontaneous Abortion Following COVID-19 Vaccination During Pregnancy*. JAMA. 2021 Oct 26;326(16):1629-1631. doi:10.1001/jama.2021.15494 **(Page 234)**

123. Hanna, N., Heffes-Doon, A., Lin, X., et al. *Detection of Messenger RNA COVID-19 Vaccines in Human Breast Milk*. JAMA Pediatr. 2022 Sep 26;e223581. doi:10.1001/jamapediatrics.2022.3581 **(Page 234)**

124. Gat, I., Kedem, A., Dviri, M., et al. *Covid-19 vaccination BNT162b2 temporarily impairs semen concentration and total motile count among semen donors*. Andrology. 2022 Sep;10(6):1016-1022. doi:10.1111/andr.13209 **(Page 237)**

125. Knapton, S. *AstraZeneca vaccine may increase risk of serious neurological condition*. Telegraph. May 28th, 2022

https://web.archive.org/web/20220528210531/https://www.telegraph.co.uk/ne
ws/2022/05/28/astrazeneca-vaccine-may-increase-risk-serious-neurological-
condition/ **(Page 237)**

126. Garrido, I., Lopes, S., Simões, M., et al. *Autoimmune hepatitis after COVID-
19 vaccine – more than a coincidence.* J Autoimmun. 2021 Dec;125:102741.
doi:10.1016/j.jaut.2021.102741 **(Page 238)**

127. Boettler, T., Csernalabics, B., Salié, H., et al. *SARS-CoV-2 vaccination can
elicit a CD8 T-cell dominant hepatitis.* J Hepatol. 2022 Sep;77(3):653-659.
doi:10.1016/j.jhep.2022.03.040 **(Page 238)**

128. Cari, L., Fiore, P., Alhosseini, M., et al. *Blood clots and bleeding events
following BNT162b2 and ChAdOx1 nCoV-19 vaccine: An analysis of
European data.* J Autoimmun. 2021 Aug;122:102685.
doi:10.1016/j.jaut.2021.102685 **(Page 239)**

129. Giovannini, F. and Pisano, G. *Dark -Field Microscopic Analysis on the Blood
of 1,006 Symptomatic Persons After Anti-COVID mRNA Injections from
Pfizer/BioNtech or Moderna.* IJVTPR, 2(2), 385–444.
doi:10.56098/ijvtpr.v2i2.47 **(Page 240)**

130. Sperber, K., Quraishi, H., Kalb, T., et al. *Selective regulation of cytokine
secretion by hydroxychloroquine: inhibition of interleukin 1 alpha (IL-1-
alpha) and IL-6 in human monocytes and T cells.* J Rheumatol. 1993
May;20(5):803-8. **(Page 245)**

131. Vincent, M., Bergeron, E., Benjannet, S., et al. *Chloroquine is a potent
inhibitor of SARS coronavirus infection and spread.* Virol J. 2005 Aug
22;2:69. doi:10.1186/1743-422X-2-69. **(Page 246)**

132. Sinha, N. and Balayla, G. *Hydroxychloroquine and COVID-19.* Postgraduate
Medical Journal 2020;96:550-555. doi:10.1136/postgradmedj-2020-137785
(Page 246)

133. Gautret, P., Lagier, J., Parola, P., et al. *Hydroxychloroquine and azithromycin
as a treatment of COVID-19: results of an open-label non-randomized clinical
trial.* Int J Antimicrob Agents. 2020 Jul;56(1):105949.
doi:10.1016/j.ijantimicag.2020.105949 **(Page 246)**

134. Satarker, S., Ahuja, T., Madhuparna Banerjee, M., et al. *Hydroxychloroquine
in COVID-19: Potential Mechanism of Action Against SARS-CoV-2.* Curr
Pharmacol Rep. 2020;6(5):203-211. doi:10.1007/s40495-020-00231-8 **(Page
246)**

135. Prodromos, C. and Rumschlag, T. *Hydroxychloroquine is effective, and
consistently so when provided early, for COVID-19: a systematic review.* New
Microbes New Infect. 2020 Nov;38:100776. doi:10.1016/j.nmni.2020.100776
(Page 246)

136. Zhang, X., Song, Y., Ci, X., et al. *Ivermectin inhibits LPS-induced production
of inflammatory cytokines and improves LPS-induced survival in mice.*
Inflamm Res. 2008 Nov;57(11):524-9. doi:10.1007/s00011-008-8007-8 **(Page
247)**

137. Caly, L., Druce, J., Catton, M., et al. *The FDA-approved drug ivermectin inhibits the replication of SARS-CoV-2 in vitro.* Antiviral Res. 2020 Jun;178:104787. doi:10.1016/j.antiviral.2020.104787 **(Page 247)**

138. Ahmed, S., Karim, M., Ross, A., et al. *A five-day course of ivermectin for the treatment of COVID-19 may reduce the duration of illness.* Int J Infect Dis. 2021 Feb;103:214-216. doi:10.1016/j.ijid.2020.11.191 **(Page 248)**

139. Bryant, A., Lawrie, T., Dowswell, T., et al. *Ivermectin for Prevention and Treatment of COVID-19 Infection: A Systematic Review, Meta-analysis, and Trial Sequential Analysis to Inform Clinical Guidelines.* Am J Ther. 2021 Jun 21;28(4):e434-e460. doi:10.1097/MJT.0000000000001402 **(Page 248)**

140. Polonikov, A. *Endogenous Deficiency of Glutathione as the Most Likely Cause of Serious Manifestations and Death in COVID-19 Patients.* ACS Infect Dis. 2020 Jul 10;6(7):1558-1562. doi:10.1021/acsinfecdis.0c00288 **(Page 248)**

141. Guloyan, V., Oganesian, B., Baghdasaryan, N., et al. *Glutathione Supplementation as an Adjunctive Therapy in COVID-19.* Antioxidants. 2020 Sep 25;9(10):914. doi:10.3390/antiox9100914 **(Page 249)**

142. Ibrahim, H., Perl, A., Smith, D., et al. *Therapeutic blockade of inflammation in severe COVID-19 infection with intravenous N-acetylcysteine.* Clin Immunol. 2020 Oct; 219:108544. doi:10.1016/j.clim.2020.108544 **(Page 249)**

143. Dominari, A., Iii, D., Kapasi, A., et al. *Bottom-up analysis of emergent properties of N-acetylcysteine as an adjuvant therapy for COVID-19.* World J Virol. 2021 Mar 25;10(2):34-52. doi:10.5501/wjv.v10.i2.34 **(Page 249)**

144. Hemilä, H. *Zinc lozenges and the common cold: a meta-analysis comparing zinc acetate and zinc gluconate, and the role of zinc dosage.* JRSM Open. 2017 May 2;8(5):2054270417694291. doi:10.1177/2054270417694291 **(Page 250)**

145. Jothimani, D., Kailasam, E., Danielraj, S., et al. *COVID-19: Poor outcomes in patients with zinc deficiency.* Int J Infect Dis. 2020 Nov;100:343-349. doi:10.1016/j.ijid.2020.09.014 **(Page 250)**

146. Grant, W., Lahore, H., McDonnell, S., et al. *Evidence that Vitamin D Supplementation Could Reduce Risk of Influenza and COVID-19 Infections and Deaths.* Nutrients. 2020 Apr 2;12(4):988. doi:10.3390/nu12040988 **(Page 250)**

147. Dofferhoff, A., Piscaer, I., Schurgers, L., et al. *Reduced Vitamin K Status as a Potentially Modifiable Risk Factor of Severe Coronavirus Disease 2019.* Clin Infect Dis. 2021 Dec 6;73(11):e4039-e4046. doi:10.1093/cid/ciaa1258 **(Page 251)**

148. Bae, M. and Kim, H. *The Role of Vitamin C, Vitamin D, and Selenium in Immune System against COVID-19.* Molecules. 2020 Nov; 25(22): 5346. doi:10.3390/molecules25225346 **(Page 251)**

149. Name, J., Souza, A., Vasconcelos, A., et al. *Zinc, Vitamin D and Vitamin C: Perspectives for COVID-19 With a Focus on Physical Tissue Barrier*

Integrity. Front Nutr. 2020 Dec 7;7:606398. doi:10.3389/fnut.2020.606398 **(Page 251)**

150. Yisak, H., Ewunetei, A., Kefale, B., et al. *Effects of Vitamin D on COVID-19 Infection and Prognosis: A Systematic Review.* Risk Manag Healthc Policy. 2021 Jan 7;14:31-38. doi:10.2147/RMHP.S291584 **(Page 251)**

151. Carrillo-Vico, A., Lardone, P., Alvarez-Sánchez, N., et al. *Melatonin: Buffering the Immune System.* Int J Mol Sci. 2013 Apr 22;14(4):8638-83. doi:10.3390/ijms14048638. **(Page 252)**

152. Grivas, T. and Savvidou, O. *Melatonin the "light of night" in human biology and adolescent idiopathic scoliosis.* Scoliosis. 2007 Apr 4;2:6. doi:10.1186/1748-7161-2-6 **(Page 252)**

153. Shneider, A., Kudriavtsev, A., and Vakhrusheva, A. *Can melatonin reduce the severity of COVID-19 pandemic?.* Int Rev Immunol. 2020;39(4):153-162. doi:10.1080/08830185.2020.1756284 **(Page 253)**

154. Zhang, R., Wang, X., Ni, L., et al. *Melatonin as a potential adjuvant treatment.* Life Sci. 2020 Jun 1;250:117583. doi:10.1016/j.lfs.2020.117583 **(Page 253)**

155. Cross, K., Landis, D., Sehgal, L., and Payne, J. *Melatonin for the Early Treatment of COVID-19: A Narrative Review of Current Evidence and Possible Efficacy.* Endocr Pract. 2021 Aug; 27(8): 850–855. doi:10.1016/j.eprac.2021.06.001 **(Page 253)**

156. U.S. Supreme Court: *Leary v. United States*, 395 U.S. 6 (1969) **(Page 254)**

157. Kovalchuk, A., Wang, B., Li, D., et al. *Fighting the storm: could novel anti-TNFα and anti-IL-6 C. sativa cultivars tame cytokine storm in COVID-19?.* Aging (Albany NY). 2021 Jan 19;13(2):1571-1590. doi:10.18632/aging.202500 **(Page 255)**

158. Nguyen, L., Yang, D., Nicolaescu, V., et al. *Cannabidiol Inhibits SARS-CoV-2 Replication and Promotes the Host Innate Immune Response.* bioRxiv. 2021 Mar 10;2021.03.10.432967. doi:10.1101/2021.03.10.432967 **(Page 255)**

159. Breemen, R., Muchiri, R., Bates, T., et al. *Cannabinoids Block Cellular Entry of SARS-CoV-2 and the Emerging Variants.* J Nat Prod. 2022 Jan 28;85(1):176-184. doi:10.1021/acs.jnatprod.1c00946 **(Page 255)**

160. State of Illinois Department of Public Health. *COVID-19 Protecting Each Other.* May 29th, 2020. https://web.archive.org/web/20211021031605/https://dph.illinois.gov/content/dam/soi/en/web/idph/files/covid19/covid-19-maskprotection2.pdf **(Page 259)**

161. Brooks, J., Beezhold, D., Noti, J., et al. *Maximizing Fit for Cloth and Medical Procedure Masks to Improve Performance and Reduce SARS-CoV-2 Transmission and Exposure, 2021.* MMWR Morb Mortal Wkly Rep 2021;70:254–257. doi:10.15585/mmwr.mm7007e1. **(Page 259)**

162. Martellucci, C., Flacco, M., Martellucci, M., et al. *Inhaled CO2 Concentration While Wearing Face Masks: A Pilot Study Using Capnograph.* Environmental Health Insights. 2022;16. doi:10.1177/11786302221112357 **(Page 261)**

163. Zheng, Y., Chen, H., Yao, M., and Li, X. *Bacterial pathogens were detected from human exhaled breath using a novel protocol.* J Aerosol Sci. 2018 Mar;117:224-234. doi:10.1016/j.jaerosci.2017.12.009 **(Page 262)**

164. Vincent, M. and Edwards, P. *Disposable surgical face masks for preventing surgical wound infection in clean surgery.* Cochrane Database Syst Rev. 2016 Apr 26;4(4):CD002929. doi:10.1002/14651858.CD002929.pub3 **(Page 264)**

165. MacIntyre, C., Seale, H., Dung, T., et al. *A cluster randomised trial of cloth masks compared with medical masks in healthcare workers.* BMJ Open. 2015 Apr 22;5(4):e006577. doi:10.1136/bmjopen-2014-006577 **(Page 264)**

166. Godoy, L., Jones, A., Anderson, T., et al. *Facial protection for healthcare workers during pandemics: a scoping review.* BMJ Glob Health. 2020 May;5(5):e002553. doi:10.1136/bmjgh-2020-002553 **(Page 265)**

167. Jefferson, T., Del Mar, C., Dooley, L., et al. *Physical interventions to interrupt or reduce the spread of respiratory viruses.* Cochrane Database Syst Rev. 2020 Nov 20;11(11):CD006207. doi:10.1002/14651858.CD006207.pub5 **(Page 265)**

168. U.S. Court of Appeals for the District of Columbia Circuit: *U.S. v. Microsoft Corp.*, 253 F.3d 34 (D.C. Cir. 2001) **(Page 271)**

169. University of Wisconsin-Madison. *Genes That Made 1918 Flu Lethal Isolated.* ScienceDaily. 31 December 2008. https://web.archive.org/web/20090102050106/www.sciencedaily.com/releases/2008/12/081229200738.htm **(Page 278)**

170. University of Wisconsin-Madison. *Virus hybridization could create pandemic bird flu.* ScienceDaily. 24 February 2010. https://web.archive.org/web/20100227022720/http://www.sciencedaily.com/releases/2010/02/100222161841.htm **(Page 279)**

171. Kerkhove, M., Mumford, E., Mounts, A., et al. *Highly Pathogenic Avian Influenza (H5N1): Pathways of Exposure at the Animal-Human Interface, a Systematic Review.* PLoS One. 2011; 6(1): e14582. doi:10.1371/journal.pone.0014582 **(Page 280)**

172. Agnandji, S., Lell, B., Soulanoudjingar, S., et al. *First Results of Phase 3 Trial of RTS,S/AS01 Malaria Vaccine in African Children.* N Engl J Med. 2011 Nov 17;365(20):1863-75. doi:10.1056/NEJMoa1102287 **(Page 280)**

173. McHugh, K., Jing, L., Severt, S., et al. *Biocompatible near-infrared quantum dots delivered to the skin by microneedle patches record vaccination.* Sci Transl Med. 2019 Dec 18;11(523):eaay7162. doi:10.1126/scitranslmed.aay7162 **(Page 287)**

174. Nuclear Threat Initiative. *Strengthening Global Systems to Prevent and Respond to High-Consequence Biological Threats.* ScienceDaily. November 2021. https://web.archive.org/web/20230122140249/https://www.nti.org/wp-content/uploads/2021/11/NTI_Paper_BIO-TTX_Final.pdf **(Page 291)**

175. Urban, H. *The Beast with Two Backs: Aleister Crowley, Sex Magic and the Exhaustion of Modernity*. Nova Religio (2004) 7 (3): 7–25. doi:10.1525/nr.2004.7.3.7 **(Page 313)**

176. U.S. Supreme Court: *United States v. Williams*, 553 U.S. 285 (2008) **(Page 314)**

177. Grove, J. and Amy, M. *Michaël Borremans: As Sweet as It Gets*. Hatje Cantz. 2014 **(Page 314)**

178. Macrae, F. *British royalty dined on human flesh (but don't worry it was 300 years ago)*. Daily Mail. May 21st, 2011. https://web.archive.org/web/20110522004803/https://www.dailymail.co.uk/news/article-1389142/British-royalty-dined-human-flesh-dont-worry-300-years-ago.html **(Page 315)**

179. Thompson, H. *Fear and Loathing in Las Vegas: A Savage Journey to the Heart of the American Dream*. Random House. July 7th, 1972. **(Page 316)**

180. Hoffer, A. *The Effect of Adrenochrome and Adrenolutin On the Behavior of Animals and the Psychology of Man*. Int Rev Neur. 1962;4: 307-371. doi:10.1016/S0074-7742(08)60025-2 **(Page 316)**

181. Nussbaum, B. *Young Global Leaders--Anderson Cooper and Leonardo DiCaprio Are In The Most Exclusive Private Social Network In The World.*. Bloomberg. March 17th, 2008. https://web.archive.org/web/20210603075926/https://www.bloomberg.com/news/articles/2008-03-17/young-global-leaders-anderson-cooper-and-leonardo-dicaprio-are-in-the-most-exclusive-private-social-network-in-the-world-dot **(Page 317)**

Human Things

Human things
believe they know many things.
Many things
about many things.
But in the grand scheme of things,
human things
do not know many things.
One could say human things
know a few things
about a few things.
Some material things
dominate human things
which influences human things
to do bad things
for tyrannical things.
Tyrannical things
who worship cruel and evil things.
So, human things
vote hard for tyrannical things
to subject other human things
to cruel and evil things
because tyrannical things
promise material things.
Controlling human things
are government things
used by tyrannical things.
Human things
believing in government things
are religious things

even though government things
are not godly things
but cruel and evil things
run by tyrannical things.
Government things
are the worst kind of things.
Human things
can do better things
than being controlled by government things
run by tyrannical things.
Human things
can evolve past needing government things
to control things
under the guise of solving things.
Government things
are the worst kind of things.
When human things
understand the reality of things
human things
fight cruel and evil things,
fight tyrannical things,
fight government things.
Government things
are the worst kind of things
to human things.

About the Author

"The sin our fathers sinned was that they did not trust liberty wholly. They thought it possible to compromise between liberty and government, believing the latter to be "a necessary evil," and the moment the compromise was made, the whole misbegotten monster of our present tyranny began to grow. Instruments which are set up to safeguard rights become the very whip with which the free are struck. Anarchism says, Make no laws whatever concerning speech, and speech will be free; so soon as you make a declaration on paper that speech shall be free, you will have a hundred lawyers proving that "freedom does not mean abuse, nor liberty license"; and they will define and define freedom out of existence. Let the guarantee of free speech be in every man's determination to use it, and we shall have no need of paper declarations. On the other hand, so long as the people do not care to exercise their freedom, those who wish to tyrannize will do so; for tyrants are active and ardent, and will devote themselves in the name of any number of gods, religious and otherwise, to put shackles upon sleeping men." – Voltairine de Cleyre, *Anarchism & American Traditions*, December 1908

People are so much more than minor descriptors that they might label themselves. However, these descriptors can be a benefit to finding like-minded individuals or understanding the principles an individual might live by. For example, I'm an anarchist, voluntarist, principled libertarian, philosopher, conspiracy theorist, U.S. Army veteran, business and solutions analyst, political analyst, cyber analyst, intelligence analyst, graphics and website designer, network and systems administrator, content creator, writer, journalist, author, vaccine risk-aware advocate, son, husband, and father. These generalized terms only provide a brief description of who and what I am -if we understand the words' definitions correctly.

The idea of anarchy elicits strong reactions from those who don't understand the definition. There are many misconceptions about what an anarchist is. Many of the negative connotations around anarchy are pushed by the government and mainstream media. Anarchy means without rulers -the absence of government- in its root definition sense. It does not mean without rules, principles, or leaders. It does not mean without hierarchies. It does not imply that an anarchist can destroy property -a natural right of others. Antifa members are not anarchists, even though its members, governments, and mainstream media claim them to be. Anarchism is a system and practice of no rulers, voluntary action -an absence of control over the innocent. It is an idea where trust is afforded to the innocent in ruling themselves.

There are different schools of thought about what an anarchist is - e.g., Anarcho-Capitalist, Anarcho-Socialist, Anarcho-Primitive, etc. However, I don't prescribe to any of them directly. I am an anarchist. I believe each anarcho- discipline and school of thought is acceptable as long as it follows the idea of the absence of government -control- over the innocent. If agreements to participate in a system and practice are voluntary -the absence of control- then it is anarchism.

I live my life through a set of principles that upholds the idea of natural rights for all, and I follow these rules and principles within a corrupt and unjust system as best I can and do what I can with what I got. I have a passion for the truth and being logical, so I was led to anarchism through the Trivium Method of Critical Thinking. I strive to live my life through these voluntary actions and value natural rights that all of us have inherently.

My goal has always been to bring truth to everyone who will listen, regardless of how it might make me look to most. Over the years, I have been viewed as a crazed individual by family, friends, and strangers while being vilified by some. I have been and continue to be censored by social media corporations for having a viewpoint different than the official government rhetoric or what is generally accepted by the masses at the time, regardless of how correct my stance is. I speak up and voice my dissent and non-consent because I stand up for innocent people who are constantly targeted and have their rights violated. Eventually, the tyranny must and will end, but that end begins with a voice to anyone who will listen. I hope that this book helps bring more to this voice that must be spoken.

I can currently be found and contacted through the following locations and accounts:

- Email
  - JeffreyHann@protonmail.com
- Website
  - https://www.journalisticrevolution.com
- Facebook
  - https://www.facebook.com/JournalisticRevolution
- Instagram
  - https://www.instagram.com/jeffrey.a.hann
  - https://www.instagram.com/journalisticrevolution
- Minds
  - https://www.minds.com/jeffreyhann/
- Steemit
  - https://steemit.com/@jeffreyahann
- Substack
  - https://jeffreyhann.substack.com/
- Telegram
  - https://t.me/JournalisticRevolution

- o   https://t.me/WelcomeToTheCollapse
- Twitter
  - o   https://twitter.com/JeffHannMADA

Here is a list of all of my published work:

- March 15th, 2016: *Why taxation is theft*
  - o   https://journalisticrevolution.com/why-taxation-is-theft.html
- July 21st, 2016: *What is a Police Enforcement Officer and what are their duties with regards to our rights?*
  - o   https://journalisticrevolution.com/what-is-a-police-enforcement-officer-and-what-are-their-duties-with-regards-to-our-rights.html
- August 16th, 2016: *Know your grammar, what is terrorism?*
  - o   https://journalisticrevolution.com/know-your-grammar-what-is-terrorism.html
- September 5th, 2016: *What made America great?*
  - o   https://journalisticrevolution.com/what-made-america-great.html
- December 24th, 2016: *Remember Remember Remember*
  - o   https://journalisticrevolution.com/remember-remember-remember.html
- January 5th, 2017: *Why I am a Libertarian and Anarchist, by definition*
  - o   https://journalisticrevolution.com/why-i-am-a-libertarian-and-anarchist-by-definition.html
- August 1st, 2017: *Taxation is theft, by definition*
  - o   https://journalisticrevolution.com/taxation-is-theft-by-definition.html
- September 18th, 2017: *Conspiracy Theory: Government and Central Banking lies about Bitcoin - CEO of JPMorgan and Director of the Federal Reserve Jamie Dimon commits fraud*
  - o   https://journalisticrevolution.com/conspiracy-theory-government-and-central-banking-lies-about-bitcoin.html
- July 11th, 2019: *To Vaccinate or Not to Vaccinate: Informed Consent*
  - o   https://journalisticrevolution.com/to-vaccinate-or-not-to-vaccinate-informed-consent.html
- May 29th, 2020: *COVID1984: A Plandemic Love Story (Part 1)*

- o https://journalisticrevolution.com/covid1984-a-plandemic-love-story-part-1.html
- May 29th, 2020: *COVID1984: A Plandemic Love Story (Part 2)*
  - o https://journalisticrevolution.com/covid1984-a-plandemic-love-story-part-2.html
- April 17th, 2022: *IN-DEPTH ANALYSIS OF COVID19: The Truth Is Out There*
  - o https://journalisticrevolution.com/in-depth-analysis-of-covid19-the-truth-is-out-there.html

Meet the future with confidence and determination